PENGUIN EDITION

PRENTICE HALL
LITERATURE

INDIANA

GRADE 8

Progress Monitoring
Assessments

Indiana

PEARSON

Prentice
Hall

Boston, Massachusetts
Upper Saddle River, New Jersey

This work is protected by United States copyright laws and is provided *solely for the use of teachers and administrators* in teaching courses and assessing student learning in their classes and schools. Dissemination or sale of any part of this work (including on the World Wide Web) will destroy the integrity of the work and is *not* permitted.

ISBN 0-13-202407-1

2 3 4 5 6 7 8 9 10   10 09 08 07

Table of Contents

Indiana Standards and Testing..iv
About the *No Child Left Behind Act*...v
About This Book..vi
Indiana Academic Standards, Grade 8..vii
The Indiana Scoring Rubrics...xiii
Reading the Reports..xvii

Tests
Screening Test 1
Diagnostic Tests 7
Benchmark Tests 43
Outcome Test..120
ISTEP+ Practice Test 133
ITBS Practice Test 153
TerraNova Practice Test 173
SAT 10 Practice Test 187

Test Reports
Benchmark Tests 205
Outcome Test..235
ISTEP+ Practice Test 240

Test Answers
Screening Test 243
Diagnostic Tests 243
Benchmark Tests 244
Outcome Test..252
ISTEP+ Practice Test 253
ITBS Practice Test 254
TerraNova Practice Test...254
SAT 10 Practice Test 255

Answer Sheets..256
Letters to Parents...261

Indiana Standards and Testing

Indiana's Academic Standards

The Indiana Department of Education has established comprehensive expectations for student learning. Indiana's Academic Standards describe the knowledge and skills that students are expected to master in a given year. These standards outline the knowledge that students need to succeed in the twenty-first century. In addition, the standards represent curriculum agreed upon by parents, teachers, administrators, academics, and community leaders.

Indiana's Academic Standards for English Language Arts are organized under three major goals: Reading, Writing, and Listening and Speaking. Each goal is supported by individual standards that specify the appropriate level of achievement for students in each grade.

The Indiana Statewide Testing for Educational Progress-Plus Test

The Indiana Statewide Testing for Educational Progress-Plus (ISTEP+) Test is administered to middle-school students as a means of measuring mastery of related academic standards. The ISTEP+ includes multiple-choice, constructed-response, and extended-response questions based on literary and informational reading passages, as well as an independent writing prompt.

For additional information regarding Indiana standards and testing, visit the Indiana Department of Education Web site. Here is the address as of this writing:

Curriculum: *http://www.doe.state.in.us/standards/welcome.html*

Testing: *http://www.doe.state.in.us/istep/welcome.html*

About NCLB

What is the *No Child Left Behind Act?*

Overview

On January 8, 2002, President Bush signed into law the *No Child Left Behind Act* of 2001 (NCLB). It changes the federal government's role in kindergarten through grade twelve education by asking America's schools to describe their success in terms of what each student accomplishes. This law is designed to revitalize America's schools and is based on four basic education reform principles: stronger accountability for results, increased flexibility and local control, expanded options for parents, and focusing resources on scientifically proven teaching methods.

As the title of the law states, the goal is that no child be left behind and that every child receives a top-notch education. *NCLB* raises expectations for states, local educational agencies, and schools. All students are expected to meet or exceed state standards in reading and math within 12 years and have the skills necessary to succeed academically and in the real world.

Adequate Yearly Progress

Accountability is at the core of *NCLB*. States must clearly explain how they will minimize achievement gaps to ensure that every student in America achieves academic proficiency. Because this new law asks America's schools to "describe their success in terms of what each student accomplishes," each state has been directed to create curriculum standards describing what a child should know and learn in each subject in each grade. Tests must be aligned with state standards and measure students' academic achievement. Another requirement, and barometer against which student performance will be measured, is the National Assessment of Education Progress (NAEP).

Although states have flexibility in determining individual content standards, these standards must be challenging and apply equally to all students. Under *NCLB*, all states must have a performance goal of 100% of the students performing at the "proficient" level or higher by 2014.

Adequate Yearly Progress (AYP) is an individual state's measure of yearly progress toward achieving state academic standards. It is the minimum level of improvement that states, school districts, and schools must achieve each year.

Reporting

Every state is required to report academic progress to parents, communities, and the federal government each year. This is done in a variety of ways, but the U.S. Department of Education ultimately requires that states provide annual state and local school district report cards to inform the general public of their progress. In order to ensure that students are provided the best education possible, *NCLB* requires that schools provide services such as tutoring or after-school help to maintain AYP.

To learn more about *NCLB*, visit the official Web site: ***www.ed.gov/nclb/***

About This Book

Because the Indiana Statewide Testing for Educational Progress-Plus (ISTEP+) must be aligned with Indiana's Academic Standards as part of NCLBA, administering tests on a consistent basis will allow you to monitor your students' proficiency levels. To be sure that all students will achieve success, student performances on these ongoing assessments should be linked to review and practice activities.

How do the Progress Monitoring Assessments Help?

This resource provides you with the following tests to detect gaps in your students' comprehension, content knowledge, and skills:

- The **Screening Test** will identify any weaknesses in basic reading comprehension and language skills. This test should be administered *at the start of the school year*. Use the percentage scored by students as a barometer to help you determine whether remediation is necessary.

- The twelve **Diagnostic Tests** will help you determine which of the two selections in a pairing a student should read. These tests should be administered *before beginning a new part* in *Prentice Hall Literature: The Penguin Edition*. The tests begin with two passages followed by a series of questions. The first passage assesses General Comprehension and the second assesses Critical Thinking. If a student does not master the Critical Thinking questions, then she or he should read the selection of lesser difficulty. The tests also consist of a series of vocabulary warm-ups.

- The twelve **Benchmark Tests** allow you to monitor your students' mastery of Indiana's Academic Standards covered in each part of *Prentice Hall Literature*. Each of the twelve tests corresponds directly to skills covered in the preceding part.

- The **Outcome Test** assesses each Academic Standard as a means of determining which standards might require further remediation.

- The **ISTEP+ Practice Test** is modeled after the content and style of the actual grade-level Reading and Writing ISTEP+ assessment. Use this test to help demystify the testing experience for your students.

The Benchmark, Outcome, and ISTEP+ Practice Tests are accompanied by comprehensive test reports that identify what concepts are being measured at any given time. Use these reports as well as the Parent Letters to communicate with parents. In addition, you may utilize the Indiana Academic Achievement Handbook in the *Prentice Hall Literature* student edition to familiarize students with the grade-level Indiana's Academic Standards, a Step Up to ISTEP+ test preparation section, and the Indiana Scoring Rubrics. Lastly, you may refer to the following link on the Indiana Department of Education Web site for ongoing updates concerning curriculum and testing in your state:

Curriculum: *http://www.doe.state.in.us/standards/welcome.html*

Testing: *http://www.doe.state.in.us/istep/welcome.html*

Indiana Academic Standards
English Language Arts
Grade 8

STANDARD 1	READING: WORD RECOGNITION, FLUENCY, AND VOCABULARY DEVELOPMENT
Vocabulary and Concept Development	
8.1.1	Analyze idioms and comparisons—such as analogies, metaphors, and similes—to infer the literal and figurative meanings of phrases. • Idioms: expressions that cannot be understood just by knowing the meanings of the words in the expression, such as *to be an old hand at something* or *to get one's feet wet* • Analogies: comparisons of the similar aspects of two different things • Metaphors: implied comparisons, such as *The stars were brilliant diamonds in the night sky.* • Similes: comparisons that use *like* or *as*, such as *The stars were like a million diamonds in the sky.*
8.1.2	Understand the influence of historical events on English word meaning and vocabulary expansion.
8.1.3	Verify the meaning of a word in its context, even when its meaning is not directly stated, through the use of definition, restatement, example, comparison, or contrast.
STANDARD 2	READING: COMPREHENSION (FOCUS ON INFORMATIONAL MATERIALS)
Structural Features of Informational and Technical Materials	
8.2.1	Compare and contrast the features and elements of consumer materials to gain meaning from documents.
8.2.2	Analyze text that uses proposition (statement of argument) and support patterns.
Comprehension and Analysis of Grade-Level-Appropriate Text	
8.2.3	Find similarities and differences between texts in the treatment, amount of coverage, or organization of ideas.
8.2.4	Compare the original text to a summary to determine whether the summary accurately describes the main ideas, includes important details, and conveys the underlying meaning.
8.2.5	Use information from a variety of consumer and public documents to explain a situation or decision and to solve a problem.

Expository (Informational) Critique	
8.2.6	Evaluate the logic, internal consistency, and structural patterns of text.
STANDARD 3	**READING: LITERARY RESPONSE AND ANALYSIS**

Structural Features of Literature

8.3.1	8.3.1 Determine and articulate the relationship between the purposes and characteristics of different forms of poetry (including ballads, lyrics, couplets, epics, elegies, odes, and sonnets). • Ballad: a poem that tells a story • Lyric: words set to music • Couplet: two successive lines of verse that rhyme • Epic: a long poem that describes heroic deeds or adventures • Elegy: a mournful poem for the dead • Ode: a poem of praise • Sonnet: a rhymed poem of 14 lines

Narrative Analysis of Grade-Level-Appropriate Text

8.3.2	Evaluate the structural elements of the plot, such as subplots, parallel episodes, and climax; the plot's development; and the way in which conflicts are (or are not) addressed and resolved.
8.3.3	Compare and contrast the motivations and reactions of literary characters from different historical eras confronting either similar situations and conflicts or similar hypothetical situations.
8.3.4	Analyze the importance of the setting to the mood, tone, and meaning of the text.
8.3.5	Identify and analyze recurring themes (such as good versus evil) that appear frequently across traditional and contemporary works.
8.3.6	Identify significant literary devices, such as metaphor, symbolism, dialect or quotations, and irony, which define a writer's style and use those elements to interpret the work. • Metaphor: an implied comparison in which a word or phrase is used in place of another, such as *He was drowning in money.* • Symbolism: the use of an object to represent something else; for example, a dove might symbolize peace • Dialect: the vocabulary, grammar, and pronunciation used by people in different regions • Irony: the use of words to express the opposite of the literal meaning of the words, often to be humorous

Literary Criticism

8.3.7	Analyze a work of literature, showing how it reflects the heritage, traditions, attitudes, and beliefs of its author.

STANDARD 4	WRITING: PROCESS
Organization and Focus	
8.4.1	Discuss ideas for writing, keep a list or notebook of ideas, and use graphic organizers to plan writing.
8.4.2	Create compositions that have a clear message, a coherent thesis (a statement of position on the topic), and end with a clear and well-supported conclusion.
8.4.3	Support theses or conclusions with analogies (comparisons), paraphrases, quotations, opinions from experts, and similar devices.
Research and Technology	
8.4.4	Plan and conduct multiple-step information searches using computer networks.
8.4.5	Achieve an effective balance between researched information and original ideas.
8.4.6	Use a computer to create documents by using word-processing skills and publishing programs; develop simple databases and spreadsheets to manage information and prepare reports.
Evaluation and Revision	
8.4.7	Review, evaluate, and revise writing for meaning and clarity.
8.4.8	Edit and proofread one's own writing, as well as that of others, using an editing checklist or set of rules, with specific examples of corrections of frequent errors.
8.4.9	Revise writing for word choice; appropriate organization; consistent point of view; and transitions among paragraphs, passages, and ideas.
STANDARD 5	WRITING: APPLICATIONS (DIFFERENT TYPES OF WRITING AND THEIR CHARACTERISTICS)
8.5.1	Write biographies, autobiographies, and short stories that: • tell about an incident, event, or situation, using well-chosen details. • reveal the significance of, or the writer's attitude about, the subject. • use narrative and descriptive strategies, including relevant dialogue, specific action, physical description, background description, and comparison or contrast of characters.
8.5.2	Write responses to literature that: • demonstrate careful reading and insight into interpretations. • connect response to the writer's techniques and to specific textual references. • make supported inferences about the effects of a literary work on its audience. • support judgments through references to the text, other works, other authors, or to personal knowledge.

8.5.3	Write research reports that: • define a thesis (a statement of position on the topic). • include important ideas, concepts, and direct quotations from significant information sources, including print reference materials and the Internet, and paraphrase and summarize all perspectives on the topic, as appropriate. • use a variety of primary and secondary sources and distinguish the nature and value of each. • organize and display information on charts, tables, maps, and graphs. • document sources with reference notes and a bibliography.
8.5.4	Write persuasive compositions that: • include a well-defined thesis that makes a clear and knowledgeable appeal. • present detailed evidence, examples, and reasoning to emotional appeals. • provide details, reasons, and examples, arranging them effectively by anticipating and answering reader concerns and counterarguments.
8.5.5	Write technical documents that: • identify the sequence of activities needed to design a system, operate a tool, or explain the bylaws of an organization's constitution or guidelines. • include all the factors and variables that need to be considered. • use formatting techniques, including headings and changing the fonts (typeface) to aid comprehension.
8.5.6	Write using precise word choices to make writing interesting and exact.
8.5.7	Write for different purposes and to a specific audience or person, adjusting tone and style as necessary.
STANDARD 6	**WRITING: ENGLISH LANGUAGE CONVENTIONS**
Sentence Structure	
8.6.1	Use correct and varied sentence types (simple, compound, complex, and compound-complex) and sentence openings to present a lively and effective personal style.
8.6.2	Identify and use parallelism (use consistent elements of grammar when compiling a list) in all writing to present items in a series and items juxtaposed for emphasis. • Correct: *Students having difficulty and needing help should stay after class.* • Incorrect: *Students having difficulty and who need help should stay after class.*
8.6.3	Use subordination, coordination, noun phrases that function as adjectives (*These gestures—acts of friendship—were noticed but not appreciated.*), and other devices to indicate clearly the relationship between ideas.

Grammar

8.6.4	Edit written manuscripts to ensure that correct grammar is used.

Punctuation

8.6.5	Use correct punctuation.

Capitalization

8.6.6	Use correct capitalization.

Spelling

8.6.7	Use correct spelling conventions.

STANDARD 7	LISTENING AND SPEAKING: SKILLS, STRATEGIES, AND APPLICATIONS

Comprehension

8.7.1	Paraphrase (restate) a speaker's purpose and point of view and ask questions concerning the speaker's content, delivery, and attitude toward the subject.

Organization and Delivery of Oral Communication

8.7.2	Match the message, vocabulary, voice modulation (changes in tone), expression, and tone to the audience and purpose.
8.7.3	Outline the organization of a speech, including an introduction; transitions, previews, and summaries; a logically developed body; and an effective conclusion.
8.7.4	Use precise language, action verbs, sensory details, appropriate and colorful modifiers (describing words, such as adverbs and adjectives), and the active (*I recommend that you write drafts.*) rather than the passive voice (*The writing of drafts is recommended.*) in ways that enliven oral presentations.
8.7.5	Use appropriate grammar, word choice, enunciation (clear speech), and pace (timing) during formal presentations.
8.7.6	Use audience feedback, including both verbal and nonverbal cues, to reconsider and modify the organizational structure and/or to rearrange words and sentences for clarification of meaning.

Analysis and Evaluation of Oral and Media Communications

8.7.7	Analyze oral interpretations of literature, including language choice and delivery, and the effect of the interpretations on the listener.
8.7.8	Evaluate the credibility of a speaker, including whether the speaker has hidden agendas or presents slanted or biased material.
8.7.9	Interpret and evaluate the various ways in which visual image-makers (such as graphic artists, illustrators, and news photographers) communicate information and affect impressions and opinions.

Speaking Applications	
8.7.10	Deliver narrative (story) presentations, such as biographical or autobiographical information that: • relate a clear incident, event, or situation, using well-chosen details. • reveal the significance of the incident, event, or situation. • use narrative and descriptive strategies to support the presentation, including relevant dialogue, specific action, physical description, background description, and comparison or contrast of characters.
8.7.11	Deliver oral responses to literature that: – interpret a reading and provide insight – connect personal responses to the writer's techniques and to specific textual references – Make supported inferences about the effects of a literary work on its audience – support judgments through references to the text, other works, other authors, or personal knowledge.
8.7.12	Deliver research presentations that: – define a thesis – research important ideas, concepts, and direct quotations from significant information sources and paraphrase and summarize important perspectives on the topic – use a variety of research sources and distinguish the nature and value of each – present information in charts, maps, and graphs
8.7.13	Deliver persuasive presentations that: – include a well-defined thesis – differentiate fact from opinion and support arguments with detailed evidence, examples, reasoning, and persuasive language – anticipate and effectively answer listener concerns and counterarguments through the inclusion and arrangement of details, reasons, examples, and other elements.
8.7.14	Recite poems (of four to six stanzas), sections of speeches, or dramatic soliloquies using voice modulation, tone, and gestures expressively to enhance the meaning.

ISTEP+ Scoring Rubrics

The following rubrics are used to score writing on the ISTEP+. Scores reflect the range of excellence in written responses to the assignment. The broad categories define the score ranges for the writing assignment and for the range of skills among students.

ISTEP+ Writing Applications Rubric

This rubric is used to score responses to the writing assessment prompts.

Score Level	Ideas and Content Does the writing sample:	Organization Does the writing sample:	Style Does the writing sample:	Voice Does the writing sample:
6	☐ Fully accomplish the task? ☐ Include thorough, relevant, and complete ideas?	☐ Organize ideas logically?	☐ Exhibit exceptional word usage? ☐ Demonstrate exceptional writing technique?	☐ Demonstrate effective adjustment of language and tone to task and reader?
5	☐ Fully accomplish the task? ☐ Include many relevant ideas?	☐ Organize ideas logically?	☐ Exhibit very good word usage? ☐ Demonstrate very good writing technique?	☐ Demonstrate effective adjustment of language and tone to task and reader?
4	☐ Accomplish the task? ☐ Include relevant details?	☐ Organize ideas logically?	☐ Exhibit good word usage? ☐ Demonstrate good writing technique?	☐ Demonstrate an attempt to adjust language and tone to task and reader?
3	☐ Minimally accomplish the task? ☐ Include some relevant details?	☐ Exhibit an attempt to organize ideas logically?	☐ Exhibit ordinary word usage? ☐ Demonstrate average writing technique?	☐ Demonstrate an attempt to adjust language and tone to task and reader?
2	☐ Only partially accomplish the task? ☐ Include few relevant details?	☐ Exhibit a minimal attempt to organize ideas logically?	☐ Exhibit minimal word usage? ☐ Demonstrate minimal writing technique?	☐ Demonstrate language and tone that may be inappropriate to task and reader?
1	☐ Fail to accomplish the task? ☐ Include very few relevant ideas?	☐ Organize ideas illogically?	☐ Exhibit less than minimal word usage? ☐ Demonstrate less than minimal writing technique?	☐ Demonstrate language and tone that may be inappropriate to task and reader?

ISTEP+ Language Conventions Rubric

This rubric applies to both writing assessment and extended-responses.

Score	Does the writing sample exhibit a good command of language skills?
4	In a Score Point 4 paper, there are no errors that impair the flow of communication. Errors are infrequent and will generally be of the first-draft variety; they have a minor impact on the overall communication. • Do words have very few or no capitalization errors? • Do sentences have very few or no punctuation errors? • Do words have very few or no spelling errors? • Do sentences have very few or no grammar or word usage errors? • Writing has very few or no paragraphing errors. • Writing has very few or no run-on sentences or sentence fragments.
Score	**Does the writing sample exhibit an adequate command of language skills?**
3	In a Score Point 3 paper, errors are occasional but do not impede the flow of communication; the writer's meaning is not seriously obscured by errors in language conventions. • Do words have occasional capitalization errors? • Do sentences have occasional punctuation errors? • Do words have occasional spelling errors? • Do sentences have occasional grammar or word usage errors? • Writing may have occasional paragraphing errors. • Writing may have run-on sentences or sentence fragments.
Score	**Does the writing sample exhibit a minimal command of language skills?**
2	In a Score Point 2 paper, errors are typically frequent and may cause the reader to stop and reread part of the writing. While some aspects of the writing may be more consistently correct than others, the existing errors do impair communication. With a little extra effort on the reader's part, it is still possible to discern most, if not all, of what the writer is trying to communicate. • Do words have frequent capitalization errors? • Do sentences have frequent punctuation errors? • Do words have frequent spelling errors? • Do sentences have frequent grammar or word usage errors? • Writing may have errors in paragraphing, or paragraphing may be missing. • Writing is likely to have run-on sentences or sentence fragments.
Score	**Does the writing sample exhibit a less than minimal command of language skills?**
1	In a Score Point 1 paper, errors are serious and numerous; they often cause the reader to struggle to discern the writer's meaning. Errors are frequently of a wide variety. There may be sections where it is impossible to ascertain what the writer is attempting to communicate. • Do words have many capitalization errors? • Do sentences have many punctuation errors? • Do words have many spelling errors? • Do sentences have many grammar and word usage errors? • Writing may have errors in paragraphing, or paragraphing may be missing. • Writing is likely to have run-on sentences or sentence fragments.

ISTEP+ Extended-Response Writing Applications Overview

This rubric is used to score answers to extended-response questions.

Score	Does the writing sample:
4	• Fully accomplish the task? • Include many relevant ideas? • Organize ideas logically? • Exhibit very good word usage? • Demonstrate very good writing technique? • Demonstrate effective adjustment of language and tone to task and reader?
Score	**Does the writing sample:**
3	• Accomplish the task? • Include relevant ideas? • Organize ideas logically? • Exhibit good word usage? • Demonstrate good writing technique? • Demonstrate an attempt to adjust language and tone to task and reader?
Score	**Does the writing sample:**
2	• Minimally accomplish the task? • Include some relevant ideas? • Exhibit an attempt to organize ideas logically? • Exhibit ordinary word usage? • Demonstrate adequate writing technique? • Demonstrate an attempt to adjust language and tone to task and reader?
Score	**Does the writing sample:**
1	• Only partially accomplish or fail to accomplish the task? • Include few relevant ideas? • Exhibit a minimal attempt to organize ideas logically? • Exhibit minimal word usage? • Demonstrate minimal or less than minimal writing technique? • Demonstrate language and tone that may be inappropriate to task and reader?

ISTEP+ Reading Comprehension Rubric

This rubric is used to score answers to open-ended constructed-response questions.

Score	
2	response includes versions of two exemplars
Score	
1	response includes version of one exemplar
Score	
0	Other

Here is an example of exemplars for an open-ended question:

---

3 List TWO details from the passage to support the idea that Tito and Bimbo shared a strong, close relationship.

1) _____

_____

2) _____

_____

Exemplars:

- As long as people could remember seeing Tito, they had seen Bimbo.

- Tito and Bimbo had been together for twelve or thirteen years.

- Bimbo was Tito's nurse, pillow, playmate, and parents.

Reading the Reports

For many of the tests contained in this workbook, there is a comprehensive test report that provides information for you and your students. Each test item is referenced to a language arts concept or skill. Here is a brief overview of how each report has been constructed:

Test Report Title
This identifies the test that corresponds to each individual report.

Indiana Benchmark Test 1: Unit 1, Part 1

Indiana Academic Standards		Test Item(s)
STANDARD 1		
READING: Word Recognition, Fluency, and Vocabulary Development		
8.1.3	Verify the meaning of a word in its context, even when its meaning is not directly stated, through the use of definition, restatement, example, comparison, or contrast.	21, 22, 23, 24, 25
STANDARD 2		
READING: Comprehension (Focus on Informational Materials)		
8.2.1	Compare and contrast the features and elements of consumer materials to gain meaning from documents.	8
8.2.5	Use information from a variety of consumer and public documents to explain a situation or decision and to solve a problem.	9, 10, SA-2
STANDARD 3		
READING: Literary Response and Analysis		
8.3.2	Evaluate the structural elements of the plot, such as subplots, parallel episodes, and climax; the plot's development; and the way in which conflicts are (or are not) addressed and resolved.	1, 2, 3, 4, 5, 6, 7, 11, 12, 13, 14, 15, 16, 17, 18, 19, 20, SA-1, SA-3, SA-4
STANDARD 5		
WRITING: Applications (Different Types of Writing and Their Characteristics)		
8.5.1	Write biographies, autobiographies, and short stories that: • tell about an incident, event, or situation, using well-chosen details. • reveal the significance of, or the writer's attitude about, the subject. • use narrative and descriptive strategies, including relevant dialogue, specific action, physical description, background description, and comparison or contrast of characters.	E-1, E-2

Language Arts Concepts
This column contains a list of the topics that were used to develop the test items.

Test Item
This column contains the list of test items that correlate to each language arts concept.

Indiana Academic Standards		Test Item(s)
8.5.4	Write persuasive compositions that: • include a well-defined thesis that makes a clear and knowledgeable appeal. • present detailed evidence, examples, and reasoning to emotional appeals. • provide details, reasons, and examples, arranging them effectively by anticipating and answering reader concerns and counterarguments.	E-3
8.5.6	Write using precise word choices to make writing interesting and exact.	E-1, E-2, E-3
8.5.7	Write for different purposes and to a specific audience or person, adjusting tone and style as necessary.	E-1, E-2, E-3
STANDARD 6		
WRITING: English Language Conventions		
8.6.4	Edit written manuscripts to ensure that correct grammar is used.	26, 27, 30, 31, 32, 33
8.6.6	Use correct capitalization.	28
8.6.7	Use correct spelling conventions.	29

Teacher Comments: _____

_____

Parent Comments: _____

_____

Comments

This space on each report allows you to add your own comments, so that monitoring the progress of each student is ongoing and meaningful.

Screening Test

Directions: Read the following passages. Then answer the questions. On the answer sheet, fill in the bubble for the answer that you think is correct.

> Telephones, faxes, and computers are company property and should be used for company business only. This includes voice mail, electronic mail, and computer files. Employees may need to use these communication tools for personal reasons from time to time. If and when that time comes, employees should keep their personal use to a minimum and should do so only during non-work hours such as lunchtime.

1 According to the passage, which of the following is _true_?
A Employees can use computers for personal use only.
B Employees are never allowed to use computers for personal reasons.
C Employees should keep their personal use of computers to a minimum.
D Employees cannot use computers during their non-work hours.

2 When are employees at this company allowed to use the telephone for personal reasons?
F when work is slow
G when taking an official break
H whenever they need to
J whenever their boss approves

3 This paragraph describes —
A how to use computers for personal reasons
B how to fix a fax machine
C the rules for taking a lunchtime break
D the rules for using office communication tools

> **To Start Your Washer:**
> 1. Measure detergent and add to basin.
> 2. Set water temperature control and number of rinses.
> 3. Close lid and pull wash cycle knob out to begin washing.

4 What information do you find in this passage?
F descriptions of temperature settings for a washer
G speeds and controls for a washer
H directions for starting a washer
J instructions for care and service of a washer

5 What is the first step in using the washer?
A setting the water temperature
B setting the number of rinses
C pulling the wash cycle knob
D measuring detergent and adding it to the basin

6 What should you do immediately before pulling the wash cycle knob?
F measure the detergent
G set the number of rinses
H close the washer lid
J add the detergent to the basin

What could chocolate and Coca-Cola possibly have in common? Both contain caffeine and are popular around the world. The main ingredient in chocolate comes from the beans of the cacao tree, and the flavoring for Coca-Cola originally came from the nuts of the kola tree. Although they grow in different parts of the world, the cacao tree and the kola tree are part of the same plant family.

7 One ingredient chocolate and Coca-Cola have in common is —
A kola nuts
B caffeine
C cacao beans
D cocoa

8 Chocolate's main ingredient —
F grows in a different part of the world than Coca-Cola's flavoring
G is more popular around the world than Coca-Cola's flavoring
H is derived from a different plant family than Coca-Cola's flavoring
J is less popular around the world than Coca-Cola's flavoring

1   "Who's that?" asked Jamey.
2   Karyn looked at the tall, athletic woman with gray hair tied back in a short ponytail. "Oh, that's my grandmother. She's training for the City Run next week."
3   The two girls finished their run and sat on the sidelines. The older woman joined them shortly.
4   "How's it going, Nanna?" Karyn asked.
5   "Pretty good," her grandmother replied. "I cut three seconds off my best time."
6   Jamey looked at the older woman. "How long have you been running?" she asked.
7   "Most of my life," Nanna replied. "But not on a team. You girls are lucky."
8   "What do you mean?" Jamey asked, confused.
9   Nanna told the girls about the old days when women had few opportunities to race. She explained how things changed when Kathryn Switzer entered the Boston Marathon in 1967. "She registered as K. Switzer so no one would know she was a woman," Nanna said. "She finished in four hours and 20 minutes, better than some men."
10 Nanna rose to her feet and said good-bye to the girls. The girls watched Nanna as she jogged to the parking lot. "Your grandma is pretty cool," Jamey said.

9 What causes Karyn to look over at the woman who was running?
A The woman is running fast.
B Jamey asks who the woman is.
C Karyn is looking for another friend.
D The woman is talking about Kathryn Switzer.

10 What effect do you think meeting Nanna will have on Jamey?
F She will like Karyn more as a friend.
G She will want to enter the Boston Marathon.
H She will appreciate being able to participate in sports.
J She will come back to the track more often.

1   Rebecca moved around in her seat nervously. Her teacher had asked the students to give oral reports on family history. All the students had wonderful stories. Robbie said his great-grandfather had been a cowboy. Angelica's ancestors had come from Ireland on a ship.

2   When her turn came, Rebecca rose slowly and walked to the front of the class. She took a deep breath and began. "My family is from Germany," she started. "They were Jewish, and in the 1930s, Adolf Hitler and the Nazis were rounding up Jews and putting them in work camps."

3   She told of how her great-grandparents decided to flee to America. "They had to walk to Germany's border," Rebecca said. "It was more than a hundred miles. They traveled at night and slept during the day. It was very hard."

4   Rebecca held up a tiny doll. "My grandmother carried this in her pocket for weeks. It's still dirty from the trip because my grandmother never washed it. She said that it reminded her of what she and her family endured for freedom."

5   The class was silent for a moment, then the students asked many questions about Rebecca's story and her family. At that moment, the butterflies in Rebecca's stomach were replaced with a glow of pride. The teacher's encouraging smile told her that she had helped her classmates learn about courage.

11 What is this story *mostly* about?
- **A** a teacher who asks her students to give reports
- **B** a girl who tells how her family came to America
- **C** a class of students who have nice stories
- **D** why some people tried to escape from the Nazis

12 What is the main idea of the last paragraph?
- **F** The teacher decides that Rebecca needs help.
- **G** The class doesn't understand Rebecca's story.
- **H** Students often ask too many questions about families.
- **J** Rebecca changes from being afraid to feeling proud.

13 Which of these is a *fact* from the story?
- **A** The teacher had asked the students to give oral reports.
- **B** Adolf Hitler and the Nazis were rounding up Jews and putting them in work camps.
- **C** Rebecca rose slowly and walked to the front of the class.
- **D** all of the above

14 Which of these is an *opinion* in the story?
- **F** Rebecca moved around in her seat nervously.
- **G** All the students had wonderful stories.
- **H** Rebecca's great-grandparents decided to flee to America.
- **J** Rebecca held up a tiny doll.

One of the most breathtaking places in the world, the Grand Canyon, lies in northwestern Arizona. It is about 277 miles long, 1 mile deep, and anywhere from 1 to 18 miles wide. In 1869, an American geologist named John Wesley Powell led a river expedition through the canyons of the Green and Colorado Rivers. Powell named the area the Grand Canyon, and his exploration of the area was one of the greatest adventures in American history. Few people remember Powell today, but he and his fellow explorers accomplished an extraordinary feat that would be difficult even with today's technology.

15 **Which of the following statements is *not* supported by the paragraph?**
 A John Wesley Powell was lazy.
 B John Wesley Powell was curious.
 C John Wesley Powell was brave.
 D John Wesley Powell was determined.

16 **After reading this paragraph, Connie thinks that a trip through the Grand Canyon would be harder than she first thought. Which words from the story cause her to think this?**
 F ". . . feat that would be difficult even with today's technology."
 G "One of the most breathtaking places in the world . . ."
 H "Powell named the area the Grand Canyon . . ."
 J ". . . Powell led a river expedition through the canyons . . ."

Directions: Read the following questions. On the answer sheet, fill in the bubble for the answer that you think is correct.

17 **Which of these describes poetry?**
 A Facts are presented so that you can understand them easily.
 B The setting is described in great detail.
 C Stage directions show the placement of characters.
 D Rhyme and rhythm help you understand the meaning.

18 **What is a great advantage of writing fiction?**
 F You can write about things that haven't happened.
 G You always write about history or real people.
 H You just tell facts and don't have to worry about a story.
 J You can use rhyme to make things sound more important.

Name _____ Date _____

Directions: Read the following passages. Then answer the questions. On the answer sheet, fill in the bubble for the answer that you think is correct.

> Daniel Parsons lives just four blocks from the hospital. Neighbors call him "Doc" and often stop to visit the retired doctor. Doc was a great doctor because he truly cared about people. When he first retired, he missed his patients. So he moved a big comfortable chair to his front porch, and he sits there when the weather permits. Doc visits with the people who pass by. Many of them are his former patients.

19 According to the story, being a good doctor means —
A living near the hospital
B having a caring personality
C getting plenty of fresh air
D enjoying many houseguests

20 Why does Daniel Parsons visit with former patients?
F He feels obligated.
G He misses them.
H He has nothing better to do.
J none of the above

Directions: Read each sentence. Choose the correct meaning of the underlined word. On the answer sheet, fill in the bubble for the answer that you think is correct.

21 Most people described Paul's personality as being rough.
A uneven
B approximate
C stormy
D harsh

22 Many of us had learned to be cautious in dealing with representatives of the press.
F push against
G news media
H a large machine
J move forward

Directions: Find the meaning of each sentence. On the answer sheet, fill in the bubble for the answer that you think is correct.

23 All hands on deck!
A a card player's demand
B a request for help
C an order to hold onto safety railing
D a command to people to show their palms

24 All the world's a stage, / And all the men and women merely players.
F Live your life while you have the chance.
G In real life, everybody has a part to play.
H Drama gives us insight into the purpose of life.
J Do not be too serious about life's meaning.

Name _____ Date _____

Directions: Read the following phrases. Then decide which of the four answers has most nearly the same meaning as the underlined word. Then fill in the bubble for the answer that you think is correct.

25 A <u>jaunt</u> in the park
   A game
   B parade
   C pony ride
   D short trip

26 A <u>massive</u> building
   F large
   G brick
   H empty
   J important

Directions: Read the following words. Look for mistakes in spelling. For each item on the answer sheet, fill in the bubble for the answer that has the mistake. If there is no mistake, fill in the last answer choice.

27 A argue
   B vauge
   C bounty
   D *(No mistakes)*

28 F drums
   G music
   H radeo
   J *(No mistakes)*

Directions: Read the following sentences. Look for mistakes in punctuation. For each item on the answer sheet, fill in the bubble for the answer that has the mistake. If there is no mistake, fill in the last answer choice.

29 A Following the Civil War, Congress passed
   B many laws protecting the rights of African
   C Americans. Most of them werent followed.
   D *(No mistakes)*

30 F Born in San Francisco California
   G Russell Freedman published his
   H first book in 1961.
   J *(No mistakes)*

Name _____   Date _____

Unit 1: Fiction and Nonfiction
Part 1 Diagnostic Test 1

Read the selection. Then, answer the questions.

Basketball is among the most popular sports in the United States and has become increasingly popular around the world in recent years. The basic idea of the game is very simple. The object is to throw the ball through its opponent's basket while stopping them from scoring. Running with the ball without bouncing it is against the rules; the ball must be dribbled, shot, or passed to another player.

The ability to shoot accurately is one of the most important skills in basketball. The lay-up shot is when a player charges in under the basket and shoots the ball. The hook is an over-the-shoulder shot that allows a player to keep his body between the opponent and the ball. Very tall players sometimes dunk the ball by leaping high over the basket and slamming it through the hoop to score two points.

Watching professional athletes play basketball is fun, but playing it is even more fun. Whether it's cold and wet outside or a beautiful balmy day, you can probably find an indoor or outdoor court to play on. Even if no one is around to play with, you can have a good time practicing different shots all by yourself.

1. According to the selection, which type of shot allows a player to keep his body between the opponent and the ball?
   - **A.** lay-up
   - **B.** hook
   - **C.** dunk
   - **D.** slam

2. What is the main goal of a basketball team?
   - **A.** to play the game in any weather
   - **B.** to show how fun the game of basketball can be and to encourage young people to play the game
   - **C.** to dribble, shoot, and pass the ball
   - **D.** to throw the ball through the opposing team's basket while stopping the other team from scoring

3. What is the writer's attitude toward the game of basketball?
   - **A.** that it is boring to watch but fun to play
   - **B.** that it has many rules and is difficult to learn
   - **C.** that it is a fun game to watch and play
   - **D.** that it is the very best game in the world

4. What advantage do tall basketball players have over shorter players?
   - **A.** They are more likely to be professional athletes.
   - **B.** They can dunk the ball into the basket.
   - **C.** They can dribble and pass the ball better.
   - **D.** They are better at hook shots.

5. At the beginning of the selection, the writer states that basketball is growing in popularity. Which of the following details provides the best explanation for why basketball is so popular?
   - **A.** Running with the ball without bouncing it is illegal.
   - **B.** Players must be able to shoot the ball accurately.
   - **C.** Types of shots include the lay-up, hook, and dunk.
   - **D.** One can always find a place to play basketball.

6. How many points does a team get for putting the ball through its opponent's hoop?
   A. one
   B. two
   C. four
   D. six

7. Which of the following methods of moving the ball is against the rules of basketball?
   A. running while holding the ball
   B. passing the ball to another player
   C. dribbling, or bouncing, the ball
   D. shooting the ball at a basket

Read the selection. Then, answer the questions.

Dragon myths have been told for thousands of years in various cultures throughout the world. Most people would be familiar with the fire-breathing dragon of European folklore. This huge, snakelike monster is almost invariably portrayed as a menace to society. Eventually, outraged citizens raise a clamor, and some valiant individual must step forward to battle the dreadful beast.

In medieval tales, it is usually a brave knight who volunteers to slay the dragon and frees the maiden it holds captive. Of course, the dragon has no intention of giving up without a fight. In the end, however, the knight's endeavor to vanquish his opponent is always successful. Despite its cunning and great physical strength, the wicked dragon is eventually slain, and his killer walks away with the treasure and the heart of the rescued maiden.

Unlike their European cousins, the dragons of Asia are usually portrayed as wise and friendly creatures. This kinder and gentler dragon seldom has wings and rarely breathes fire. Asian dragons can be distinguished by the number of toes they have. A three-toed dragon is Japanese; a four-toed dragon is Indonesian or Korean; and a five-toed dragon, or Lung, is Chinese.

8. Where can dragon myths be found?
   A. in Europe
   B. in Asia
   C. in both Europe and Asia
   D. throughout the world

9. How do European dragons contrast with Asian dragons?
   A. European dragons are fierce fire-breathing monsters, while Asian dragons are friendly and wise.
   B. European dragons are snake-like and have three toes, while Asian dragons have four or five toes.
   C. European dragons are misunderstood victims, while Asian dragons are secretly fierce in nature.
   D. Both European and Asian dragons are menaces to society and must be slain by brave knights.

10. According to the selection, in European legend, what does a knight receive as a reward for slaying the dragon?
    A. money from grateful villagers
    B. treasure and the rescued maiden
    C. fame and magical abilities
    D. great strength and valor

11. Which of the following is the best statement of the main idea of this selection?

    A. Myths about dragons can be found in almost all cultures throughout the world.

    B. Most of us are familiar with the fire-breathing dragon of European folklore.

    C. Despite its cunning and great physical strength, the wicked dragon is eventually slain.

    D. Asian dragons can be distinguished from one another by the number of toes they have.

12. What does the writer assume about the reader's knowledge of dragons?

    A. that the reader knows nothing about dragon legends

    B. that the reader knows how dragons look and behave

    C. that the reader is more familiar with European dragon legends

    D. that the reader is more familiar with Asian dragon legends

13. Which of the following is a conclusion one can draw about Asian dragon legends based on the selection?

    A. Asian dragons are actually just as fierce as European dragons.

    B. Asian dragons steal treasure and kidnap innocent maidens.

    C. Asian villagers do not want dragons living anywhere near them.

    D. Asian dragons are not usually attacked and slain by knights.

14. What makes the dragon a worthy opponent for the brave knight of European legends?

    A. It is an intelligent and friendly creature.

    B. It is an intelligent and dangerous creature.

    C. It likes to collect treasures and innocent young women.

    D. Its legends have been passed down for centuries.

15. From which country does a five-toed Asian dragon come?

    A. Japan

    B. Indonesia

    C. Korea

    D. China

Name _____ Date _____

Read the selections. Then, answer the questions.

In 1933, when Franklin Delano Roosevelt became president, the United States was in its fourth year of the devastating crisis known as the Great Depression. The crisis began in October 1929 when the stock market crashed. The price of stocks in companies all over America fell dramatically. An estimated $30 billion was lost. Many individuals' savings were wiped out. Companies cut back or closed, and people lost their jobs. The country was stricken with fear of financial catastrophe.

President Herbert Hoover was in office at the time. Unfortunately, he lacked a deep understanding and clear recognition of what had happened. He believed the country's problems were caused primarily by the normal ups and downs of business and would resolve on their own. As a result, President Hoover did little to change things.

Soon, 25 percent of able workers were unemployed. Banks also failed. In December 1931, the Bank of the United States went broke, losing $200 million in depositor's savings.

By 1932, many Americans had lost faith in Hoover's leadership and wanted a take-charge president who could guide the country out of its misery. They got one when they elected Franklin Delano Roosevelt, soon known by all as "FDR." FDR established many new programs that many people believe brought the country out of the Great Depression.

1. What is the main idea of this selection?
   A. During the Great Depression, many people lost their jobs and their entire life's savings.
   B. Herbert Hoover did not understand what had happened.
   C. Because of the misery caused by the Great Depression, people wanted a new president.
   D. Franklin Delano Roosevelt was a strong president.

2. What initially caused many people to lose their jobs during the Great Depression?
   A. Stock prices fell dramatically.
   B. Companies cut back or closed.
   C. Hoover did not understand the crisis.
   D. Banks went broke and lost people's money.

3. Why didn't President Hoover try to change things during the Great Depression?
   A. He believed the bad economy was simply a result of the normal business cycle and would fix itself.
   B. He did not care that so many Americans were poor, hungry, and unemployed.
   C. He was not very intelligent and did not have any good ideas for fixing the problems.
   D. He knew that Roosevelt would do a better job than he could and wanted to step aside.

4. Which of the following details from the selection best supports the idea that Americans were disappointed in Hoover's approach to the crisis?
   A. 25 percent of workers were unemployed.
   B. Hoover did not understand what had happened.
   C. The Bank of the United States went broke.
   D. Voters chose Franklin D. Roosevelt in 1932.

5. What was President Roosevelt's approach to the Great Depression?
   A. He was stricken with fear of causing further financial catastrophes.
   B. He did not change things because he believed the problems would fix themselves.
   C. He forced companies to give workers their jobs back and banks to reopen.
   D. He started many new programs that were meant to help end people's suffering.

6. What was a result of President Hoover's lack of action?
   A. The stock market crashed.
   B. Problems began to fix themselves.
   C. Many more people lost their jobs.
   D. People's faith in Hoover grew.

7. What happened to many people's savings during the Great Depression?
   A. They gave it away to those who were less fortunate.
   B. They lost it in the stock market crash or in failed banks.
   C. Their savings grew under Hoover and shrank under Roosevelt.
   D. Their savings were not directly affected by the Great Depression.

8. Based on the information in the selection, what caused the Great Depression?
   A. the loss of many people's jobs and savings
   B. the stock market crash of 1929
   C. the failure of the Bank of the United States
   D. the election of Herbert Hoover

Read the selection. Then, answer the questions.

At the dawn of the twentieth century, few people dared to speculate that human beings would ever be able to fly. Yet, two brothers named Orville and Wilbur Wright, were about to make that dream come true.

The adventurous Wright brothers had never been afraid of a challenge. Together, as young men, they opened a bicycle shop in Dayton, Ohio. Their business was a commercial success, but simply making money was not enough to satisfy the Wright brothers. Their curiosity led to an interest in flying and they started building a series of gliders. Fearing that the gliders would be unable to withstand strong winds, they built a sturdier airplane powered by a lightweight gasoline engine. They took their new airplane to Kitty Hawk, North Carolina to test it.

On December 17, 1903, the brothers tossed a coin to see who would go up first. Orville won. He flew for 12 seconds and traveled 120 feet. Although the farthest the plane flew that day was only 825 feet, the airborne brothers were rightfully proud of their extraordinary aerial feat. It didn't take very long for people around the world to realize that the Wright brothers' invention could change the course of history.

9. What did the Wright brothers do for a living?
   A. They had a bicycle shop in Dayton, Ohio.
   B. They built lightweight gasoline engines.
   C. They invented war machines for the United States government.
   D. They did not work because they were independently wealthy.

10. Why did the Wright brothers decide to build an airplane powered by a gasoline engine?

    A. They liked adventure, and a gasoline-powered airplane was more dangerous than a glider.

    B. They feared that gliders would not be able to withstand strong winds.

    C. They became tired of pedaling their early inventions, which were based on bicycles.

    D. They flipped a coin to decide what kind of airplane they would build.

11. How far did the Wright's airplane fly during its first flight in Kitty Hawk, North Carolina?

    A. 12 feet

    B. 120 feet

    C. 825 feet

    D. 1,000 feet

12. What two details help you conclude that both Orville and Wilbur wanted to pilot the first flight?

    A. They built gliders first, and they went to Kitty Hawk, North Carolina.

    B. They sold bicycles, and they built a gasoline-powered flying machine.

    C. They did not fly very far the first day, but they knew they had made history.

    D. They flipped a coin to decide who would fly first.

13. What is the main idea of this selection?

    A. The Wright brothers were adventurous men who were never afraid of a challenge.

    B. The Wright brothers made history when they invented a gasoline-powered airplane.

    C. Simply making money was not enough for the Wrights, who had a passion for flying.

    D. The brothers were very proud of their first test flights in Kitty Hawk, North Carolina.

14. What quality made the Wright brothers very different from most people in the early twentieth century?

    A. They dared to believe that human beings could fly.

    B. They were extremely intelligent and loved machines.

    C. They owned their own successful bicycle sales business.

    D. They were brothers who were very fond of each other.

15. Based on the information in the selection, which of the following might have prevented the Wrights from inventing a gasoline-powered airplane?

    A. if they had run out of money

    B. if they had been more interested in bicycles

    C. if their gliders had been successful

    D. if they had been satisfied with running their business

Unit 2: Short Stories
Part 1 Diagnostic Test 3

MULTIPLE CHOICE

Read the selection. Then, answer the questions.

No one knows for sure when the game of chess was invented. An early version of the game was popular at end of the tenth century. The modern game was developed in southern Europe a few centuries later.

Players in the sixteenth century wanted others to study their games in order to become better players. The best players were proclaimed "masters" and were highly honored. Books on chess were soon being read all over the world and the game grew in popularity.

After the Russian Revolution, the Russian government deliberately set out to dominate world chess. It set up a program of chess education for children. It offered financial support to the country's best players. Russian players dominated the game throughout the twentieth century.

Computer programs that play chess first appeared in the 1960s, but these programs were no match for the top human players. It was not until 1997 that a chess computer called Deep Blue was able to narrowly defeat world champion Garry Kasparov in a series of games. Kasparov concealed his disappointment as best he could, but he could not hide the embarrassment he felt over losing to a machine.

1. When was the game of chess invented?
   A. the end of the tenth century
   B. during the sixteenth century
   C. after the Russian Revolution
   D. No one knows for sure.

2. What is Deep Blue?
   A. the code name for a great chess master's winning strategy
   B. the name of the Russian government's plan to dominate chess
   C. a computer that was able to defeat a human chess master
   D. the prize that the top chess player wins at the world championships

3. How did the Russian government help Russian players to dominate world chess during the twentieth century?
   A. It threatened Russian citizens into playing the game and winning.
   B. It sponsored chess classes for children and paid the country's best players.
   C. It gave them computers that could help them learn the play the game better.
   D. It proclaimed its players to be masters and published books about chess.

4. Why would chess players in the sixteenth century want others to study their games?
   A. so that everyone would play chess the same way
   B. so that Russia could one day dominate the game
   C. so that they would become famous and perhaps be declared chess masters
   D. so that they could teach others to play chess

5. Why was Garry Kasparov embarrassed about his encounter with Deep Blue?
   A. He felt bad about Deep Blue's miserable loss and was embarrassed for its designers.
   B. He mistook Deep Blue for a great Russian world chess champion.
   C. He was the first human chess champion to lose the game to a computer.
   D. He did not know the very simple game strategy of Deep Blue.

6. The selection states that experts developed a computer that can compete with the best human chess champions in the World. What is the benefit of this development to the game of chess?
   A. It will force human players to think like computers and use better strategies in order to win.
   B. People of all ability levels can practice and improve their game with computers.
   C. It will allow countries, other than Russia, to have a chance to win world chess championships.
   D. People no longer have to play the game themselves since they can simply watch computers do it.

7. What details explain why many Europeans in the sixteenth century wanted to learn, practice, and improve their chess strategies?
   A. Chess masters were honored and books were written about their strategies.
   B. Chess was invented in the tenth century and the modern game centuries later.
   C. Their governments provided chess classes to children and generously paid winners.
   D. Some day, they would need to be good enough to defeat a chess-playing machine.

Read the selection. Then, answer the questions.

San Francisco's Chinatown is the second largest Chinese community in the United States. Rebuilt after the 1906 earthquake, it became a major tourist attraction in the 1920s. Today, tourists from all over flock to Chinatown to visit the many fascinating shops and superb restaurants that line the crowded streets.

Begin your tour at the Chinatown Gate. Stroll along Grant Avenue and peek into some of the crowded shops you pass along the way. You'll find that the shop windows have encased unusual objects of every description. Some shops sell everything from valuable antiques to inexpensive trinkets. Others concentrate on one specific kind of item. Of course, you don't have to enter every shop you see to find out what's inside. A quick peek at the window display will usually reveal the kinds of things being offered for sale.

With so many tempting restaurants to choose from, deciding where to have lunch can be a problem. Looking at menus displayed outside the restaurants can help you make your choice.

The most interesting part of a visit to Chinatown, of course, is seeing the people who live there. Be sure to visit the teeming fruit and vegetable stands on Stockton Street. There, you will find many local people doing their daily grocery shopping.

8. Why do tourists flock to Chinatown?
   A. It has inexpensive hotels and restaurants.
   B. It is an interesting and colorful cultural neighborhood.
   C. It has good bargains on Chinese and other Asian goods.
   D. Its shops sell items that cannot be found anywhere else in the world.

9. How does the writer make this selection about Chinatown more interesting to the reader?

   A. by creating a visual tour with only words

   B. by comparing Chinatown to other neighborhoods

   C. by describing the people of Chinatown in great detail

   D. by pointing out both good and bad things about Chinatown

10. What main point is the writer trying to make about Chinatown?

   A. It has a long and rich history.

   B. It is a fascinating community.

   C. It is a major tourist attraction.

   D. It has many interesting shops.

11. According to the selection, what is the most interesting part of Chinatown?

   A. the Chinatown Gate

   B. the many unique shops

   C. the variety of restaurants

   D. the people who live there

12. What helps Chinatown's visitors decide which restaurant to choose?

   A. helpful tour guides

   B. advice from people who live there

   C. menus outside the restaurants

   D. sample trays inside the restaurants

13. According to the selection, what can visitors do to find out what is sold in the shops in Chinatown?

   A. They can ask local people.

   B. They can look at the shop windows.

   C. They can go inside every shop.

   D. They can read the signs on the shops.

14. Which detail best supports the statement that Chinatown's shops are unique and fascinating?

   A. Chinatown was rebuilt after the 1906 earthquake.

   B. Some shops sell a wide variety of goods.

   C. Some shops sell only a specific kind of item.

   D. Shop windows display objects of every description.

15. According to the selection, what can be found on Stockton Street?

   A. fruit and vegetable stands

   B. many excellent restaurants

   C. souvenir shops for tourists

   D. a view of Chinatown Gate

Unit 2: Short Stories
Part 2 Diagnostic Test 4

MULTIPLE CHOICE

Read the selection. Then, answer the questions.

Jacques Cousteau was an ocean explorer who believed that people could live and work underwater. In the early 1960s, he developed a project called the Continental Shelf Station as a trial underwater living space. Aquanauts—deep-sea versions of astronauts—found the setting hostile and not at all a comfortable place to live. For example, in the dark ocean there is no natural light. The pressure of the deep ocean requires breathing helium, which creates an odd, high-pitched voice. The aquanauts lost their appetite in the strange environment. They also lost their privacy in the too-tight quarters.

Still, Cousteau's experiment created interest. In 1964, a popular exhibit at the World's Fair showed a variety of ways to take advantage of the underwater world. Among the different ideas were people living underwater, vacationing underwater, and drilling for oil. Only one of these, drilling for oil, is widely done.

However, the idea of underwater vacations is not completely lost. In Key Largo, Florida, an ocean research facility called La Chalupa has been turned into an underwater hotel. Guests scuba dive 21 feet down to enter the hotel. These "aqua-vacationers" enjoy private bedrooms and gourmet meals. Windows nearly four feet high allow them to watch creatures moving in the peaceful atmosphere of the sea.

1. What was Jacques Cousteau's Continental Shelf Station?
   A. an underwater station used to drill for oil
   B. an experimental underwater living space
   C. a World's Fair exhibit about the underwater world
   D. an underwater hotel that was once a research station

2. The 1964 World's Fair included ideas for a variety of ways to take advantage of the underwater world. What is the only idea that is widely used today?
   A. people living underwater
   B. people vacationing underwater
   C. deep sea oil drilling
   D. undersea research stations

3. Based on aquanauts' complaints about living underwater and the lack of modern underwater living quarters, what conclusion might scientists draw about humans living under the sea?
   A. Humans will soon live happily under the sea.
   B. Humans are simply not comfortable living underwater.
   C. With a few small adjustments, living underwater will be possible.
   D. The aquanauts would have been much happier in an undersea hotel.

4. Why is La Chalupa successful as an underwater hotel?
   A. It was built and run by Jacques Cousteau himself.
   B. It has private bedrooms, gourmet meals, and huge windows.
   C. Guests enjoy breathing helium and hearing their strange, high voices.
   D. It makes guests feel like they are real aquanauts living in a hostile ocean.

5. Based on the aquanauts' comments about underwater living, how do you think they felt at the end of the experiment?
   A. depressed and unhealthy
   B. optimistic and proud
   C. excited but cautious
   D. unhappy but boastful

6. Why might scientists be so interested in ways to use the underwater world?
   A. because they want to save endangered sea creatures
   B. because they believe that space exploration is not practical
   C. because so much of the earth's surface is covered by water
   D. because they want to have their work featured in future World's Fairs

7. Where is the former underwater research station La Chalupa located?
   A. on the Continental Shelf
   B. at the World's Fair
   C. near Houston, Texas
   D. near Key Largo, Florida

Read the selection. Then, answer the questions.

The first great wave of Chinese immigrants came to Canada around the mid 1800s. Countless men, women, and children fled from Hong Kong during the Opium Wars in order to escape poverty and political unrest. The gold rush of 1858 brought even more Chinese to British Columbia.

In the 1880s, cheap labor was needed to build the new Canadian Pacific Railroad. More than 5,000 Chinese workers were recruited from China and another 7,000 from California. The Chinese were excellent workers who deftly performed whatever tasks were required of them. With despair, however, they soon realized that their employers had little concern for their comfort or safety. Chinese workers were housed in flimsy canvas tents. Many were killed each night by falling rocks. The mood of the workers was somber to say the least. They were also perplexed to discover that non-Chinese workers were earning five times as much for their labor! Not only that, but the Chinese worked on the most dangerous sections of the railroad. Many died on the 300 miles of track that passed through the Rocky Mountains. Those who lived to tell about their experience vividly recalled the long days of back-breaking labor that was the plight of the Chinese railroad workers.

8. Why did Canadian railroad builders decide to hire so many Chinese workers?
   A. The Chinese immigrants were cheap and worked hard.
   B. The Chinese immigrants were far stronger than other workers.
   C. They wanted to help the Chinese immigrants escape the Opium Wars.
   D. They wanted to bring more of the fascinating Chinese culture to Canada.

9. Based on the information in the selection, what do you think the railroad owners did when too many Chinese workers died?
   A. They began paying the remaining workers more to finish.
   B. They recruited more Chinese immigrants.
   C. They worked to pass laws to protect railroad workers.
   D. They tried to improve working conditions.

10. Why did many Chinese people want to leave China during the mid 1800s?
    A. to escape poverty and war
    B. to fight for workers' rights around the world
    C. to learn how to build railroads
    D. to get good jobs building the Canadian railroad

11. Which detail explains why Chinese railroad workers despaired about their situation?
    A. The railroad considered the Chinese to be cheap labor.
    B. Thousands of them were recruited from China and California.
    C. They were excellent workers who deftly performed any task.
    D. They realized their employers did not care about their safety.

12. How were Chinese workers treated compared to other railroad workers?
    A. They were fired more often than others because of their laziness and lack of skills.
    B. They were given much better housing and were paid a bit more than other workers.
    C. They were assigned to the most dangerous sections of the railroad and were paid less.
    D. They were valued more than other workers because of their willingness to work hard.

13. According to the selection, what was one of the greatest dangers railroad workers faced?
    A. falling rocks
    B. political unrest
    C. being sent back to China
    D. attacks from other workers

14. How many Chinese workers were recruited from China and California to work on the Canadian railroad?
    A. a few hundred
    B. about 5,000
    C. about 7,000
    D. more than 12,000

15. How did the housing that was provided to Chinese workers affect their safety?
    A. They had unsafe housing at first but demanded better shelter.
    B. Their sturdy shelters saved many lives, much to their surprise.
    C. Their flimsy tents did nothing to protect them from falling rocks.
    D. Their housing did not affect their safety either way.

Name _____   Date _____

Unit 3: Types of Nonfiction
Part 1 Diagnostic Test 5

MULTIPLE CHOICE

Read the selection. Then, answer the questions.

On July 4, 1776, representatives of the thirteen colonies in North America came together to declare their independence from Great Britain. The difficulties between the colonists and England had begun long before. Many people still had faith that the problems could somehow be resolved peacefully. Others believed, however, that the situation would worsen as time went on. The colonists chose men of the noblest character to represent them at a Continental Congress. After much debate, the members of Congress agreed to perform whatever tasks were necessary to win their precious liberty. Thomas Jefferson of Virginia was given the task of drafting a document declaring colonial independence.

The glory of the Declaration of Independence lies in both its noble ideas and its beautiful language. Jefferson worded his argument clearly and concisely, writing that all men are born with equal rights. He believed that these rights were fundamental and could not be taken away by the government. Governments exist to serve the people, not the other way around. Furthermore, people have the right and duty to throw off an unjust government. Many people were inspired by Jefferson's bold statements and they agreed that the king of England should no longer rule the American colonies.

1. What was the main disagreement among representatives at the Continental Congress?
   A. Some representatives believed that a government exists to serve the people, while others believed the opposite to be true.
   B. Some believed that all people are born equal, while others believed that some people are born with more rights than others.
   C. Some believed that Thomas Jefferson should write the Declaration of Independence, while others wanted different writers.
   D. Some believed their problems with Britain could still be worked out, while others believed they should fight for their independence.

2. Which phrase from the selection best reveals the writer's attitude toward the Declaration of Independence?
   A. came together to declare their independence
   B. whatever was necessary to win their precious liberty
   C. both its noble ideas and its beautiful language
   D. the right and duty to throw off an unjust government

3. How did most of Jefferson's fellow colonists react to the ideas he included in the Declaration of Independence?
   A. They were frightened by the boldness of his ideas.
   B. They were inspired by his statements and supported the document.
   C. They disagreed completely and demanded many changes.
   D. They thought the document was perfect, but they were afraid.

4. According to the Declaration of Independence, what should people do about an unjust government?
   A. threaten it
   B. throw it off
   C. wait for it to get better
   D. have meetings to discuss it

5. What was the purpose of the Declaration of Independence?
   A. to declare war on the king of Great Britain
   B. to establish the government of the United States
   C. to let the British king know that the colonists no longer accepted his rule
   D. to persuade the British king to change his government to please the colonists

6. Which of the following most clearly states the main idea of this selection?
   A. The Declaration of Independence helped inspire American colonists to throw off British rule.
   B. Thomas Jefferson was a truly great writer whose greatest work was the Declaration of Independence.
   C. Representatives of the thirteen colonies met to discuss what to do about their problems with Britain.
   D. Some representatives believed the colonists' problems with Great Britain could still be worked out.

7. Which of the following best reflects Jefferson's attitude toward governments?
   A. No government can ever be trusted to do what is right.
   B. In a perfect world, there would be no governments at all.
   C. People should be loyal to their government, no matter what.
   D. A government should serve its people, not the other way around.

Read the selection. Then, answer the questions.

Coretta Scott King was married to the great civil rights leader Dr. Martin Luther King, Jr. After his murder in 1968 in Tennessee, she continued to carry on his unfinished work.

Coretta Scott grew up on a farm in a small hamlet near Marion, Alabama. She was an excellent student and graduated at the top of her high school class. She enrolled at Antioch College as a major in music and education. Unfortunately, the local public schools refused to accept any African American student teachers.

She then decided to become a professional singer. While studying at the New England Conservatory of Music in Boston, Coretta met a theology student named Martin Luther King, Jr. They soon married and moved to Montgomery, Alabama, where Dr. King began his work as a minister. Due to their strong belief in equal rights for everyone, the Kings soon became influential leaders in the civil rights movement. They gave many speeches and led many marches. Just days after her husband's death, Coretta led fifty thousand people in a civil rights march. She then traveled to other countries to speak out for equal rights. She eventually founded the King Center to educate people about Dr. King's work and beliefs.

8. Where did Coretta Scott King grow up?
   A. Marion, Alabama
   B. Boston, Massachusetts
   C. Montgomery, Alabama
   D. Nashville, Tennessee

9. What was the first career Coretta tried to pursue?
   A. music teacher
   B. professional singer
   C. church minister
   D. civil rights leader

10. Why was Coretta unable to pursue her first career choice?
   A. She could not find a college that would accept her as a music student.
   B. She realized very quickly that her true passion was for the civil rights movement.
   C. She married Martin Luther King, Jr. and moved to Montgomery, Alabama.
   D. None of the local public schools would accept an African American student teacher.

11. What detail from the selection helps you understand why Coretta Scott King wanted to fight against racial injustice?
   A. She grew up on a small farm.
   B. She married the great civil rights leader, Martin Luther King, Jr.
   C. No one would let her student teach.
   D. She was unable to become a singer because of her race.

12. The Kings believed in using peaceful methods to fight for equal rights. What detail from the selection supports this idea?
   A. The Kings gave speeches and led marches.
   B. Dr. King was murdered in 1968 in Tennessee.
   C. Dr. King was a minister in Montgomery, Alabama.
   D. Coretta traveled to other countries to speak out for equal rights.

13. According to the selection, what did Coretta Scott King do within days of her husband's death?
   A. She attended music school in Boston.
   B. She led a huge civil rights march.
   C. She traveled to other countries.
   D. She founded the King Center.

14. Which of the following most clearly states the main idea of this selection?
   A. Dr. Martin Luther King, Jr. was a great civil rights leader who was murdered in 1968.
   B. The Kings gave many speeches and led many marches in their fight for equal rights.
   C. Coretta Scott King continued her husband's unfinished civil rights work after his death.
   D. Coretta Scott King was outraged when she was not able to pursue her first career choice.

15. What is the writer's attitude toward Coretta Scott King?
   A. pity
   B. admiration
   C. indifference
   D. gratefulness

Unit 3: Types of Nonfiction
Part 2 Diagnostic Test 6

MULTIPLE CHOICE

Read the selection. Then, answer the questions.

Depending on what kind of railway car you were riding in, traveling by train in the late 1800s could be either a grand experience or an awful one. If you were in a Pullman train car, you could expect considerable luxury and a great deal of service. George Mortimer Pullman introduced his Pullman Sleeping Car in 1857. Pullman's ambition was to design a railroad car that would be comfortable for overnight travel.

In 1865, a Pullman car was attached to the funeral train carrying President Lincoln's body to his home in Illinois. Pullman gained fame and his business took off. Four years later, he introduced his Pullman Palace Car. It boasted leather seats, lamps with silk shades, chandeliers, and gourmet food. Naturally, just about everyone would have preferred to ride in a Pullman car, but only the wealthy could afford it. For the rest, a long train ride could be a very cheerless experience, due to hard seats, lousy food, and bad smells. It seemed that no season was an ideal time to travel by train. In the winter, there was a constant risk of fire from coal heaters. In the summer, passengers would be drenched in sweat.

1. What was Pullman's main goal when he designed his train cars?
   - A. to figure out a way to air-condition a railroad car
   - B. to take away the danger of fires from coal heaters
   - C. to design a railroad car that only the very wealthy could afford
   - D. to design a railroad car that would be comfortable for overnight travel

2. What effect did people seeing a Pullman car carrying President Lincoln's body have on Pullman's business?
   - A. It had not effect because people were too upset about the president's death to notice the train car.
   - B. Pullman became famous and his luxury passenger car business took off.
   - C. Pullman realized he would have to make many improvements to his design.
   - D. People were outraged that the luxurious car took attention away from Lincoln.

3. What conclusion can you draw about the Pullman Palace Car based on the selection's description of it?
   - A. It was probably the most luxurious train car that had ever been seen at the time.
   - B. It had many design flaws, but it was still better than riding in a regular train car.
   - C. It was probably the same design as the Pullman Sleeping Car with no big changes.
   - D. Its excessive luxury would have offended President Lincoln if he had lived to see it.

4. According to the selection, what could a passenger expect from a ride in a Pullman car?
   - A. considerable luxury and great service
   - B. a high danger of fire from coal heaters
   - C. faster travel times than in regular cars
   - D. hard seats, lousy food, and bad smells

5. Who rode in Pullman cars?
   A. all train passengers
   B. wealthy passengers
   C. only Pullman's friends and family
   D. the first few people to board the train

6. Which of the following words best summarizes what a ride in a regular train car was like?
   A. luxurious
   B. satisfactory
   C. miserable
   D. adventurous

7. Why does the writer include a description of a regular train car?
   A. to show how Pullman and his train cars became so famous and successful
   B. to criticize a passenger's decision to choose a regular train car over a ride in a Pullman car
   C. to demonstrate how Pullman cars were not really so different from regular cars
   D. to contrast the poor traveling conditions with the comfort of the Pullman cars

8. What is the main idea of this selection?
   A. No one wanted to ride in regular train cars.
   B. Pullman train cars were luxurious and comfortable.
   C. Pullman train cars had chandeliers and air-conditioning.
   D. A Pullman car was attached to the train that took Lincoln home.

Read the selection. Then, answer the questions.

Over the centuries, wigs have been both popular accessories as well as a way to enhance beauty. In ancient Egypt, both men and women of nobility wore wigs on special occasions. These wigs were made of human hair and they were usually adorned with flowers and gold ornaments. There are even paintings of dead Egyptians wearing wigs. Egyptians believed that everything needed in the afterlife must be buried with the dead.

In ancient Rome, women believed that blond hair was better than dark hair. They therefore had wigs made from the hair of blond captives.

Throughout history the wearing of wigs was a sign of prosperity. It was the wealthy that cared about and could afford the elaborate headpieces when they were in fashion. Wigs would go in and out of style, often based on the whims of a king or queen. For example, King Louis XIII of France went bald at an early age, so he wore a wig of long and curly locks.

In the 1700s, wigs for women were designed with support wires and powder that raised hair three feet in the air. Some included cages with live birds and miniature ships. It would take an agile woman to move easily in such a headpiece without tipping over!

9. In the past, who would have most likely worn wigs?
   A. men
   B. women
   C. the poor
   D. the wealthy

10. The selection states that ancient Egyptians buried their dead wearing wigs. What other detail helps the reader understand that wigs were very important to Egyptians?

    A. They used captives' hair to make blond wigs.

    B. The adorned their wigs with flowers and gold ornaments.

    C. Both men and women wore wigs made of human hair.

    D. They believed that everything needed in the afterlife must be buried with them.

11. What color hair did the women of ancient Rome prefer?

    A. blond

    B. black

    C. brown

    D. red

12. Why did King Louis XIII of France wear a wig?

    A. he believed he would need it in the afterlife

    B. because he enjoyed putting birds and ships in it

    C. because he went bald at a very early age because

    D. because he preferred long hair over short

13. According to the selection, what did King Louis XIII's wig look like?

    A. It had cages with live birds in it.

    B. It was long and had curly locks.

    C. It was decorated with gold and flowers.

    D. It was made of human hair.

14. Why did women in the 1700s wear decorated wigs that were as high as three feet tall?

    A. They wanted to appear taller than they actually were.

    B. They were inspired by the wig fashions of ancient Rome.

    C. They wanted to show off their wealth by wearing elaborate wigs.

    D. They wished to exercise the muscles in their necks and shoulders.

15. What is the main idea of this selection?

    A. Ancient Egyptians and Romans wore wigs.

    B. Women who wore very tall wigs had to be agile.

    C. Over the centuries, wigs have been popular accessories.

    D. Wig styles were sometimes determined by kings and queens.

Unit 4: Poetry
Part 1 Diagnostic Test 7

MULTIPLE CHOICE

Read the selection. Then, answer the questions that follow.

International Space Station Alpha is a cooperative effort of the U.S. along with other countries, including Russia, Canada, and Japan. The science facility has been inhabited by astronauts continually since November 2000.

Due to the Earth's circular orbit, the space station orbits the Earth sixteen times a day. It is the job of Alpha astronauts to study changing conditions on the planet. They make careful observation using expert data from scientific equipment. They then add their own informal field notes from their observations.

Alpha crews describe the heart-pounding sensations that come from getting a stars-eye look at Earth. They also worry about troubling developments. Astronaut Frank Culbertson piloted shuttle missions in the early 1990s. He took command of ISS Alpha in 2001. An immediate surprise was the change in what he could observe of Earth's face. Pollution now creates a far more cloudy view than in the decade before. "There is smoke and dust in wider-spread areas than we have seen before. . . ," he explained in an interview. He also recalled the magnificent light shows on Earth's surface at night. "It's quite amazing to see how many people actually live down there . . . ," he marveled.

1. How many times per day does ISS Alpha orbit around Earth?
   A. 1
   B. 6
   C. 16
   D. 26

2. According to the information in the selection, what is the main purpose of ISS Alpha?
   A. to study the Earth and help us to understand our world better
   B. to see how long people can live and work in space
   C. to find out if people from different countries can work together
   D. to develop advanced weapons systems that will work in space

3. According to the selection, what is one troubling development that concerns ISS Alpha crews?
   A. night-time light shows from Earth's huge population
   B. conflicts between crew members from different countries
   C. faulty equipment on the space station giving incorrect data
   D. increasing smoke and dust from pollution in Earth's atmosphere

4. How does Frank Culbertson know that pollution is wider-spread now than it was a decade ago?
   A. He sees how many people live on the planet and realizes they must be spreading pollution.
   B. He was a shuttle pilot in the 1990s and saw less pollution from space then.
   C. He is simply drawing a logical conclusion that pollution must have spread during that time.
   D. He was told by others that pollution has spread over the last ten years.

5. Why do the night-time light shows on Earth's surface amaze Frank Culbertson?

    A. They look like tiny, twinkling holiday lights.

    B. They completely cover the face of the planet.

    C. There are not as many lights as he would have thought.

    D. They are evidence of how many people live on the planet.

6. Why do you think this selection was written?

    A. to inform readers about ISS Alpha

    B. to entertain readers with stories about life on ISS Alpha

    C. to persuade readers to fight pollution

    D. to make readers feel proud of the U.S. role in ISS Alpha

7. Which of the following choices best describes Frank Culbertson's reaction to his first view of Earth from ISS Alpha?

    A. fear and regret

    B. thrill and wonder

    C. joy and confusion

    D. amazement and concern

Read the selection. Then, answer the questions.

Like modern scientists, ancient astronomers learned a great deal from observing the stars. However, because they did not have the sophisticated instruments of modern astronomers, the ancients made a very important, but incorrect, assumption. For thousands of years, these astronomers believed that the Earth was at the center of the universe.

It was not until 1543 that Nicolaus Copernicus of Poland proposed a strange and intriguing theory: the Earth revolved around the sun. Many found it impossible to accept this sudden, abrupt turnabout from a long-held belief. Earth, as the center of the universe, placed humans in the central role. Copernicus's theories were rejected as false.

In the early 1600s, a crude telescope was invented. In Italy, Galileo Galilei refined the design to make it twenty times stronger than the human eye. Upon first using it, he immediately found undiscovered stars. He also located four moons revolving around Jupiter. He made other discoveries that similarly supported Copernicus's idea that the Earth, in fact, does revolve around the sun. However, it wasn't until the late 1600s that the English scientist Sir Isaac Newton had new evidence that finally convinced people that Galileo and Copernicus were correct. "If I have seen further it is by standing upon the shoulders of giants," Newton wrote. Modern astronauts would surely agree.

8. What is the main focus of this selection?

    A. the ancient idea that the universe revolves around the Earth

    B. the lives of astronomers Copernicus, Galileo, and Newton

    C. how astronomers proved that the Earth revolves around the sun

    D. how modern scientists are more intelligent than ancient astronomers

9. The selection states that ancient astronomers learned about the stars and planets by simple observation. What was the main problem with relying on what could be seen with the naked eye?

    A. They made incorrect assumptions.

    B. They could not see anything useful.

    C. They did not share their findings.

    D. Each person saw something different.

10. What was the main reason why people rejected Copernicus's idea that the Earth revolves around the sun?
    A. because the first crude telescopes showed them that the sun was revolving around Earth
    B. because they thought Copernicus misunderstood his data
    C. because they did not want to think that humans were not at the center of the universe
    D. because their observations clearly told them that the opposite was true

11. What effect did the invention of the telescope have on the controversy about whether or not the Earth revolves around the Sun?
    A. It had no effect because Galileo was unable to find anything to support or disprove Copernicus's theory.
    B. Galileo was able to find some evidence that supported Copernicus's theory.
    C. It distracted most astronomers from the controversy, so the theory was forgotten for some time.
    D. Galileo was able to prove Copernicus's theory once and for all.

12. How did Galileo's discovery of new stars and of moons orbiting Jupiter effect Copernicus's theory?
    A. It was logical to assume from this discovery that the Earth, like Pluto, orbits the sun.
    B. It showed that Jupiter is a larger planet than Earth, so Earth must not be the center of the universe.
    C. He saw that some stars orbit Jupiter, so the entire universe must not be orbiting around Earth.
    D. He still assumed that the new stars and Jupiter were revolving around Earth, the center of the universe.

13. How long did it take to prove Copernicus's theory?
    A. almost 50 years
    B. a little less than 100 years
    C. about 150 years
    D. more than 200 years

14. Whose evidence convinced people that Earth revolves around the sun?
    A. Galileo Galilei
    B. Nicolaus Copernicus
    C. modern scientists
    D. Sir Isaac Newton

15. Why would modern astronauts agree with Newton's statement about "standing upon the shoulders of giants"?
    A. because stars and planets look like giants from space
    B. because they know that early astronomers Copernicus and Galileo were right about Earth revolving around the sun
    C. because all astronauts admire Sir Isaac Newton and his discoveries
    D. because they would not be able to go into space without the discoveries and inventions of those who came before them

Name _____ Date _____

Part 2 Diagnostic Test 8

MULTIPLE CHOICE

Read the selection. Then, answer the questions that follow.

The word *supermarket* was first used in the late 1920s in the United States. However, early supermarkets were not nearly as large as today's high-volume, self-service stores. Several important developments mark this transition from small general stores to one-stop mega-supermarkets.

In 1910, the Great Atlantic and Pacific Tea Company opened the so-called economy store format. On their shelves, they placed attractive displays of such items as tea, coffee, and canned foods. This company kept their prices fairly low by selling in high volume. This practice became a feature of later supermarkets as well. They also introduced the idea of "cash and carry." Customers had to pay cash, and delivery was not offered. This also helped keep grocery prices low.

Any discussion of the history of the supermarket must include mention of two more important developments. The introduction of the motor vehicle is one, and the invention of the home refrigerator is the other. Both of these products allowed people to buy large quantities of food at one time.

By the 1930s, the supermarket concept was becoming more and more popular. Convenient locations, parking lots, self-service, and low prices have kept shoppers flowing to stores for more than seventy years.

1. When was the word *supermarket* first used in the United States?
   A. 1910
   B. 1920s
   C. 1930s
   D. 1940s

2. Why is the Great Atlantic and Pacific Tea Company's economy store so important in the history of supermarkets?
   A. It was the first to use the term *supermarket.*
   B. It did not succeed, so it set supermarkets back many years.
   C. It was the first supermarket to offer refrigerated foods and parking lots.
   D. It introduced many new ideas that became features of later supermarkets.

3. What practices helped keep prices low in the Great Atlantic and Pacific Tea Company's economy store?
   A. keeping a very limited stock on the shelves
   B. offering delivery service and lines of credit
   C. selling in high volume while keeping prices low
   D. building parking lots for customers with automobiles

4. What does "cash and carry" mean?
   A. Customers could only get the low prices if they paid cash.
   B. Customers had to pay cash for the store's delivery service.
   C. Customers had the option of either paying cash or using credit.
   D. Customers could not use credit, and the store was self-service.

5. Based on the information in the selection, what can you assume about how people shopped before supermarkets were introduced?
   - A. They bought large amounts of food at one time so they would not have to shop as often.
   - B. They had to go to many small stores to buy all the goods they needed.
   - C. They had to park their cars far away since the stores did not have parking lots.
   - D. They paid cash and carried their groceries home themselves.

6. Why was the invention of motor vehicles important to the development of supermarkets?
   - A. Shoppers would not go to stores without parking lots.
   - B. People could carry more food home much more easily.
   - C. Store owners had to charge more to pay for their vehicles.
   - D. People needed all their products in one place to save gasoline.

7. The selection states that shoppers were able to buy much more food at one time after the invention of refrigerators. What does this imply about how people shopped before the invention of refrigerators?
   - A. They had to pay far more for perishable foods but did not have to worry about spoilage.
   - B. They were able to buy great quantities of perishable foods.
   - C. They had to buy perishable foods in smaller amounts and much more frequently.
   - D. They were unable to buy or eat any perishable foods.

8. What is the main idea of this selection?
   - A. Supermarkets keep their prices low and sell in volume.
   - B. Many factors influenced the development of supermarkets.
   - C. The invention of home refrigerators helped supermarkets grow.
   - D. The concept of a supermarket was introduced in the early 1900s.

Read the selection. Then, answer the questions.

Born in 1847, Alexander Graham Bell was a distinguished scientist and educator who is best known today for inventing the telephone.

With the help of his partner, Thomas Watson, Bell began to work on an electrical device that would transmit sound over telegraph wires. The two men struggled vainly for years in their efforts to get the device to work. Then, one day in 1876, Bell and Watson were working on their invention in separate rooms. Bell spilled some acid on himself. Agitated by the accident, he said, "Mr. Watson, come here. I want you!" To the astonishment of both men, Watson heard Bell's voice through the device on his workbench. Bell's telephone had become a reality!

Bell and Watson were soon giving demonstrations of the amazing new invention. It was not long before the first telephone company was established. Bell and his new wife then set sail for England to introduce the telephone to the people of Europe. When the French government awarded him a prize for his important work, Bell used the money to set up a laboratory devoted to helping the deaf. Bell continued to make many important contributions to science throughout his life. Forty-five years after inventing the telephone, Alexander Graham Bell died.

9. Which of the following is a direct result of the invention of the telephone?
   A. It took years for Bell and Watson to succeed.
   B. Bell wanted to work with the deaf.
   C. The first telephone company was established.
   D. Bell spilled acid on himself.

10. How did Bell and Watson discover that their invention worked?
   A. Bell called out for Watson, who heard Bell's voice through the device.
   B. Bell spilled acid on the device, and Watson saw that it started working.
   C. They took it to Europe to show to other scientists, who told them that it worked.
   D. They were able to call someone in the French government.

11. How did Bell use his award money from the French government?
   A. He retired and never invented anything again.
   B. He used it to invent the first working telephone.
   C. He opened the first telephone service company.
   D. He set up a laboratory devoted to helping the deaf.

12. Which of the following details from the selection helps explain why Bell and Watson were completely surprised when their invention worked?
   A. Watson was Bell's partner for many years.
   B. Bell was a distinguished scientist and educator.
   C. Bell and his wife took the telephone to Europe.
   D. They had been trying for years without success.

13. What is the main idea of this selection?
   A. The invention of the telephone changed the course of history.
   B. Thomas Watson rarely gets credit for inventing the telephone.
   C. Bell and Watson were surprised when their invention worked.
   D. Alexander Graham Bell is best known for inventing the telephone.

14. What is the main purpose of this selection?
   A. to persuade readers to use telephones more often
   B. to inform readers about Bell's invention of the telephone
   C. to give Thomas Watson credit for inventing the telephone
   D. to entertain readers with amusing stories about Bell and Watson

15. About how old was Bell when he died?
   A. 45 years old
   B. 29 years old
   C. 74 years old
   D. 50 years old

Unit 5: Drama
Part 1 Diagnostic Test 9

MULTIPLE CHOICE

Read the selection. Then, answer the questions.

History is filled with tragic examples of cities going up in flames. Among the first recorded major fire disasters, is the burning of Rome in July of 64 A.D. Most fires are fed by oxygen in the air, and accounts show that wind fanned the flames. The fire is thought to have started among the wooden shops and goods in a merchant area of the city. In the narrow streets, flames spread quickly, trapping people who were then unable to get away, causing many deaths.

A side story to this great fire is the role of Emperor Nero. A famous myth is that "Nero fiddled while Rome burned." He was accused of being outside the city, playing music while watching the fire. Although Nero was known as an entertainer, the thought that he might sing a ballad of Rome's destruction at such a time seems unlikely. In fact, Nero was hailed for his response to the fire. His actions included opening his royal gardens and surviving public buildings to the homeless. He also directed the rebuilding of Rome. Following the fire, the preference for marble and stone over wood created a more fireproof city.

1. What is the purpose of the first paragraph in this selection?
   A. to show that fires in large cities can be very dangerous
   B. to discuss Emperor Nero's role in the Rome fire of 64 A.D.
   C. to explain the factors that caused the Rome fire to start and spread
   D. to state that fewer people would have died if Rome had been fireproofed

2. Why are the dates of the Rome fire important to understanding why the fire may have started and spread?
   A. One can assume from the dates that it started on a very hot and dry summer day.
   B. One can assume from the dates that the fire started on an extremely windy day.
   C. Historians know that Emperor Nero was not in the city on those particular dates.
   D. The merchant area of Rome may not have been open for business on those days.

3. How did oxygen affect the fire?
   A. The oxygen in the air made the fire start.
   B. The fire did not ruin the parts of the city where it was the windiest.
   C. The oxygen in the air helped to stop the fire from spreading.
   D. It was a windy day, so the oxygen in the air fueled the fire.

4. Why were so many people trapped in the Rome fire?
   A. because Emperor Nero was not in the city to help them escape
   B. because it was a hot Italian summer day and people were asleep
   C. because they did not know the way out of their own neighborhoods
   D. because the streets were narrow and lined with shops built of wood

5. What evidence helps to disprove the story that "Nero fiddled while Rome burned"?
    A. The fire is thought to have started among the wooden shops of Rome.
    B. Nero was hailed for his response to the fire.
    C. Nero did much to help the homeless and rebuild Rome after the fire.
    D. Nero was known as an entertainer and a good fiddler.

6. Why was Nero praised?
    A. for playing beautiful music
    B. for helping victims after the fire
    C. for putting out the fire
    D. for running away from the fire

7. Why did Roman builders prefer marble and stone over wood when rebuilding after the fire?
    A. to block the wind better
    B. to stay cooler in the summer
    C. to make the city more fireproof
    D. to please Nero, who disliked wood

Read the selection. Then, answer the questions.

We may think of fish as residing in comfortable oblivion in watery homes, unaware of more than their immediate surroundings. However, the salmon is a good example of the complexity of the ocean's ecosystem.

Salmon live in the sea but make a difficult journey upstream to fresh water to spawn, or reproduce. A female lays thousands of eggs in a stream nest, which are fertilized by a male. After the eggs hatch, the young salmon go through the different growth stages. Eventually they return to the ocean to mature into adult salmon. Then, as if they swore oaths and promised to return to their birthplace, they travel back upstream to spawn. There they usually die. The decomposing fish add nutrients to the water that flows downstream to the sea.

Relationships among sea dwellers can also be complicated. An interesting example involves the shark. Weak and injured creatures, violently thrashing or quietly mewling, attract the shark. Yet along with the shark come slender pilot fish, befriended by this fearsome predator. The shark, of course, is not a friend to humans. However, it helps the pilot fish by letting it eat its leftovers without attacking this "freeloading" fish.

8. What is spawning?
    A. reproducing
    B. freeloading
    C. swimming upstream
    D. maturing to adulthood

9. Where do salmon go to mature into adult fish?
    A. freshwater streams
    B. the open ocean
    C. their birthplace
    D. shark feeding areas

10. According to the selection, how do dead salmon contribute to the cycle of life?
    A. They add nutrients to the water.
    B. They keep away predators that threaten the baby fish.
    C. They are food for the baby salmon.
    D. They help other salmon find their way upstream to spawn.

11. What detail about the salmon's life cycle helps to disprove the idea that fish are not aware of more than their immediate surroundings?
   A. Salmon die in their birthplace after they lay their eggs.
   B. Female salmon lay thousands of eggs in their nests.
   C. Salmon swear oaths, promising to return to their birthplace.
   D. Salmon are able to return to their far-away birthplaces to spawn.

12. What attracts sharks?
   A. fresh water
   B. dead salmon
   C. freeloading pilot fish
   D. weak and injured creatures

13. Which of the following sentences from the selection fails to support the main idea of the last paragraph?
   A. Relationships among sea dwellers can also be complicated.
   B. Yet along with the shark come slender pilot fish, befriended by this fearsome predator.
   C. The shark, of course, is not a friend to humans.
   D. However, it helps the pilot fish by letting it eat its leftovers without attacking this "freeloading" fish.

14. How do you know that the writer assumes readers do not know much about the ocean's ecosystems?
   A. The first sentence says that people might think fish are "oblivious."
   B. The second example is of the relation-ship between sharks and pilot fish.
   C. The first example is of the salmon's complex and interesting life cycle.
   D. The selection is written in simple lan-guage, as if it was meant for children.

15. What is the main idea of this selection?
   A. Fish live in comfortable oblivion.
   B. Salmon swim upstream to spawn.
   C. The ocean's ecosystem is complex.
   D. Sharks allow pilot fish to eat leftovers.

Unit 5: Drama
Part 2 Diagnostic Test 10

MULTIPLE CHOICE

Read the selection. Then, answer the questions.

Sarah Breedlove, an African American woman better known as Madame C.J. Walker, founded her own business in the first decade of 1900. Within 15 years she was a millionaire—the first black woman to attain that achievement.

What propelled Sarah toward her road to success was what you might call a disastrous hair day! She developed a scalp problem and lost patches of hair. She was ashamed of her appearance and, in her embarrassment, she began mixing and experimenting with hair products to find a cure. In the process, she discovered not only the source of her future company but her skill as a businesswoman.

In 1905, Sarah married Charles Joseph Walker. She took his name—initials and all—and began producing "Madame Walker's Wonderful Hair Grower." Soon she had a line of hair-care products for African-American women and was presenting them door to door. She visited with women in their homes, demonstrating her products and always looking for new ways to sell them. Madame Walker was the picture of hard work and industry, and before long her business was thriving.

At the high point of her company's success, more than 3,000 people, many of them women, were dependent on her for employment, and she supported them with good jobs.

1. According to the selection, Sarah Breedlove was the first African-American woman to attain what achievement?
   A. have employees
   B. become a millionaire
   C. start a line of hair-care products
   D. become a door-to-door salesperson

2. What caused Sarah to experiment with hair-care products?
   A. She developed an embarrassing scalp problem.
   B. Her husband encouraged her to start a business.
   C. She wanted to become wealthy and famous.
   D. She liked visiting other women in their homes.

3. What most likely inspired Madame C.J. Walker to develop more hair-care products after she invented "Madame Walker's Wonderful Hair Grower"?
   A. successful sales of her "Hair Grower"
   B. the need to keep her employees busy
   C. her love of selling things door to door
   D. her husband's unquestioning support

4. How did Sarah sell her products at first?
   A. catalogs
   B. general stores
   C. door to door
   D. her own shop

5. How do you know that there probably were not many hair-care products for African American women available before Madame C.J. Walker introduced her line?

   A. Madame C.J. Walker had many employees, many of them women, dependent on her for their income.

   B. Walker's products became very successful very quickly, so there probably was not much competition at the time.

   C. African-American women were willing to let her into their homes for product demonstrations.

   D. The products that were available made her hair fall out in clumps, so they probably had not been made for African American hair.

6. At the height of her company's success, how many workers did Madame C.J. Walker employ?

   A. 15

   B. 1,900

   C. 3,000

   D. 5,000

7. What was the main reason for Madame C.J. Walker's success?

   A. her scalp problem

   B. her husband's name

   C. the number of workers she employed

   D. her willingness to work hard

Read the selection. Then, answer the questions.

Maya Angelou is one of the most popular poets of recent times. She has enjoyed great success, though not just as a poet. She is also known as an author, a playwright, an actress, a dancer, a director, a producer, and an educator. Angelou is a fluent speaker of half a dozen languages and uses them as she travels the world, spreading her message of love and social equality. Millions of people have been touched by Angelou's expressive readings of her work on television and at live performances. Her powerful and animated reading of her poem "On the Pulse of Morning" was a highlight of President Clinton's 1993 inauguration. The poem asks the people of America to work together to build a more loving nation.

In her poetry, Maya Angelou uses short lines and everyday vocabulary to describe the great joy and terrible sadness she has known in her life. The words she prefers to use may not be very fancy. Still, the feelings and ideas she expresses through her poetry are anything but bland. Her poems are filled to overflowing with strong emotions and powerful images. Maya Angelou clearly understands that language is a gift to be cherished and used wisely.

8. Which of the following choices contains three of the roles in which Maya Angelou has found success?

   A. author, scientist, and doctor

   B. lawyer, photographer, and politician

   C. poet, actress, and educator

   D. playwright, translator, and chef

9. The selection states that Angelou knows a half dozen languages. How does this help her with her life's mission?

   A. She is able to write poetry in all six languages.

   B. She is able to spread her message around the world.

   C. She can write poems about the joy and sadness in her life.

   D. She was able to act as an ambassador for President Clinton.

10. What are the main messages that Maya Angelou wishes to spread?
    A. love and social equality
    B. hard work and compassion
    C. anger and rebellion
    D. talent and creativity

11. What is the message of "On the Pulse of Morning," which Angelou read at President Clinton's 1993 inauguration?
    A. to wake up early each day and work hard
    B. to learn many languages and travel the world
    C. to cherish the gift of language and use it wisely
    D. to work together to build a more loving nation

12. Which of the following phrases from the selection best shows that the writer admires Angelou's oral readings of her work?
    A. her powerful and animated reading
    B. short lines and everyday vocabulary
    C. a gift to be cherished and used wisely
    D. readings of her work on television

13. The selection states that Angelou chooses to use short lines and everyday vocabulary in her writing. How does this affect her poetry?
    A. It makes it seem somewhat childish and simple.
    B. It is quite bland but appeals to a wider audience.
    C. It still reveals strong emotions and powerful images.
    D. It is not very easy to understand for the average reader.

14. What evidence in the selection best supports the idea that Angelou understands language is a "gift to be cherished and used wisely"?
    A. She has found success in a great many fields.
    B. She chooses to use simple rather than fancy words.
    C. She has known great joy and terrible sadness in her life.
    D. She uses language to influence people to be more loving.

15. What is the main idea of this selection?
    A. Maya Angelou has found success in many different fields and can speak a half dozen languages.
    B. Maya Angelou read one of her poems, "On the Pulse of Morning," at the 1993 inauguration of President Clinton.
    C. Maya Angelou uses short lines and everyday vocabulary in her poetry because she prefers simple language.
    D. Maya Angelou is a talented woman who uses her skills with language to spread her messages of love and social equality.

Unit 6: Themes in American Stories
Part 1 Diagnostic Test 11

MULTIPLE CHOICE

Read the selection. Then, answer the questions.

Alexander Graham Bell's invention of the telephone grew out of observing the trials of communication for his mother and wife, both of whom were deaf. Growing up, the needs of the deaf were part of his everyday life. His father taught deaf students and his mother lived the challenges of the deaf. Many people attempted to speak to her through a tube in her ear. Bell had a theory that vibrations from his voice would be a better way to communicate with her. He tested his idea by getting close to her forehead and speaking to her in low, deep tones. It is not clear how successful he was, however, each experience strengthened his inward resolve to understand sound transmission.

As an adult, Bell began teaching at a school for the deaf. There, he met Mabel Hubbard, a student he would later marry. Wanting to help his wife, mother, and others to communicate better, he was determined to continue his studies of the ear and his experiments with sound. In 1875, he successfully transmitted the first sounds over a wire, and in 1876, he invented the telephone. And so the telephone was born from a world of silence.

1. What inspired Bell to investigate how sound is transmitted?
   - **A.** his fascination with the use of wires and tubes
   - **B.** his mother's and wife's constant urging
   - **C.** his father's devotion to teaching the deaf
   - **D.** his desire to help deaf people communicate

2. How did most people try to speak to Bell's mother?
   - **A.** with sign language
   - **B.** by shouting very loudly
   - **C.** through a tube in her ear
   - **D.** by getting close to her forehead

3. The selection states that it is unclear how successful Bell's experiments were with using vibrations to speak to his mother. Based on the information in the selection, what is the most likely explanation for this?
   - **A.** His method was not scientific and his findings could not be measured.
   - **B.** His mother became frustrated and angry at his efforts.
   - **C.** He lost interest in his experiments with how sound is transmitted and heard.
   - **D.** His experiments were a failure, so he was too embarrassed to discuss them.

4. Which of the following most likely motivated Bell to teach at a school for the deaf?
   - **A.** his father's career teaching deaf students
   - **B.** his desire to test his inventions on deaf people
   - **C.** his belief that he would meet his wife there
   - **D.** his unsuccessful experiments with his mother

5. What effect did teaching at a school for the deaf have on Bell?
   A. He lost interest in his ideas about sound vibrations and transmitting sound with wires.
   B. He became even more determined to learn about how sound is transmitted and heard.
   C. He despaired of meeting a woman who could understand his passion for studying sound.
   D. He began to pity deaf people and think that there was no way to help them communicate.

6. How did Bell meet his wife?
   A. His mother introduced Mabel Hubbard to her son.
   B. His father once taught Mabel at a school for the deaf.
   C. She was a fellow scientist, also trying to invent a telephone.
   D. She was a student at the school for the deaf where he taught.

7. What is the main idea of this selection?
   A. Alexander Graham Bell invented the telephone in 1876.
   B. A young Bell began experimenting with the idea that deaf people might be able to hear the vibrations of a low voice.
   C. As an adult, Bell began teaching at a school for the deaf.
   D. Bell's observations of the struggles of deaf people to communicate made him want to learn how sound is transmitted and heard.

Read the selection. Then, answer the questions.

The largest and most famous carnival in the United States is the colossal Mardi Gras celebration held every year in New Orleans. Each year, tourists flock from all over the country to view amazing floats and listen to lively marching bands. Men and women in fantastic costumes balance on the highest tier of multi-level floats and shower the crowd below with colorful beads and trinkets. It is truly a sight to see!

Those who prefer quiet celebrations, however, should stay away. The noise level at Mardi Gras can be excessive, and the crowds that line the parade route tend to get rowdy. The local police are kept very busy trying to keep the public safe during Mardi Gras season.

After the parade, the party continues at fancy costume balls decorated in the official colors of the carnival: purple, which stands for justice; green, which stands for faith; and gold, which stands for power. While most tourists think of Mardi Gras as just an excuse to enjoy a party, some local people continue to honor the customs and traditions that reflect the carnival's ancient origins as a religious festival. Either way, everyone has a good time at Mardi Gras.

8. Mardi Gras is considered to be which of the following?
   A. a modest parade
   B. a religious festival
   C. a colossal party
   D. a violent demonstration

9. Which of the following is presented in the selection as a problem of Mardi Gras?
   A. The level of noise and that people tend to get rowdy.
   B. Police work hard to ensure public safety.
   C. Parade participants throw beads to the crowd.
   D. There are fancy costume balls after the parade.

Name _____   Date _____

10. What are the official colors of Mardi Gras?
   A. blue, red, and green
   B. green, yellow, and silver
   C. purple, green, and gold
   D. purple, red, and orange

11. What does the color green represent at Mardi Gras?
   A. justice
   B. faith
   C. power
   D. tradition

12. According to the selection, what happens after the Mardi Gras parade?
   A. People throw beads.
   B. The tourists all go home.
   C. There is a religious festival.
   D. There are fancy costume balls.

13. What is the origin of Mardi Gras?
   A. It was once a religious festival.
   B. It was once just a small parade that grew to what it is today.
   C. It is an excuse to have a party.
   D. It was invented by the city of New Orleans as a tourist attraction.

14. Which details from the selection most clearly indicates that the writer has probably been to Mardi Gras?
   A. It is truly a sight to see!
   B. Each year, tourists flock from all over the country to view amazing floats and listen to lively marching bands.
   C. People have a good time at Mardi Gras.
   D. Some local people continue to honor the customs and traditions that reflect the carnival's ancient origins.

15. What is the main idea of this selection?
   A. Mardi Gras participants wear costumes and throw beads.
   B. There is a huge parade at Mardi Gras, which tourists enjoy.
   C. Crowds get very loud and rowdy at the Mardi Gras celebration.
   D. Mardi Gras is a huge celebration held in New Orleans each year.

Unit 6: Themes in American Stories
Part 2 Diagnostic Test 12

MULTIPLE CHOICE

Read the selection. Then, answer the questions.

No one knows exactly when the first library was founded. People began writing down information and ideas thousands of years ago. The earliest records were kept on clay tablets and scrolls of papyrus, a primitive form of paper. Almost 2000 years ago, the rulers of ancient Egypt borrowed papyrus scrolls from distant lands and made copies of them. The establishment of the Alexandrian Library made Alexandria, Egypt, a great center of culture and learning. The library, teeming with information, contained more than 700,000 scrolls. These scrolls never left the building. Scholars came from far and wide to study them. An aura of wonder hung over this very special place where educated people could gather to study and to teach.

The oldest library in the United States was started at Harvard University in 1638. A century later, Benjamin Franklin founded the first subscription library in the country. For a small fee, subscribers could borrow books in exchange for their solemn pledge to return the books to the library. Other libraries supported themselves with voluntary donations from the people who used them. The first tax-supported free libraries in the United States appeared in the early 1800s. Today, public libraries can be found in almost every community in the nation.

1. How many scrolls did the Alexandrian Library contain?
   A. a few thousand
   B. about 550,000
   C. more than 700,000
   D. over 1,000,000

2. What effect did the establishment of the great library have on Alexandria, Egypt?
   A. It became a center of culture and learning.
   B. It became a sanctuary for scholars from around the world.
   C. It became the brand new capital of Egypt.
   D. It became famous for use of subscriptions.

3. Based on the information in the selection, how did the Alexandrian library get many of its scrolls?
   A. by hiring scholars to write them for the library
   B. by trading scrolls with libraries in other places
   C. by borrowing them from scholars who studied there
   D. by borrowing and copying scrolls from distant lands

4. Who started the oldest library in the United States?
   A. Benjamin Franklin
   B. Harvard University
   C. the United States government
   D. the city of Alexandria, Virginia

5. How did Benjamin Franklin ensure that library subscribers would return the books they borrowed?
   A. He charged fees of those who failed to return the books.
   B. He did not allow people to remove the books from the library.
   C. He asked subscribers to make donations to support the library.
   D. He asked them to make promise that they would return the books.

6. Most community libraries today are funded by tax dollars. If you connect this information to details in the selection concerning the history of American libraries, what conclusion can you draw about how early American libraries were funded?

   A. Donations and small fees were not enough to support them.

   B. People did not want their taxes increased to pay for libraries.

   C. People did not value libraries very much in the early days.

   D. The ones that were supported by taxes were not successful.

7. What is the main idea of this selection?

   A. Libraries are centers of learning and culture.

   B. The history of libraries is long and fascinating.

   C. There was a great library in ancient Alexandria, Egypt.

   D. American libraries tried many ways of supporting themselves.

Read the selection. Then, answer the questions.

Imagine a wall of brick and stone, fifteen feet wide and twenty-five feet high. Imagine that it spans some fifteen hundred miles. That's roughly the distance from New York City to Omaha, Nebraska. Imagine a wall so vast that astronauts orbiting Earth can see it from space! Believe it or not, you've just imagined one of the seven wonders of the world—the Great Wall of China.

Built entirely by hand, the Great Wall was begun around the 7th century BCE. It took many hundreds of years to complete. The first segments were built thousands of years ago to keep out invaders from the north. Nearly paralyzed by the fear of being overrun by barbarians, Chinese emperors ordered that a wall be built in order to protect the people.

When nomadic Mongols entered the country through gaps in the wall, the emperors ordered more walls built to fill in the gaps. Millions of laborers were enlisted to help at the bustling work sites that sprang up across the country.

Today, people come from all over the world to walk along the Great Wall and marvel at its beauty. Protecting the ancient Wall from damage without halting tourism has been an ongoing concern for the Chinese government.

8. What is the purpose of the first paragraph in the selection, in which the writer asks the reader to imagine the Great Wall of China?

   A. to persuade readers to visit the Great Wall of China

   B. to argue for the protection and preservation of the wall

   C. to hook readers' attention with visual images of the wall

   D. to compare the Great Wall to other wonders of the world

9. What are the measurements of the Great Wall?

   A. 5 feet wide, 15 feet high, and 1000 miles long

   B. 15 feet wide, 25 feet high, and 1500 miles long

   C. 25 feet wide, 50 feet high, and 2500 miles long

   D. 50 feet wide, 100 feet high, and 3000 miles long

10. What is a unique feature of the Great Wall of China compared to other ancient structures?
    A. It is built of brick and stone.
    B. It was built entirely by hand.
    C. It took a very long time to complete.
    D. It is so large it can be seen from space.

11. Why was the Great Wall built?
    A. to protect China from barbarian invaders
    B. to make Chinese emperors feel important
    C. to create something that could be seen from space
    D. to have a tourist attraction that would last for centuries

12. How long did it take to complete the Great Wall?
    A. about ten years
    B. over 100 years
    C. many hundreds of years
    D. thousands of years

13. What effect did Mongol invasions have on the building of the wall?
    A. They slowed down the wall building for centuries.
    B. They finally brought the building of the Great Wall to a stop.
    C. They caused the emperors to speed up building to close the gaps.
    D. They did not affect the building of the Great Wall in any significant way.

14. Why did it take so long to complete the Great Wall?
    A. It was built entirely by hand.
    B. There were many worker rebellions.
    C. Emperors kept getting distracted.
    D. Invaders repeatedly destroyed the wall.

15. What detail from the selection supports the idea that the modern Chinese government is experiencing conflict about the Great Wall?
    A. Mongols entered the country through gaps in the wall.
    B. They want to protect the wall without ending tourism.
    C. The Great Wall is huge and can be seen from space.
    D. Early Chinese emperors were terrified of barbarians.

Unit 1: Fiction and Nonfiction
Part 1 Benchmark Test 1

MULTIPLE CHOICE

Reading Skill: Predicting

Answer the questions below.

1 What are the two MAIN things you should consider in order to make accurate predictions in a story?

  ○ the author and the personalities of the characters

  ○ the title and the names of the characters

  ○ the plot and the cultural context of the work

  ○ story details and your own experience

2 What is the BEST procedure for making predictions as you read a story?

  ○ Make a prediction as you read, and then keep reading to see if it comes true.

  ○ Make a prediction as you read, and then peek at the ending to see if you are right.

  ○ Never change a prediction you make, no matter what new details the story provides.

  ○ Read the story backwards so that you know everything that will happen before it happens.

3 What MAIN effect does making predictions have on most readers?

  ○ It removes all the suspense from the plot of a story.

  ○ It cuts down on the reader's interest in the story.

  ○ It makes the story seem more realistic and believable.

  ○ It helps keep the reader actively engaged in the story.

4 Read these sentences from a story and choose the BEST prediction of what will happen next.

  In the early morning, Cara stood at the bus stop on Round Lake Road. She clutched her textbooks to her side and stamped her feet to try to keep warm.

  ○ Cara will greet her brother when he comes home from school on the bus.

  ○ Cara will get on the bus when it comes in order to go to school.

  ○ Cara will read her textbooks as she takes the bus to the movies.

  ○ Cara and her family will move to a warmer climate.

5 Which of these details MOST CLEARLY predict that a bad storm is coming?

  ○ A siren sounds as a character looks out the window.

  ○ The sky darkens and the winds begin to blow.

  ○ A character takes a sailboat to a place called Storm Island.

  ○ A character listens to a weather report and shakes her head.

Read the following excerpt from a story. Then answer questions 6–7.

In the ballroom, the orchestra began to play. Jorge listened, tapping a foot to the rhythm. Across the table Anna smiled, tapping a foot as well. Jorge rose from his chair at the table and smiled back at Anna. "Shall we?" he said, motioning toward the dance floor. The tablecloth hung low between them, and as Jorge moved forward, he stepped on it. Then, his legs in a tangle, he fell flat on his face.

6 From the details in the first five sentences of the selection, which of these predictions seems MOST LIKELY to happen?
   ○ Jorge will refuse to ask Anna to dance with him.
   ○ Jorge and Anna are going to get up and dance.
   ○ Anna will refuse to dance with Jorge when he asks.
   ○ Jorge is going to trip and fall on his face.

7 Which detail in the selection should make you reconsider your first prediction and expect a different outcome than before?
   ○ Jorge taps his foot to the music.
   ○ Jorge motions toward the dance floor.
   ○ Anna taps her foot to the music.
   ○ Jorge steps on the tablecloth.

Reading Skill: Using Text Aids

Answer the questions below.

8 Which of these are examples of consumer documents?
   ○ atlases and almanacs
   ○ textbooks and encyclopedias
   ○ labels and warranties
   ○ newspapers and magazines

9 What does the legend on a map provide?
   ○ the meaning of the maps' symbols
   ○ directions (north, south, east, west)
   ○ the scale to which the map is drawn
   ○ an old tale about places on the map

10 What is the term for a document that lists arrival and departure times in rows and columns?
   ○ a legend
   ○ a schedule
   ○ an orientation
   ○ an itinerary

Literary Analysis: Plot, Conflict, and Literary Devices

Answer the questions below.

11 What is the term for the part of a story that provides background information about main characters and their situation?
   ○ exposition
   ○ falling action
   ○ flashback
   ○ resolution

12 Which of these choices is the BEST definition of the climax of a story?
- ○ the point at which the conflict is introduced
- ○ the point where new complications to the conflict are introduced
- ○ the point of highest tension or suspense
- ○ the point at which all the loose ends of a plot are tied together

13 Which of these is an example of an internal conflict?
- ○ A knight struggles to defeat a fire-breathing dragon.
- ○ A lawyer struggles to prove the innocence of her client.
- ○ A farmer struggles to bring his crops through a bad drought.
- ○ A student struggles to come to the right decision.

14 In what part of the story are problems worked out so that the conflict is eliminated?
- ○ exposition
- ○ rising action
- ○ foreshadowing
- ○ resolution

15 What does foreshadowing usually help to create?
- ○ suspense
- ○ flashbacks
- ○ external conflict
- ○ internal conflict

16 What does it mean when a story has a chronological narrative structure?
- ○ The narrator presents events that happened in a long-ago time.
- ○ The narrator presents events in the order in which they happened in time.
- ○ The narrator jumps around in time in order to provide his or her memories.
- ○ The narrator introduces a character who goes on to tell a story within the story.

Read the story below. Then answer the questions 17–20.

(1) Jean, a high school student, was such a good swimmer that she was able to get a summer job as a lifeguard at the local pool. (2) She had no idea that the experience would test her skill and quick thinking more than anything ever before. (3) One Thursday afternoon, Dean and Frank Rinaldo showed up at the pool. (4) Noisy and reckless, the two teenaged brothers quickly drove the other swimmers away. (5) They paid no attention when Jean told them to behave. (6) Jean was just about to phone her supervisor when she saw the brothers crash into each other and begin to sink. (7) No one was there to help as Jean dove into the pool and struggled to pull them out. (8) They were very heavy, but she finally managed to drag out first Dean and then Frank. (9) Dean was conscious but in pain. (10) Frank was unconscious, and Jean had to give him mouth-to-mouth resuscitation. (11) When he finally began breathing, Jean raced to her cell phone and called an ambulance. (12) After the brothers recovered, they apologized to Jean and never behaved badly at the pool again.

17 Which part of the story is the exposition?
- ○ sentence 1
- ○ sentence 2
- ○ sentence 3
- ○ sentence 12

18 Which sentence in the story is an example of foreshadowing?
- ○ sentence 1
- ○ sentence 2
- ○ sentence 5
- ○ sentence 6

19 Around what conflict do the events in the story center?

- ○ Jean and the doctors' struggle to save the lives of the injured Rinaldo brothers.
- ○ Jean's struggle to control the crowds at the swimming pool.
- ○ Jean's struggle to get the Rinaldo brothers to behave at the swimming pool.
- ○ Jean's struggle to be the best swimmer she can be.

20 Where does the climax of the story take place?

- ○ sentence 3
- ○ sentences 4–5
- ○ sentences 6–11
- ○ sentence 12

Vocabulary: Prefixes

Answer the questions below.

21 Which statement is true about the prefixes *pre-* and *re-*?

- ○ *Pre-* and *re-* usually have similar meanings.
- ○ *Pre-* and *re-* often have opposite meanings.
- ○ *Pre-* and *re-* are never used with the same roots.
- ○ *Pre-* is much more frequently used than *re-*.

22 Based on your understanding of the prefix *pre-*, where in a textbook chapter would you probably find a *preview*?

- ○ before the chapter starts
- ○ in the middle of the chapter
- ○ at the end of every section
- ○ at the end of the entire chapter

23 Based on your understanding of the prefix *re-*, when are you likely to *regain* something?

- ○ when you never had it
- ○ when you had it at least once before
- ○ when you do not want it
- ○ when you understand it fully

24 Which choice explains how the prefix *pre-* is part of the meaning of the word *prefix*?

- ○ A *prefix* is something you fix, or attach, before a word or a root.
- ○ A *prefix* is something you fix in your mind beforehand.
- ○ A *prefix* is something that happens before something else.
- ○ A *prefix* is something you determine over and over until it is fixed in your mind.

25 Based on your understanding of the prefix *re-*, what do you conclude the italic word in this sentence must mean?

As she sang the song, the singer kept having trouble with the high notes of the *refrain*.

- ○ the opening notes of a song
- ○ an introductory part of a song that has a different tune that the rest
- ○ the highest notes in a song
- ○ a line or stanza that is sung over and over in a song

Grammar

Answer the questions below.

26 Which statement is true about common and proper nouns?
   ○ A proper noun is more specific than a common noun.
   ○ A proper noun is more polite than a common noun.
   ○ A common noun usually begins with a capital letter.
   ○ A proper noun usually does not begin with a capital letter.

27 How many proper nouns are there in this sentence?

   Sally Harding and her brother visited the D-Day Museum in New Orleans.
   ○ two
   ○ three
   ○ four
   ○ six

28 Which sentence below uses correct capitalization?
   ○ Carmine saw the United Nations and a museum when he visited New York City.
   ○ Carmine saw the United Nations and a Museum when he visited New York City.
   ○ Carmine saw the united Nations and a museum when he visited New York city.
   ○ Carmine saw the United Nations and a museum when he visited new york city.

29 Which of these spelling rules is accurate?
   ○ To form the plural of any noun that ends in *y*, change the *y* to an *i* and add *-es.*
   ○ To form the plural of any noun that ends in *y*, just add *-s.*
   ○ To form the plural of a noun that ends in a vowel + *y*, change the *y* to an *i* and add *-es.*
   ○ To form the plural of a noun that ends in a consonant + *y*, change the *y* to an *i* and add *-es.*

30 Which of these sentences uses plural nouns correctly?
   ○ The wifes used knifes to cut bunchies of berrys from the leafs.
   ○ The wives used the knives to cut bunches of berries from the leaves.
   ○ The wives used the knives to cut bunchies of berries from the leavs.
   ○ The wifes used the knifes to cut bunches of berryes from the leaves.

31 What do you call a noun that names something that can be perceived by one or more of the five senses?
   ○ A common noun
   ○ A proper noun
   ○ a concrete noun
   ○ an abstract noun

32 Which word in this sentence is an abstract noun?

   The child showed great kindness to the stray puppy that she found on the street.
   ○ child
   ○ kindness
   ○ puppy
   ○ street

33 Which of these sentences uses possessive nouns correctly?

○ The Miller brothers' invention was a children's game in which each player's marker was a different zoo animal.

○ The Miller brother's invention was a childrens' game in which each player's marker was a different zoo animal.

○ The Miller brother's invention was a children's game in which each players' marker was a different zoo animal.

○ The Miller brothers' invention was a childrens' game in which each players' marker was a different zoo animal.

ESSAY

Writing

1 Think of a children's story that you read or heard when you were younger. Then, on a separate piece of paper, write a very short version of the story and give it a new ending. You can include details that help point to the new ending, or you can make it a complete surprise.

2 Think of a new experience you have had that might be of interest to others. It can be something you did recently or something you recall from the past. Then, on a separate piece of paper, write a letter to a close friend in which you describe this experience.

3 Think of a person in your town or neighborhood who has made a strong impression on you. Then, on a separate piece of paper, write a short description of this person. Explain what he or she is like and why he or she has made such a strong impression on you.

SHORT ANSWER

Reading Skill: Predicting

1 What is the BEST procedure for making predictions as you read a story?

Reading Skill: Using Text Aids

2 What does the legend on a map show?

Literary Analysis: Plot, Conflict, and Literary Devices

3 What is the climax of a story?

4 What does it mean when a story has a chronological narrative structure?

Unit 1: Fiction and Nonfiction
Part 2 Benchmark Test 2

MULTIPLE CHOICE

Reading Skill: Author's Purpose

Answer the questions below.

1 In a detective story or mystery, what is usually the author's MAIN purpose?
   - ○ to entertain readers with an interesting puzzle
   - ○ to inform readers about police procedures
   - ○ to describe the appearance of a crime scene
   - ○ to persuade readers that crime does not pay

2 For which type of writing is the author's MAIN purpose usually to persuade readers to think or act in a certain way?
   - ○ biography and autobiography
   - ○ nonfiction travel writing
   - ○ newspaper editorial
   - ○ magazine articles

3 Which of these MOST OFTEN signal writing that is written to inform the reader?
   - ○ highly emotional language
   - ○ images and figurative language
   - ○ interesting characters and situations
   - ○ facts and technical language

4 For which type of writing is it MOST IMPORTANT to question and evaluate the author's statements and check the author's facts?
   - ○ persuasion
   - ○ description
   - ○ explanation
   - ○ narration

Read the personal narrative below. Then answer questions 5–7.

When I was a young man, I worked as an extra in Hollywood. I appeared in the crowd scenes in several films. Since it was easier to get jobs if you supplied your own costumes, I had a closet stuffed with costumes, including a cowboy outfit, a Roman toga, and a suit of armor. I wore the toga when I worked on a film called *Spartacus* about a slave revolt in ancient Rome. I had to arrive at the Hollywood sound stage at five A.M. each day. It was so early, I wore my watch to make sure I got there on time. During shooting one day, I forgot to take off my watch. No one on the set noticed, and no one noticed it later when they were making the final cut of the film. So if you ever see *Spartacus*, look for the Roman slave wearing a modern wristwatch. That fellow would be me.

5 What is the MAIN purpose of this narrative?
   - ○ to inform
   - ○ to entertain
   - ○ to explain
   - ○ to persuade

6 What is the specific purpose of this narrative?

○ to inform the reader about the difficulties in making a film that is set in the past

○ to convince the reader to see the film *Spartacus*

○ to share the writer's interesting and amusing experiences as an extra in films

○ to explain the process by which a person can become an extra in films

7 What type of detail MOST CLEARLY points to the MAIN purpose of the narrative?

○ the technical language

○ the factual information

○ the reasons for the author's behavior

○ the surprising event at the end

Read the following excerpt from a magazine article about snoring. Then answer questions 8–10.

Snoring: Comical Ailment or Serious Symptom?

Snoring is often the subject of comedy, but it can be more serious than most people realize. Sometimes it is a sign of obstructive sleep apnea, a medical condition in which the upper air passages narrow during sleep because of the combined effect of a blockage, relaxed muscles, and gravity. As the air passages narrow, breathing lessens, the oxygen level in the blood drops, and the patient snores to try to get more air. When the throat tissues collapse further, the patient stops breathing altogether, at which point he or she awakens, regains control of the throat muscles, and begins breathing normally. The patient then falls back asleep, but the cycle repeats throughout the night. In fact, a patient suffering from severe sleep apnea may awaken more than a hundred times a night. In most cases, since the patient awakens only partially, he or she is unaware of what is happening.

8 What is the MAIN purpose of this magazine article?

○ to entertain

○ to inform

○ to narrate

○ to persuade

9 Which phrase BEST describes the attitude of the magazine article's author?

○ humorous and witty

○ serious and informative

○ serious and sad

○ tense and frightening

10 Imagine that you are doing a science report on snoring. What is the FIRST thing you should do when you come across this magazine article?

○ Preview it to see if it will be a useful source of information.

○ Take detailed notes on the information that it supplies.

○ Compare it to another article on the subject to see which is longer.

○ Summarize the article in language that you can understand.

Literary Analysis: Mood, Tone, and Author's Style

Answer the questions below.

11 In a discussion of literature, to what does the term *mood* refer?

  ○ the author's attitude toward his or her subject or audience

  ○ the attitude or feelings that each character expresses

  ○ the time and place in which the work happens

  ○ the feeling or atmosphere that the work creates for the reader

12 In a discussion of literature, to what does the term *tone* refer?

  ○ the author's attitude toward his or her subject and audience

  ○ the loudness or softness of the dialogue that characters speak

  ○ the polished literary style that some authors display

  ○ the feeling or atmosphere that the work creates for the readers

13 Which of these details are MOST LIKELY to contribute to the mood of a story?

  ○ the title and the events

  ○ the characters and the ending

  ○ the images and the setting

  ○ the characters and the dialogue

Read the story below. Then answer questions 14–17.

> A cold wind raked across the barren moor and night was beginning to set in when we reached our final destination. The horses' hooves beat a steady drum as the carriage proceeded up the sweeping length of the driveway. At last we came to a stop in front of a crumbling mansion. One light shined brightly near an upper window, but the rest of the house was in inky darkness.

14 Which phrase BEST describes the mood of the passage?

  ○ sad and mournful

  ○ bleak and eerie

  ○ angry and resentful

  ○ charming and whimsical

15 Which of these images from the selection MOST CLEARLY contribute to the mood?

  ○ the cold wind raking across the moor

  ○ the steady drum of the horses' hooves

  ○ the sweeping length of the driveway

  ○ the light shining in an upper window

16 Which of these words from the passage MOST CLEARLY contribute to the mood?

  ○ *steady, sweeping,* and *shined*

  ○ *sweeping, brightly,* and *inky*

  ○ *final, crumbling,* and *brightly*

  ○ *barren, crumbling,* and *inky*

17 Based on the selection, which of these qualities seems characteristic of the author's style?

  ○ a highly emotional tone

  ○ fairly long sentences

  ○ lack of imagery

  ○ frequent use of slang

Literary Analysis: Fictional and Nonfictional Narratives

Answer the questions below.

18 Which of these elements must a fictional narrative contain?
  ○ plot   ○ figurative language
  ○ dialogue   ○ true events

19 Which type of writing is a nonfiction narrative?
  ○ a novel   ○ a stage drama
  ○ a biography   ○ a poem that tells a story

Read the story below. Then answer questions 20–21.

  Aaron and I had hiked quite a distance and were tired when we made camp. By the time dinner was over, we were more than ready for bed. Because of our exhaustion, we did not clean up properly. I should have known better than to leave food around in Yellowstone Park at night. At any rate, some time during the night, I was awakened by a noise. Glancing over, I saw a big, dark shape in the dim light. Blinking my eyes, I realized it was a grizzly bear. The leftovers we had foolishly left near camp had attracted the menacing beast! Deeply afraid, I remained very still and hoped that Aaron would do the same. I breathed a sigh of relief when the bear went lumbering off into the night.

20 How would you describe the mood of this nonfiction narrative?
  ○ lighthearted and humorous   ○ tense and exciting
  ○ sad and sentimental   ○ serious and unemotional

21 In what way does this nonfiction narrative borrow from the elements of fictional narratives?
  ○ It includes invented characters and   ○ It emphasizes certain details to add
    events.   excitement.
  ○ It resets the events in an imaginary   ○ It uses flashbacks to recount events
    setting.   that happened in the past.

Vocabulary

Answer the questions below.

22 How does the suffix *-ize* or *-yze* affect the word or root to which it is attached?
  ○ It turns the word or root into a verb   ○ It turns the word or root into a noun.
  ○ It turns the word or root into an   ○ It makes the word or root have an
    adjective.   opposite meaning.

23 Which of these words is generally used a noun?
  ○ invent   ○ reinvent
  ○ inventive   ○ invention

24 In this sentence, what does word in italics mean?

The potters will *individualize* each mug by putting a different design on the handle.

- ○ people who show unique qualities
- ○ to make special or appropriate to each person
- ○ to turn something into something else
- ○ special or unique

Grammar

Answer the questions below.

25 What do personal pronouns do?
- ○ replace nouns in sentences
- ○ describe or modify nouns
- ○ connect nouns to prepositions
- ○ indicate people but not other things

26 How many personal pronouns does this sentence contain?

Jane and I asked the boys to find the book for us, but they could not find it in time.

- ○ one
- ○ two
- ○ three
- ○ four

27 What is the case of the personal pronoun in this sentence?

The tune is borrowed, but the words are mine.

- ○ nominative
- ○ objective
- ○ possessive
- ○ reflexive

28 What is the complete antecedent of the pronoun *ourselves* in this sentence?

Since the train was nearly empty, Yvonne and I had a whole car to ourselves.

- ○ Yvonne
- ○ I
- ○ Yvonne and I
- ○ train and car

29 Which sentence uses pronouns correctly?
- ○ The boys tried to take care of the problem themselves.
- ○ Alyson and myself went to the computer store.
- ○ You students should do yourself a favor and study more.
- ○ No one but myself understood the situation.

30 Which of these sentences uses pronouns correctly?
- ○ Each of the girls had their own bicycle.
- ○ All of the girls had her own bicycle.
- ○ Both of the girls had their own bicycle.
- ○ Few of the girls had her own bicycle.

Spelling

Answer the questions below.

31 Which word is spelled correctly?

- ○ allways
- ○ agravate
- ○ bussiness
- ○ career

32 In which sentence is the italicized word spelled correctly?

- ○ Mom's birthday is an important *occassion* in our house.
- ○ *Parallell* lines run side-by-side and never meet.
- ○ They took *possession* of the house last Tuesday.
- ○ I am waiting *untill* six o'clock before I turn the soup on.

33 What should you do to spell the italic word in this sentence correctly?

I hope that you will *reccommend* me for this job.

- ○ Drop one of the *c*'s only.
- ○ Drop one of the *m*'s only.
- ○ Drop one *c* and one *m*.
- ○ Leave the word alone; it is correct as is.

ESSAY

Writing

1 Think of something that happened to you that changed your view of someone or something. Then, on a separate piece of paper, write a brief personal narrative about the incident.

2 Think about a situation in your school that could be improved. Then, on a separate piece of paper, write a journal entry about the situation. Indicate the problem and your ideas about the solution.

3 Recall an incident in your life that you think others would find entertaining or interesting to read about. Then, on a separate piece of paper, write a brief autobiographical essay about the incident. Tell what happened, how you felt at the time, and why the experience has made an impression on you.

SHORT ANSWER

1 What is the general purpose of a newspaper editorial?

2 What kind of details do you often find in writing that aims to inform?

3 What is the mood of a story?

4 Name three elements that a fictional narrative usually contains.

Unit 2: Short Stories
Part 1 Benchmark Test 3

MULTIPLE CHOICE

Reading Skill: Compare-and-Contrast

Answer the questions below.

1 Which of these sentences contains a comparison?

○ Many tourists visit Brazil during the festival known as Carnival.

○ Rio de Janeiro is a large city in Brazil, although it is not the capital.

○ Like Rio de Janeiro, São Paolo is a large city on the coast of Brazil.

○ People in Brazil speak Portuguese, for Brazil was once a colony of Portugal.

2 Which of these statements expresses a contrast?

○ The Nile, like the Amazon, is a very long river.

○ The Nile is in Africa, while the Amazon is in South America.

○ Both rivers have always been important to the people along their banks.

○ Only some portions of the Nile and the Amazon are easily navigated.

Read the following essay about Sherlock Holmes. Then answer questions 3–6.

Most people have heard of Sherlock Holmes, the fictional London detective created by Sir Arthur Conan Doyle. Fewer people know, however, that Doyle borrowed the idea for Holmes from American author Edgar Allan Poe. Several decades before Doyle wrote, Poe created Inspector Dupin of Paris, France, a detective who used his amazing intellect to solve puzzling crimes. The similarities can be seen in one of the very first Sherlock Holmes stories, "A Scandal in Bohemia," which involves a stolen document in a plot quite similar to the plot of Poe's earlier tale "The Purloined Letter."

3 What basic comparison does the essay make between Sir Arthur Conan Doyle and Edgar Allan Poe?

○ Neither author's works are well known today.

○ Both authors wrote detective stories.

○ Each author borrowed ideas from the other.

○ Both were important American authors.

4 According to the essay, how is the character of Inspector Dupin like the character of Sherlock Holmes?

○ He is French.

○ He lives in London.

○ He is based on a real person.

○ He is very clever.

5 Which words show that the second sentence of the essay contrasts with the first?

○ *fewer* and *however*

○ *however* and *idea*

○ *borrow* and *idea*

○ *fewer* and *people*

6 What similarity or difference between Doyle's and Poe's works does the essay point out?

- ○ "A Scandal in Bohemia" has events similar to those of "The Purloined Letter."
- ○ Both works are set in Paris.
- ○ "A Scandal in Bohemia" has no similarities with "The Purloined Letter."
- ○ Both works are set in London.

Read the following description of two characters. Then answer questions 7–8.

Olivia was a hard worker who put in long hours at the plant. Yet she always had a kind word for her fellow workers, from the plant manager to the cleaning staff. Her sunny disposition cheered people up, and coworkers often came to her for advice and assistance. Her brother Franz, on the other hand, would never win any popularity contests. "You ought to stop doing favors for the whole world," he often told his sister, "and start looking out for Number One." Still, Franz worked as hard as Olivia did at the plant. Eager to be promoted, he often agreed to come in on weekends.

7 Which contrast MOST CLEARLY applies to the characters?

- ○ Franz is kinder than his sister.
- ○ Franz is smarter than his sister.
- ○ Franz is more trusting than his sister.
- ○ Franz is more selfish than his sister.

8 What is similar about the perspectives of the two characters?

- ○ Both believe in hard work.
- ○ Both believe in stepping on toes to get ahead.
- ○ Both believe in helping others.
- ○ Nothing is similar about the two characters' perspectives.

Reading Skill: Compare an Original to a Summary

Answer the questions below.

9 Which of these types of writing MOST OFTEN consists of a summary?

- ○ a weekly editorial found in a local newspaper
- ○ a description of a TV show in a TV guide
- ○ the instructions that come with a bottle of medicine
- ○ a book-length biography of a famous person

10 How should a summary compare or contrast with the work it summarizes?

- ○ It should be more interesting to read than the work it summarizes.
- ○ It should be the same length as the work it summarizes.
- ○ It should include the main ideas of the work it summarizes.
- ○ It should not discuss the underlying meaning of the work it summarizes.

Literary Analysis: Setting

Answer the questions below.

11 What do details about the setting MOST OFTEN help establish in a work of fiction?
- ○ plot
- ○ mood
- ○ character traits
- ○ resolution

12 In which type of literature would the MOST IMPORTANT aspects of the setting probably be the customs and beliefs of the characters and the era in which the action takes place?
- ○ a historical novel
- ○ a contemporary drama
- ○ a children's fantasy
- ○ a spy thriller

Read the story below. Then answer questions 13–14.

The road was a dead end into the heart of the country. Where the woodland broke into a field, the sun poured down like honey from the vivid blue sky. Usually this was a quiet spot, but today— the first really warm day of spring—was a little different. The warm sun had melted the snows to create temporary pools of water, and in those pools thousands of frogs were hatching. They made a joyful symphony, higher pitched than the calls of birds but more tuneful than any insects'. It would last only for a day or two, and then it would be over.

13 Which aspect of the setting is MOST IMPORTANT in this description?
- ○ the customs and beliefs of the characters and the physical features of the land
- ○ the physical features of the land and the weather or season of the year
- ○ the weather or season of the year and the historical era in which the action takes place
- ○ the physical features of the land and the customs of the characters

14 What mood do the details in this description help create?
- ○ an eerie, somewhat frightening mood
- ○ a quiet and sad mood
- ○ a calm and cheerful mood
- ○ a tense and hectic mood

Literary Analysis: Character

Answer the questions below.

15 Which sort of character is the MOST complex?
- ○ a flat, static character
- ○ a flat, dynamic character
- ○ a round, static character
- ○ a round, dynamic character

16 For which of these purposes do writers often use static characters?
- ○ to serve as the main character
- ○ to create conflict for the main character
- ○ to show how people change and grow
- ○ to help establish the mood of a story

Read the story below. Then answer questions 17–20.

Leona was a goodhearted, outgoing person, but she did like to gossip. She did not realize that her gossiping could cause problems for others. After all, her gossip was never unkind; she liked to spread the news, not make snide comments about it. One day at the mall, she saw Elise Mondego. Then, at the other end of the mall, she saw Elise's boyfriend, Charley Parks. Smiling broadly, she told Charley she had just seen Elise and then asked if they were meeting up for lunch. Angrily, Charley stated that Elise had told him that she was visiting her grandmother. The next day, a furious Elise told everyone about Leona's big mouth. Leona learned the dangers of gossip, and from then on she was much more careful about the news she spread.

17 Which of these is a character trait that Leona displays?
- ○ friendliness
- ○ shyness
- ○ nastiness
- ○ sensitivity

18 Which of these is a character trait that Elise displays?
- ○ honesty
- ○ loyalty
- ○ friendliness
- ○ vengefulness

19 What type of character is Charley Parks?
- ○ flat and static
- ○ flat and dynamic
- ○ round and static
- ○ round and dynamic

20 What makes Leona a dynamic character?
- ○ She is a basically good person with one flaw.
- ○ She has a lively personality.
- ○ She learns a lesson and changes as a result.
- ○ She speaks to more than one character.

Vocabulary

Answer the questions below.

21 From which language does the root -*similis*- come?
- ○ English
- ○ French
- ○ Greek
- ○ Latin

22 Based on your understanding of roots and their meaning, what do you conclude the italic word in this sentence must mean?

Because she is color blind, she is unable to *differentiate* between red and green.
- ○ to identify characteristics
- ○ to appreciate qualities
- ○ to identify similarities
- ○ to identify differences

23 Based on your understanding of roots and their meaning, what do you think *spectators* are?
- ○ people who watch something
- ○ people who have fun
- ○ people who argue with each other
- ○ people who participate in sports

24 How is the root -*similis*- reflected in the meaning of the literary term *simile*?
- ○ in the idea that a simile uses language not meant to be taken literally
- ○ in the idea that a simile tells how one thing is like another
- ○ in the idea that a simile is different from a metaphor
- ○ in the idea that a simile is a device often found in poetry

25 Based on your understanding of the root -*spect*-, what is a pair of *spectacles*?
- ○ pants
- ○ shorts
- ○ eyeglasses
- ○ scissors

Grammar

Answer the questions below.

26 Identify the action verb in the following sentence.

The twins usually arrive on time for the gym class, but today they are late.
- ○ arrive
- ○ time
- ○ gym
- ○ are

27 Identify the sentence in which the verb in italics is a linking verb.
- ○ As he walked through the garden, he *smelled* the roses.
- ○ The roses *smelled* fragrant.
- ○ He *saw* several new bushes in the corner by the trellis.
- ○ Some of the bushes *had grown* very tall.

28 What are the principal parts of regular verbs?
- ○ present, past, present participle, past participle
- ○ present, past, future, participle
- ○ present, base, present participle, past participle
- ○ present, past, future, perfect

29 Which is true of regular verbs?
- ○ Their present and present participle have the same form.
- ○ Their past participle ends in -*ing*.
- ○ Their past and past participle have the same form.
- ○ Their present participle ends in -*ed*.

30 Which form of the verb correctly completes this sentence?

Cindy was _____ at the clown.
- ○ smile
- ○ smiles
- ○ smiling
- ○ smiled

31 Which form of the verb correctly completes this sentence?

Yesterday the dress still _____ fifty dollars.
- ○ costs
- ○ cost
- ○ costed
- ○ costing

32 Which form of the verb correctly completes this sentence?

Jonathan has _____ an essay about his summer job.

- ○ write
- ○ writed
- ○ wrote
- ○ written

33 In which sentence is the verb in italics used correctly?

- ○ The auctioneer *has spoke* into the microphone.
- ○ She *has put* the chair up for bidding.
- ○ Jamal *bringed* an auction guide with him.
- ○ He *bidded* twice on the chair.

ESSAY

Writing

1 Think of a place that you really like or really hate. Then, on a separate piece of paper, write a one-paragraph description of this setting.

2 Think of a character in a TV show or a film who made a strong impression on you. On a separate piece of paper, write a one-paragraph profile of this character.

3 Recall two movies or TV shows that you have seen lately and consider what you liked or did not like about them. On a separate piece of paper, jot down your ideas for a critical review of the two movies or shows.

SHORT ANSWER

Reading Skill: Compare-and-Contrast

1 Write a sentence that makes a comparison.

2 Write a sentence that states a contrast.

Literary Analysis: Setting

3 What do the details describing a setting often help establish in a work?

Literary Analysis: Character

4 In terms of flat, round, static, and dynamic, which combination makes for the MOST COMPLEX character?

Unit 2: Short Stories
Part 2 Benchmark Test 4

MULTIPLE CHOICE

Reading Skill: Making Inferences

Answer the questions below.

1 What is an *inference*?
- ○ a logical assumption about something an author leaves unstated
- ○ a reader's appreciation of an author's skills or techniques
- ○ a conversation in which characters have to read between the lines
- ○ the central idea or insight expressed in a literary work

2 Which of these steps is basic to making inferences?
- ○ focusing on the main ideas
- ○ connecting several details
- ○ separating fact from opinion
- ○ restating in simpler words

Read the story below. Then answer questions 3–6.

Marlena wheeled her cart down the aisle and paused in front of the cold cereals. She took a box of bran flakes from the shelf without comparing prices as she usually did. Her mind was elsewhere—on the science test her teacher had announced a few hours before. Marlena always got high grades in school, but she still worried about tests. She was worrying now as she went into the bread aisle and absently dropped a package of regular English muffins into her cart, even though she and her parents preferred the whole-wheat muffins. As she approached the checkout area, Marlena hoped the lines were not too long because she wanted to get home and study before supper.

3 From the details in the story, what inference can you make about Marlena's location?
- ○ She is in a supermarket.
- ○ She is at a drug store.
- ○ She is in a department store.
- ○ She is on her way to school.

4 Which details in the story help you infer that the events take place on a weekday afternoon?
- ○ "as she went into the bread aisle" and "as she approached the checkout area"
- ○ "wheeled her cart down the aisle" and "absently dropped a package"
- ○ "her teacher had announced a few hours before" and "study before supper"
- ○ "was worrying now" and "get home and study before supper"

5 From the details in the story, what inference can you draw about the character of Marlena?
- ○ She is smart but lazy.
- ○ She is foolish and impulsive.
- ○ She is selfish and unkind.
- ○ She is studious and responsible.

6 What do the details about Marlena's purchases suggest about her and her family?
- ○ They eat healthy food.
- ○ They love sweets.
- ○ They eat a lot of red meat.
- ○ They pay little attention to cost.

Reading Skill: Making Generalizations

Answer the questions below.

7 What are rational appeals in advertisements?
- ○ the excuses people make to buy a product they cannot afford
- ○ images that engage the feelings or emotions of consumers
- ○ factual details used to convince consumers to buy a product
- ○ inaccurate but strong details used to convince consumers to buy a product

8 Which of these lines from an advertisement contains generalizations that cannot be proved?
- ○ Scorpion: The car driven by athletes, movie stars, and corporate executives.
- ○ Anyone who buys a Scorpion before August 31 gets a $500 rebate.
- ○ The Scorpion has passed all the safety tests that the government has performed.
- ○ Everyone loves the new Scorpion—the most glamorous car on the road.

9 Which of these lines from an advertisement makes a bandwagon appeal?
- ○ Scorpion: The car driven by athletes, movie stars, corporate executives . . . and you!
- ○ Anyone who buys a Scorpion before August 31 gets a $500 rebate.
- ○ The Scorpion has passed all the safety tests that the government has performed.
- ○ The new Scorpion is the most glamorous car on the road.

10 Which words in this advertisement are examples of loaded language?

The ShowerPower umbrella combines plush fabric and sturdy metal in the best traditions of umbrella making. Buy one today!

- ○ *power, combines,* and *today*
- ○ *plush, sturdy,* and *traditions*
- ○ *plush, best,* and *buy*
- ○ *sturdy, buy,* and *today*

Literary Analysis: Point of View

Answer the question below.

11 What is the point of view of a story?
- ○ the author's attitude toward his or her subject or audience
- ○ the perspective from which the story is told
- ○ the customs of the period or society in which the work takes place
- ○ the central idea, insight, or message that the story conveys

Read the following passage from a story. Then answer question 12.

The New House

Arlen was impressed by the new house. He especially liked the high gables on the second floor and the large porch that ran along the whole front of the house. "I'd love to live in a house like that," he thought to himself.

Eva considered the house an awful monstrosity, way too big for the small plot of land on which it stood. "It's like an elephant on a postage stamp," she told herself, though she did not share her thoughts with Arlen.

12 What is the point of view of the story?
- ○ first person, narrated by Arlen
- ○ third person, limited to the thoughts and impressions of the character telling the story
- ○ first person, narrated by Eva
- ○ third person, providing the thoughts and impressions of more than one character

Read the following passage from a story. Then answer questions 13–14.

Our Farm

Our farm was on Stone Church Road near the parkway. I was very upset when my parents sold it, but Dad said the buyers made him an offer he couldn't refuse. Mom agreed with the decision. "We're not getting any younger, Johnny," she told me. "And the price they offered was a good one."

13 What is the point of view of the story?
- ○ third person, providing the thoughts and impressions of more than one character
- ○ first person, narrated by Johnny
- ○ third person, limited to the thoughts and impressions of only one character
- ○ first person, narrated by the father

14 Which pronouns in the story help indicate the point of view?
- ○ *my*, *him*, and *he*
- ○ *our*, *we*, and *they*
- ○ *our*, *I*, and *me*
- ○ *him*, *he*, and *we*

Literary Analysis: Theme

Answer the questions below.

15 Which statement about the theme of a work is true?
- ○ There is usually just one correct interpretation of a work's theme.
- ○ The theme of a work is usually directly stated at the end.
- ○ The theme of a work is never directly stated but is always implied.
- ○ The theme of a work is often a generalization about life or people.

16 When used as a symbol, what does a four-leaf clover commonly represent?
- ○ joy   ○ innocence   ○ a second chance   ○ good luck

Name _____ Date _____

Read the fable below. Then answer questions 17–20.

Once a lion captured a mouse and was about to eat it. "Spare me!" cried the mouse. "I am but a small mouthful to you, yet my family needs and loves me. If you let me go, I will help you in return." The lion did not think that anything so small could ever help him, but he was touched by the tiny creature's plight and amused by the bold claim of future aid, so he decided to let the mouse go. Years later, the lion was captured by some men. He was tied up in a cage when the mouse came by and saw him. When the men went to sleep, the mouse slipped into the cage and gnawed through the ropes. Later, when the men opened the cage to feed him, the lion was able to escape. The mouse had saved the creature who had spared his life, thereby proving that kindness will be rewarded.

17 What is the stated theme of the fable?
- ○ My family needs and loves me.
- ○ I will help you in return.
- ○ He decided to show compassion.
- ○ Kindness will be rewarded.

18 Which of these is an additional theme?
- ○ Do not judge capability based only on appearances.
- ○ Those who love their families will show compassion to others.
- ○ Do not let great changes catch you sleeping.
- ○ Human beings are stronger and cleverer than the strongest beast.

19 What does the mouse in the fable seem to symbolize, or represent?
- ○ wisdom
- ○ smallness
- ○ boastfulness
- ○ compassion

20 What does the lion in the fable seem to symbolize, or represent?
- ○ size and ambition
- ○ cruelty and greed
- ○ strength and power
- ○ endangered species

Vocabulary

Answer the questions below.

21 What is the origin of the word *evidence*?
- ○ It comes from a Greek word meaning "reason."
- ○ It comes from a Greek word meaning "truth."
- ○ It comes from a Latin word meaning "see."
- ○ It comes from a Latin word meaning "clue."

22 How is the origin of the word *monologue* reflected in its meaning?
- ○ A *monologue* is a speech by one person.
- ○ A *monologue* is the study of communication.
- ○ A *monologue* is something an actor must memorize.
- ○ A *monologue* is a speech that you see, rather than hear.

23 In what language does the word *indicate* have its origin?
- ○ Greek
- ○ Latin
- ○ French
- ○ German

24 The prefix *pro-* can mean "before." Based on your understanding of word origins, what do you conclude the italic word in this sentence must mean?

I read the *prologue* and went on to read Chapter 1.

- ○ a final chapter
- ○ a logical summary
- ○ an argument in favor of an issue
- ○ words that come before the main part

Grammar

Answer the questions below.

25 Which sentence uses a verb in the future tense?
- ○ Angela usually goes to the mall every Saturday.
- ○ Angela will probably go to the mall next Saturday.
- ○ Since October, Angela has gone to the mall every Saturday.
- ○ By tomorrow, Angela will have gone to the mall every Saturday in October.

26 What tense is the italic verb in this sentence?

Kristin *has boiled* the water for tea.

- ○ present
- ○ past
- ○ present perfect
- ○ past perfect

27 Which verb correctly completes this sentence using the subjunctive?

I wouldn't do that if I _____ you.

- ○ was
- ○ were
- ○ will be
- ○ have been

28 How do you form perfect tenses of verbs?
- ○ Use the helping verb *will* and the base form of the verb.
- ○ Use a form of the helping verb *be* and the past participle of the verb.
- ○ Use a form of the helping verb *have* and the present participle of the verb.
- ○ Use a form of the helping verb *have* and the past participle of the verb.

29 Which sentence uses correct subject-verb agreement?
- ○ Among the items were a box of eggs.
- ○ There was only eleven eggs in the box.
- ○ Some of the eggs was broken.
- ○ Gregory and Stuart eat a lot of eggs.

30 Which sentence uses correct subject-verb agreement?
- ○ A nest of robins sits in the tree.
- ○ There is two birds in the nest.
- ○ Sandy and Joanne sits near the nest.
- ○ One of the girls scare the birds.

Spelling

Answer the questions below.

31 Which word is spelled correctly?
- ○ athelete
- ○ sherbet
- ○ cockeroach
- ○ arthuritis

32 In which sentence is the italic word spelled correctly?

○ Sally is a *mischievious* child.   ○ My sister is applying to *college*.

○ That author is *writting* a new novel.   ○ I was sad to hear your cat *drownded*.

33 What should you do to spell the italic word in this sentence correctly?

I hope that you can visit *tommorrow*.

○ Drop one of the *m*'s only.   ○ Drop an *m* and an *r*.

○ Drop one of the *r*'s only.   ○ Leave the word alone; it is correct as is.

SHORT ANSWER

Reading Skill: Making Inferences

1 What is an inference?

2 If you read this sentence in a selection, what inference would you make about where Marlena is and what she is doing?

Marlena wheeled her cart down the aisle and paused in front of the cold cereals.

Literary Analysis: Point of View

3 What is the point of view of a story?

Literary Analysis: Theme

4 Usually, what kind of statement is the theme of a work?

ESSAY

Writing

1 Sometimes people avoid saying exactly how they feel. On your paper or a separate sheet, write a brief dialogue between two people who are trying to hide their feelings. Try to make the characters' feelings clear to the reader without having either character express those feelings directly.

2 Recall a fictional book, film, or TV drama that taught a life lesson you think applied to your own experiences. In a brief personal essay below or on a separate sheet, explain how the theme or lesson of that work applied to your own experience.

3 Think of a value you hold dear or an observation you have made about life or human behavior. How could you convey that value or observation by telling a story? On your paper or a separate sheet, jot down ideas for a short story that conveys your value or observation as its main theme.

Unit 3: Types of Nonfiction
Part 1 Benchmark Test 5

MULTIPLE CHOICE

Reading Skill: Main Idea

Read the following paragraph about the Missouri Compromise. Then answer questions 1–3.

The argument over whether slavery should be legal in the United States became heated when Missouri applied to become a state in 1817. At the time, there were an equal number of states that did not support slavery and states that did. Slavery was legal in Missouri. If it joined the Union, there would no longer be a balance. The Missouri Compromise was reached, which said that Maine would be accepted as a free state and Missouri would be a slave state. From then on, slavery was banned from the territories north of Missouri's border. This compromise seemed to settle the issue. However, the conflict between the North and the South over slavery continued to grow worse.

1 Which of the following details helps the reader understand the implied main idea of the paragraph?
   - ○ The Louisiana Territory was opened for settlement.
   - ○ The Missouri Compromise was reached by the U.S. Senate.
   - ○ The admittance of Missouri as a state would upset the balance between slave and free states.
   - ○ There were an equal number of slave states and free states.

2 Which of the following BEST states the implied main idea of the paragraph?
   - ○ The Missouri Compromise settled the argument between free states and slave states by keeping the balance.
   - ○ The Missouri Compromise was important because it allowed Missouri and Maine to become states in the Union.
   - ○ The Missouri Compromise settled the issue of slavery by banning slavery in territories north of the Missouri border.
   - ○ The Missouri Compromise kept the balance between free and slave states, but it did not stop the argument over slavery.

3 Which of the following statements supports the main idea?
   - ○ Slavery was legal in Missouri.
   - ○ The conflict between the North and the South over slavery grew worse than ever.
   - ○ Missouri wanted to become a state.
   - ○ Slavery was banned from the territories when Missouri applied to become a state.

Read the story below. Then answer questions 4–6.

Stuart had at least an hour before his report was due. After six weeks of work, he was finally finished. Stuart had already printed the report and checked it for errors. All he had left to do was to attach a cover and deliver it. He was filled with relief. Stuart was proud that he had completed what he had at first thought was an impossible task. He now realized that he could do anything that he set his mind to.

4 Which of the following is the BEST statement of the main idea?

○ Stuart finished his report an hour before it was due and felt proud of himself.

○ Stuart learned to believe in himself because he completed the challenging task of writing his report.

○ Stuart worked on his report for six weeks and delivered it on time.

○ Stuart felt relieved after completing his paper, which was long and difficult to write.

5 Which of the following details BEST supports the main idea?

○ Stuart printed the paper and checked it for errors.

○ Stuart needed to attach a cover.

○ Stuart worked for six weeks on his report.

○ Stuart was proud of himself.

6 Which of the following statements about the main idea is true?

○ The main idea is directly stated in the first sentence.

○ The main idea is directly states in the middle of the paragraph.

○ The main idea is implied in the first sentence.

○ The main idea is implied in the last two sentences.

Read the following passage on the history of baseball. Then answer questions 7–10.

As early as 1744, a popular book described playing a game called base ball. A pitcher threw a ball to a batter who attempted to hit the ball with a bat that had a flat end. A catcher stood behind the batter. If the batter hit the ball, he ran to a base and back again to score a point. The bases were marked with posts rather than the modern-day bags, and the pitcher threw the ball underhand.

In 1828, another book described a game called rounders. It was very much like modern baseball, with a diamond-shaped infield and a base on each corner. A batter was out after three strikes. If he hit a pitch, he could run. A fielder who caught the ball could throw out the runner by throwing the ball and hitting him with it.

7 Which of the following BEST states the main idea of the first paragraph?

○ Early baseball was completely unlike modern baseball.

○ The game of baseball has been played since 1744.

○ A game called base ball was played as early as 1744, but it differed in key ways from modern baseball.

○ Baseball was started in 1744 using flat bats.

8 Which of the following BEST states the main idea of the second paragraph?

○ The game of rounders was similar to modern baseball because batters were out after three strikes.

○ Rounders was a game similar to baseball.

○ A game called rounders, similar to modern baseball, was played in 1828.

○ A game called rounders was played with bats and bases.

9 Which of the following might be the main idea of an essay containing these two paragraphs?

○ Games similar to modern baseball have been played for over 200 years.

○ There are many different types of baseball.

○ Modern baseball has been around for several hundred years.

○ The game of baseball has gone through many changes in the last fifty years.

10 Which of the following is a KEY detail that supports the main idea of the first paragraph?

○ A popular book described a game called base ball.

○ Bases were marked with posts rather than bags.

○ A batter attempted to hit the ball thrown to him.

○ Batters scored a point if they hit the ball.

Literary Analysis: Narrative Essay

Read the following story about President Lincoln. Then answer questions 11–13.

The day was April 14, 1865. It was springtime in Washington, D.C., and a heavy burden had recently been lifted from President Abraham Lincoln. The Civil War was over at last, after four long and bloody years. The slaves had been freed, and the Union had held together. That evening President Abraham Lincoln and his wife decided to attend a play at Ford's Theater. They sat in the special presidential box. The play was a comedy, and just at the moment when the audience was laughing the loudest, a man named John Wilkes Booth stepped into the box and shot President Lincoln in the head. Booth jumped down onto the stage and disappeared. President Lincoln was carried to a room in a building across the street. The doctor desperately tried to save his life, but he died the following morning.

11 Which of the following is the MOST IMPORTANT event in this selection?

○ The Civil War had ended.

○ Spring had arrived in Washington, D.C.

○ President Lincoln was shot.

○ President Lincoln attended a play.

12 Who are the two MOST IMPORTANT people in this selection?

○ President Lincoln and Mrs. Lincoln

○ President Lincoln and the doctor

○ President Lincoln and John Wilkes Booth

○ John Wilkes Booth and Mrs. Lincoln

13 Which BEST describes the location of the most important event in this selection?

○ Washington, D.C.

○ Ford's Theater

○ the presidential box in Ford's Theater

○ the stage of Ford's Theater

Literary Analysis: Biographical and Autobiographical Essay

Read the biography below. Then answer questions 14–16.

John Wilkes Booth was born in 1838, one of ten children in a theatrical family. Booth had a talent for acting. In 1860, he had a successful acting tour through the Deep South. He became a strong supporter of the South and of slavery and often expressed his hatred of Abraham Lincoln. In 1864, Booth planned to kidnap President Lincoln, but his plans never worked out. Finally, in 1865, he planned to murder the President. On April 14, 1865, Booth succeeded in entering the presidential box of Ford's Theater and shooting the President in the head. After the shooting, he leapt onto the stage and shouted "The South is avenged!" Even though he broke his leg when jumping, he was able to escape. However, on April 26, Federal troops found Booth hiding in a barn at a farm in Virginia. Booth refused to surrender and died of a gunshot wound.

14 What is the subject of this biography?
  ○ John Wilkes Booth   ○ President Lincoln
  ○ Booth's acting career   ○ slavery and the South

15 Which of the following BEST explains why this selection is biographical?
  ○ The writer tells about an important event in the life of another person.
  ○ It tells about an important event that the writer experienced.
  ○ It tells about an important event in the life of John Wilkes Booth.
  ○ It gives the years of the birth and death of John Wilkes Booth.

16 Which describes the MOST IMPORTANT event in the biography?
  ○ Booth's successful acting career   ○ Booth's plan to kidnap Lincoln
  ○ Booth's trip through the Deep South ○ Booth's assassination of Lincoln

Literary Analysis: Types of Organization

Answer the questions below.

17 Which type of organization is used in the preceding biography of John Wilkes Booth?
  ○ cause and effect   ○ comparison and contrast
  ○ chronological   ○ problem and solution

18 That type of organization would you MOST LIKELY use to describe what happens when a hurricane strikes a city or town?
  ○ chronological   ○ order of importance
  ○ cause and effect   ○ comparison and contrast

19 For which of the following topics would you MOST LIKELY use comparison-and-contrast organization?
  ○ educational systems in Japan and the ○ feeding habits of dolphins
     United States   ○ a football game
  ○ the Revolutionary War

20 Why would chronological order be a good way to organize an essay about how people become infected with the flu virus, get sick, and get better?

○ You could explain where the flu virus comes from and how vaccines can be used to prevent the flu.

○ You could explain the step-by-step process of what happens when the virus enters a human body and then makes a person sick.

○ You could explain each of the symptoms that a person gets and how it affects how the person feels.

○ You could explain how the flu virus affects different parts of the body and how the person's immune system reacts.

Vocabulary: Synonyms

Answer the questions below.

21 Which of the following words is a synonym for *obstacles* as it is used in the following sentence?

She had to work hard to overcome many obstacles before she finished her education.

○ passages   ○ drawbacks
○ difficulties   ○ enemies

22 The word *ingenious* can mean "clever." Which of the following words is the BEST synonym for *ingenious* as it is used in the following sentence?

His plan for winning the game was ingenious.

○ smart   ○ unusual
○ witty   ○ simplistic

23 Which of the following sentences contains a synonym of *elated*?

○ He was overjoyed that the team won its first game of the season.

○ The birth of the new baby was a happy occasion.

○ No one received an "A," but most students were pleased with their grades.

○ Everyone at the party was in a cheerful mood.

24 The word *approach* can be used as a verb or a noun. Which of the following words is a synonym of *approach* as it is used in the following sentence?

What approach do you want to use to try to beat the other team?

○ act   ○ close
○ method   ○ join

Grammar: Adjectives and Articles

Answer the questions below.

25 Which of the following sentences contains an article that answers the question "which one?"
- ○ Harry tried to help me.
- ○ Anna was very late to class.
- ○ Dr. James prescribed some medicine.
- ○ Andrew was the last to arrive.

26 Which question does the adjective in the following sentence answer?

Jerry quickly grabbed the last piece of pizza.
- ○ which one?
- ○ how much?
- ○ whose?
- ○ how many?

27 Which word does the adjective in the following sentence modify?

The hungry man quickly looked around the park trying to spot a place where he could eat his lunch.
- ○ he
- ○ looked
- ○ park
- ○ man

Grammar: Adverbs

Answer the questions below.

28 The word *joyfully* answers which of the following questions?
- ○ to what extent?
- ○ in what manner?
- ○ where?
- ○ when?

29 Which word in the following sentence is an adverb?

Wild animals are usually cautious when they sense the presence of human beings.
- ○ usually
- ○ wild
- ○ cautious
- ○ presence

30 Which of the following adverbs answers the question "when?"
- ○ especially
- ○ largely
- ○ always
- ○ deliberately

Grammar: Comparative and Superlative Forms

Answer the questions below.

31 Which of the following is true of the comparative form?
- ○ It is used to compare three or more items.
- ○ It ends in *-ly*.
- ○ *Most* is used with two-syllable adverbs.
- ○ It is used to compare two items.

32 Which word in the following sentence is a superlative form of an adjective?

Even though the flashlight helped us see the path more clearly, it did little good in the darkest part of the forest.

- ○ little
- ○ clearly
- ○ more
- ○ darkest

33 Which of the following words would be used to compare two items?

- ○ most
- ○ better
- ○ fastest
- ○ least

SHORT ANSWER

1 What is the implied main idea of the first selection, which appears on page 1?

2 What is the MOST IMPORTANT event in the fourth selection, which appears on page 3?

3 What is the definition of a biographical essay?

4 Explain why chronological order would be a good way to organize an essay about how people become infected with the flu virus, get sick, and get better.

ESSAY

Writing: How-to Essay

1 Think of some activity that you enjoy, such as playing a particular sport, planting flowers, or cooking a particular dish. Then imagine that you are going to explain the activity to someone who has never done it. Write a brief essay explaining each step in the process.

Writing: Biographical Sketch

2 Think of someone who did something that you admire. The person might be a historical figure, a teacher, a friend, a neighbor, or a family member. Write a brief essay describing the person's action and explaining why you admire it.

Writing: Reflective Composition

3 Write a brief reflective essay about something that has recently made an impression upon you. It might be a story in the news, a movie, a book, a poem, or an article in a magazine. Tell why it has impressed you and how it relates to your life.

Unit 3: Types of Nonfiction
Part 2 Benchmark Test 6

MULTIPLE CHOICE

Reading Skill: Fact and Opinion

Read the following excerpt about the women's rights movement in Great Britain. Then answer questions 1–4.

Until the twentieth century, women were denied the right to vote in Great Britain. The movement to gain voting rights for women began in England in 1792. Many women in the movement, known as suffragists, were sent to prison, where they continued to work for their cause by staging hunger strikes. Bill after bill was introduced in the British Parliament during the 1800s and early 1900s, but with no success. Public support for women's voting rights slowly grew and, in 1918, an act was passed that allowed women age 30 or over to vote. In 1928, this age was lowered to 21, the same as for men. After more than a century, women finally achieved equal voting rights.

1 Which of the following statements is a fact?
   ○ Women were treated unfairly.
   ○ In 1928, the voting age for women was 21.
   ○ Women were impatient.
   ○ The British Parliament acted unjustly.

2 Which of the following is an opinion?
   ○ Many bills were introduced in Parliament.
   ○ Women achieved equal voting rights.
   ○ By 1918 women age 30 and over could vote.
   ○ British Parliament was unfair.

3 Which of the following sentences contains a clue word indicating a judgment?
   ○ Being denied the vote was the worst injustice.
   ○ Parliament moved slowly.
   ○ Nothing was done for women for centuries.
   ○ Women were treated unequally.

4 Which of the following statements supports the opinion that women were treated unfairly?
   ○ Many women fought for all women's right to vote.
   ○ Women were not allowed to vote in Great Britain.
   ○ Public support for women's rights grew.
   ○ The movement for women's rights began in 1792.

Read the following excerpt about the Hubble Space Telescope. Then answer questions 5–10.

On April 25, 1990, the crew of the space shuttle *Discovery* placed the most sophisticated telescope ever created in orbit around the Earth. The Hubble Space Telescope was named for Edwin Hubble, the most important American astronomer of the 20th century. Unlike telescopes on Earth, the Hubble telescope can see deep into space without the interference of Earth's atmosphere. The images received by Hubble are much brighter and clearer than anyone could have imagined. With the Hubble Space Telescope, people are able to clearly see the breathtaking beauty of the universe.

5 Which of the following opinions could be supported by facts?

○ The space shuttle crew performed a great service for humanity.

○ It is important for scientists to see objects in outer space.

○ Hubble is the most sophisticated telescope ever created.

○ Hubble is a wonderful invention that will make the world better.

6 Which of the following statements can be considered a faulty opinion?

○ People will benefit from Hubble by learning more about the universe.

○ People on Earth are lucky to have the Hubble.

○ The Hubble can help scientists learn much more about the universe.

○ Most astronomers consider the Hubble an important invention.

7 Which of the following statements BEST describes the author's opinion of the Hubble Space Telescope?

○ It is an important invention that will benefit science and humanity.

○ The Hubble took a great effort to put in place, but it was worth it.

○ It is a technologically advanced invention that will benefit scientists.

○ Without the Hubble, scientists would know very little about the universe.

8 Which of the following questions would be helpful in evaluating the support for the author's opinion?

○ Can the author prove how the Hubble was placed in orbit?

○ Can the author prove how the Hubble will be a benefit?

○ Where does the author get information about the Hubble?

○ Why does the author seem to like the Hubble?

Reading Skill: Organizational Structure

Answer the questions below.

9 How does the author use comparison and contrast in the paragraph?

○ comparing the Hubble to telescopes on Earth

○ contrasting Edwin Hubble with other astronomers

○ comparing Earth's atmosphere to outer space

○ comparing light rays on Earth to light in space

10 Which of the following details from the paragraph is an example of cause and effect?

○ The crew of the shuttle placed the Hubble in orbit.

○ Earth's atmosphere absorbs light, which limits vision.

○ The Hubble Space Telescope was named for Edwin Hubble.

○ Images received by Hubble are much brighter and clearer.

Literary Analysis: Persuasive Techniques

Read the following excerpt about the Peace Corps. Then answer questions 11–13.

In 1960 President Kennedy challenged young people to join the Peace Corps. Why might someone want to join the Peace Corps? Peace Corp volunteers help people in developing nations. Peace Corps volunteers might counsel teens in Belize, launch a computer center in Armenia, or teach chemistry in a high school in Ghana. Since the 1960s, more than 178,000 Peace Corps volunteers have had the satisfaction of living and helping others in 138 countries around the world. Individuals who join the Peace Corps know that they have served their country, served humanity, and made a difference in the world.

11 What is the author attempting to persuade the reader of in the paragraph?

   ○ President Kennedy wanted to bring world peace with the Peace Corps.

   ○ People should work for world peace by doing volunteer work.

   ○ Peace Corps volunteers serve humanity and the cause of peace.

   ○ Peace Corps volunteers can bring world peace.

12 How is the rhetorical question in the paragraph answered?

   ○ by listing the countries to which Peace Corps volunteers travel

   ○ by describing how Peace Corps volunteers help others around the world

   ○ by explaining what Peace Corps volunteers do in Belize

   ○ by explaining the numbers of volunteers who have joined the Peace Corps

13 To which emotions does the phrase "served their country, served humanity" appeal?

   ○ pride and a desire for peace

   ○ pride and patriotism

   ○ pride and a desire to help others

   ○ patriotism and the desire to help others

Literary Analysis: Word Choice

Read the following excerpt about the Civil Rights Movement. Then answer questions 14–18.

The Civil Rights Movement was a remarkable time in American history. Using nonviolent demonstrations, African Americans brought attention to the injustice of their situation. For generations they had been segregated, or kept apart from the white population. The "sit-in" movement was begun by young black people, who insisted on being served at a lunch counter in Greensboro, North Carolina. These courageous demonstrators suffered abuse, physical violence, and even the threat of death. Yet they remained firm and succeeded in achieving desegregation across the nation. Their courage, and the courage of all those who participated in the Civil Rights Movement, helped awaken the conscience of white Americans and bring justice to those who had been oppressed.

14 Which of the following phrases from the paragraph BEST conveys a positive feeling?

   ○ The "sit-in" movement was begun by young African Americans.

   ○ For generations, African Americans had been segregated.

   ○ African Americans brought attention to the injustice of their situation.

   ○ Their courage helped awaken the conscience of white Americans.

15 Which of the following words from the paragraph has negative connotations?

- ○ participated
- ○ oppressed
- ○ nonviolent
- ○ desegregation

16 Which word in the following sentence helps convey the author's attitude of admiration?

These courageous demonstrators suffered abuse, physical violence, and even the threat of death.

- ○ courageous
- ○ demonstrators
- ○ abuse
- ○ threat

Literary Analysis: Tone

17 What is the overall tone of the author in this paragraph?

- ○ admiring
- ○ playful
- ○ impersonal
- ○ critical

18 Which of the following details BEST conveys the author's tone?

- ○ The "sit-in" movement was begun by young people.
- ○ Their courage helped awaken the conscience of white Americans.
- ○ They brought attention to the injustice of their situation.
- ○ They succeeded in achieving desegregation.

Vocabulary

Answer the questions below.

19 Which is the definition of antonyms?

- ○ words with similar meanings
- ○ words that sound alike
- ○ words with opposite meanings
- ○ words that have multiple meanings

20 Which of the following pairs of words are antonyms?

- ○ accurate / factual
- ○ credible / unbelievable
- ○ their / there
- ○ support / uphold

21 Which of the following sentences contains an antonym of the word *biased*?

- ○ He is well known for his straight talk and level-headed thinking.
- ○ The judge is noted for making fair-minded decisions.
- ○ Many people think his decisions are often unfair.
- ○ The letters to the editor often contain incredible statements.

22 Which of the following definitions fits the word *supports* as it is used in this sentence?

The supports underneath this house have been weakened by age and weather.

- ○ props that hold something
- ○ give approval
- ○ to bear the weight of something
- ○ means of staying alive

23 In which of the following sentences is the word *fair* an antonym of the word *biased*?

- ○ Their team does not play fair.
- ○ He presented the facts in a fair manner.
- ○ We bought some craft items at the fair.
- ○ It looks like this will be a fair day.

24 Which of the following sentences uses the word *ground* as a noun meaning "the topic or subject"?

- ○ You should ground your arguments in facts, not opinions.
- ○ The tribe was confined to a small hunting ground.
- ○ The pilot realized that the weather would keep him on the ground.
- ○ Let's review the ground that we have already discussed.

Grammar

Answer the questions below.

25 Which of the following is the BEST definition of conjunctions?

- ○ words that separate sentences
- ○ words that connect sentence parts
- ○ words that add information
- ○ words that change sentence meanings

26 Which of the following sentences contains a conjunction?

- ○ Everyone in the club wanted to go to the home team's opening game.
- ○ There were not enough tickets for all of them to go to the game.
- ○ It rained in the morning, but the sun came out in the afternoon.
- ○ It was a great day for the opening of the baseball season.

27 Which of the following is a true statement about prepositions?

- ○ They can join two sentences or sentence parts together.
- ○ They can change the meaning of words.
- ○ They can separate two complete sentences.
- ○ They are used to add information to sentences.

28 Which of the following sentences contains a prepositional phrase?

- ○ Many people attempted to win the tournament.
- ○ Bad weather forced the tournament to be postponed.
- ○ When the tournament finally resumed, most spectators had left.
- ○ The judge presented flowers to the winner.

29 Which of the following would you use to connect two independent clauses or two words of equal rank?

- ○ coordinating conjunction
- ○ subordinating conjunction
- ○ compound subject
- ○ compound sentence

30 Which of the following sentences contains a subordinating conjunction?
- ○ Because the closest star is so far away, humans will probably never travel there.
- ○ Many people believe that there is undiscovered life on other planets in our galaxy.
- ○ There are billions of stars in our galaxy, and our galaxy is only one of millions.
- ○ Scientists continue to listen for messages sent by intelligent life on other planets.

Spelling: Homonyms and Homophones

Answer the questions below.

31 Which of the following is the definition of a homophone?
- ○ words that sound alike and have the same meanings
- ○ words that sound alike but have different meanings and spellings
- ○ two or more words that have the same meaning
- ○ words that are spelled alike but have different sounds

32 Which of the following pairs of words are homophones?
- ○ bored / bared
- ○ like / dislike
- ○ bored / board
- ○ fair / fair

33 Which of the following sentences contains a homophone of the word *allowed*?
- ○ He was very proud to be one of the players on the team.
- ○ They were not permitted to attend the game.
- ○ Members of the losing team behaved in an aloof manner.
- ○ The names of the winners were read aloud.

ESSAY

Writing

1 What current issue do you feel strongly about? Issues at school? Curfew? The environment? Write a brief newspaper editorial stating and defending your opinion on the issue. Be sure to include reasons and evidence to support your opinion and to use persuasive techniques to convey your message.

2 Think of a short piece of nonfiction that you have read recently in which the author has made an argument for or against something. It might be a letter to an editor of your newspaper or an article in a magazine or textbook. Write a brief response to the idea, explaining whether you agree or disagree with it.

3 What is your favorite television commercial? What techniques does the commercial use to persuade you to buy a product? Write a brief evaluation of the commercial. Describe the persuasive techniques, such as repetition or rhetorical questions, used in the piece. Evaluate the overall effectiveness of the commercial.

SHORT ANSWER

1   List one fact from the selection on page 1 on voting rights for women in Great Britain.

2   Explain why the statement, "People on Earth are lucky to have the Hubble Space Telescope" can be considered a faulty opinion.

3   What is the author attempting to persuade readers of in the selection on page 3 on the Peace Corps?

4   What is the overall tone of the author in the selection on page 3 on the Civil Rights Movement?

Unit 4: Poetry
Part 1 Benchmark Test 7

MULTIPLE CHOICE

Reading Skill: Context

Read the following excerpt from a poem by Henry Wadsworth Longfellow. Then answer questions 1–4.

My life is cold, and dark, and dreary;

It rains, and the wind is never weary;

My thoughts still cling to the mouldering Past,

But the hopes of youth fall thick in the blast,

And the days are dark and dreary.

Be still, sad heart! and cease repining;

Behind the clouds is the sun still shining;

Thy fate is the common fate of all,

Into each life some rain must fall,

Some days must be dark and dreary.

—from **"The Rainy Day"**
by **Henry Wadsworth Longfellow**

1 Which of these is the MOST LIKELY definition of *mouldering* in Longfellow's poem?
   ○ burning   ○ decaying   ○ inspiring   ○ darkening

2 Which of these BEST helps you determine a possible meaning for *mouldering*?
   ○ the word *past*, which suggests some-   ○ the phrase *fond hopes*, which suggests
      thing that has died or is dying   inspiration
   ○ the phrase *dark and dreary*, which   ○ the phrase *thick in the blast*, which
      suggests sadness   suggests fire or burning

3 Which of these is a possible meaning for the word *repining* in the poem?
   ○ expressing uncertainty   ○ expressing happiness
   ○ expressing determination   ○ expressing discontent

4 In the poem, what type of context clue for *repining* is the word *shining*?
   ○ explanation   ○ definition   ○ synonym   ○ antonym

Read the following excerpt from the poem "Boat Song." Then answer questions 5–8.

THE RIVER calmly flows,

Through shining banks, through lonely glen,

Where the owl shrieks, though ne'er the cheer of men

Has stirred its mute repose,

Still if you should walk there, you would go there again.

The stream is well alive;

Another passive world you see,

Where downward grows the form of every tree;

Like soft light clouds they thrive:

Like them let us in our pure loves reflected be.

—from **"Boat Song"**
by **Ralph Waldo Emerson**

5 Which of these is the BEST definition of *repose* in Emerson's poem?

- ○ silence
- ○ depth
- ○ rest
- ○ liveliness

6 Which word in the first stanza of Emerson's poem is a clue to the meaning of *repose*?

- ○ calmly
- ○ mute
- ○ shining
- ○ lonely

7 What is the MOST LIKELY meaning of *passive* in Emerson's poem?

- ○ flowing
- ○ inactive
- ○ calming
- ○ busy

8 Which of these is a context clue to the meaning of *passive* in Emerson's poem?

- ○ downward grows
- ○ reflected be
- ○ soft light clouds
- ○ Another, world

Read the following directions from a recipe. Then answer questions 9–10.

Whisk together the flour and eggs until they are thoroughly mixed. Gradually add the milk and water, stirring to combine. Add the salt and butter, and beat until smooth. Then heat a lightly oiled frying pan over medium high heat. Pour the batter into the pan. Tilt the pan with a circular motion so that the batter coats the surface evenly. Cook the crepe for about 2 minutes. Then loosen the crepe with a spatula, turn, and cook the other side.

9 What context clue BEST helps you figure out the meaning of *whisk*?

- ○ gradually
- ○ mixed
- ○ add
- ○ heat

10 Based on the context in which it is used, what is the MOST LIKELY meaning of *spatula*?

- ○ a tool for heating food
- ○ a tool for mixing food
- ○ a tool for frying food
- ○ a tool for lifting food

Literary Analysis: Sound Devices

Answer the questions below.

11   What type of sound device is used in the following line of poetry?

A tapering turret overtops the work,

- ○ alliteration
- ○ onomatopoeia
- ○ rhyme
- ○ repetition

12   Which sound device uses words to imitate sounds?

- ○ rhythm
- ○ onomatopoeia
- ○ alliteration
- ○ rhyme

13   Which of these is the BEST example of the use of rhythm as a sound device?

- ○ A snail trail streamed across the summer porch.
- ○ When I wished upon a star, the star winked back at me.
- ○ The water in the hot pan hissed and sputtered.
- ○ Four farmers toiled tirelessly in their fields.

Literary Analysis: Figurative Language

Answer the questions below.

14   Which of these is an example of the use of figurative language?

- ○ The breeze rustled the leaves of the tall elms.
- ○ A sudden breeze cooled our hot faces as we worked.
- ○ The grain stalks bowed to one another in the breeze.
- ○ The wind chimes dinged and clanged in the breeze.

15   Which choice contains a simile?

- ○ The sheriff was a hearty, loud-talking fellow.
- ○ The stream gurgled its way over the rocks.
- ○ Her curiosity led her to learn a great deal.
- ○ Pynchon's Pond was as smooth as glass.

16   Which of the following is an example of personification?

- ○ A rusted stove crouched in the corner.
- ○ The trail goes left toward the creek.
- ○ In the race, Evan ran like a gazelle.
- ○ She sat sleepily nodding her head.

17   Which of these BEST defines the use of personification in making comparisons?

- ○ Two unlike things are compared using *like* or *as*.
- ○ A nonhuman subject is given human characteristics.
- ○ Two unlike things are compared by saying that one is the other.
- ○ Human behavior is described in terms of animal behavior.

Literary Analysis: Humor

Read the following excerpt from the poem "Casey at the Bat." Then answer questions 18–19.

The sneer is gone from Casey's lip, his teeth are clenched in hate;

He pounds with cruel violence his bat upon the plate;

And now the pitcher holds the ball, and now he lets it go,

And now the air is shattered by the force of Casey's blow.

Oh, somewhere in this favored land the sun is shining bright,

The band is playing somewhere, and somewhere hearts are light:

And somewhere men are laughing, and somewhere children shout,

But there is no joy in Mudville—mighty Casey has struck out.

—from **"Casey at the Bat"**
by **Ernest L. Thayer**

18 Which of these BEST describes a literary device in the excerpt from "Casey at the Bat"?

○ pairing images that do not usually go together

○ using personification and metaphor for effect

○ describing a situation from an unusual perspective

○ using words that appeal to the senses of sight and sound

19 Which technique BEST contributes to the poem's humorous effect?

○ using irony so that readers are surprised to learn what happens at the end

○ combining two points of view in an unusual way

○ using images that appeal to the senses of touch and taste

○ describing a common situation from an unusual perspective

Vocabulary: Suffixes

Answer the questions below.

20 What is the meaning of *virtuous* in the following sentence?

The poem is about a virtuous man who is tricked into committing a crime.

○ one who suffers bad luck

○ the process of doing good

○ relating to hard work

○ full of good qualities

21 What is the BEST definition of *development* in the following sentence?

Development of a good poem can take months or even years.

○ having many parts

○ relating to the act of writing

○ concerned with outcome

○ the act of putting together

22 Which definition BEST fits the word *nervous* in the following sentence?

Paul felt nervous as he mounted the stage to recite his poem.

- ○ having the quality of uneasiness
- ○ relating to being proud
- ○ one who has courage
- ○ a state of readiness

23 Which of these BEST defines *amusement* in the following sentence?

For amusement, Oscar read aloud a humorous poem by Ogden Nash.

- ○ the state of being entertained
- ○ in order to pass the time
- ○ one who enjoys poetry
- ○ relating to recreation

24 Which definition BEST fits the word *wondrous* in the following sentence?

The poet Mary Oliver can make ordinary things seem wondrous.

- ○ in an amazing manner
- ○ one who inspires wonder
- ○ having an extraordinary quality
- ○ the act of marveling

25 What is the meaning of *contentment* in the following sentence?

True contentment is writing a poem that says exactly what you feel.

- ○ a process that brings happiness
- ○ full of pleasant feelings
- ○ one who is feeling happy
- ○ the state of being satisfied

Grammar

Answer the questions below.

26 Which sentence contains a predicate adjective as a subject complement?
- ○ Maggie is walking with her dog.
- ○ The small farm on the hill was tidy.
- ○ Jay and Art are both photographers.
- ○ The salesperson who called was he.

27 Which sentence contains a predicate pronoun as a subject complement?
- ○ We wondered what happened to him.
- ○ The best person for the job is she.
- ○ Are they coming to our play?
- ○ He was the poet laureate in 2001.

28 Which sentence contains a predicate noun used as a subject complement?
- ○ The walk through the tunnel was eerie.
- ○ What nationality are you?
- ○ My dog is master of the household.
- ○ The ground is sloping and uneven.

29 What is the direct object in the following sentence?

Olivia fed a cracker to the gray mule in the pen.

- ○ Olivia
- ○ cracker
- ○ mule
- ○ pen

30 Which sentence contains an indirect object?
- ○ Elyssa handed her dad the purple iris.
- ○ Jack hung the lantern on the nail.
- ○ Dad gave the horse's reins to me.
- ○ That coat is too large for Marco.

31 What is the indirect object in the following sentence?

The high bluff afforded us a broad view of the river valley.

- ○ bluff
- ○ us
- ○ view
- ○ valley

32 Which of these BEST defines a verb in the passive voice?

- ○ Its subject receives the action.
- ○ The performer is important.
- ○ The verb lacks strength.
- ○ Its subject is unclear.

33 Which sentence shows a verb in the active voice?

- ○ A loud screech was heard in the tree.
- ○ The baby is sleeping soundly.
- ○ Are the streets really paved in gold?
- ○ The new park was finished at last.

ESSAY

Writing

1 Imagine that you have been asked to write an introduction for a favorite recorded song that you will play for other students. You want to draw students' attention especially to the words of the song and their effect on you. On a separate sheet of paper, jot down two or three ideas about how you will explain why the words of this song are important to you. Mention any use of sound devices such as alliteration, onomatopoeia, rhyme, or rhythm in the song.

2 Jot down notes for a poem about a walk in the woods. Begin by listing some things you might see, hear, smell, touch, and taste in the woods. Then choose three things on your list and write phrases that make comparisons using one example each of a simile, a metaphor, and personification.

3 Imagine that you are writing for assessment and have expressed the following main idea in response to a writing prompt. On your paper, list at least three details that you might use to support this main idea.

Poetry often reassures us that someone else shares our thoughts and feelings.

SHORT ANSWER

Reading Skill: Context

1 What is the MOST LIKELY definition of *mouldering* in Longfellow's poem on page 1?

2 What word is a context clue to the meaning of *repose* in Emerson's poem on pages 1–2?

Literary Analysis: Sound Devices

3 What sound device uses words to imitate sounds?

Literary Analysis: Figurative Language

4 How is personification used in making comparisons?

Name _____ Date _____

Unit 4: Poetry
Part 2 Benchmark Test 8

MULTIPLE CHOICE

Reading Skill

Read the following excerpt from a poem by Ralph Waldo Emerson. Then answer questions 1–3.

Announced by all the trumpets of the sky,

Arrives the snow, and, driving o'er the fields,

Seems nowhere to alight: the whited air

Hides hill and woods, the river, and the heaven,

And veils the farmhouse at the garden's end.

The sled and traveller stopped, the courier's feet

Delayed, all friends shut out, the housemates sit

Around the radiant fireplace, enclosed

In a tumultuous privacy of storm.

—from **"The Snowstorm"**
by **Ralph Waldo Emerson**

1 Which is the BEST paraphrase of lines 1–2 of Emerson's poem?
- ○ The sky is full of wonder.
- ○ Great horns are blowing.
- ○ A snowstorm has come.
- ○ Wind blows over the fields.

2 Which BEST expresses the meaning of lines 3–5 of Emerson's poem?
- ○ The snow falls softly on the land.
- ○ The snow blots out everything.
- ○ Snow falls but does not stick.
- ○ The weather is cold and gloomy.

3 Which BEST restates lines 6–9 of Emerson's poem?
- ○ Neighbors are isolated from one another by the storm.
- ○ Travelers stop to admire the beauty of the woods.
- ○ Families enjoy sitting around the fire together.
- ○ People are staying indoors during the storm.

Read the following excerpt from a poem by John Masefield. Then answer questions 4–6.

I must go down to the seas again, for the call of the running tide

Is a wild call and a clear call that may not be denied;

And all I ask is a windy day with the white clouds flying,

And the flung spray and the blown spume, and the sea-gulls crying.

I must go down to the seas again, to the vagrant gypsy life,

To the gull's way and the whale's way where the wind's like a whetted knife;

And all I ask is a merry yarn from a laughing fellow-rover,

And quiet sleep and a sweet dream when the long trick's over.

—from **"Sea Fever"**
by **John Masefield**

4 Reading Masefield's verse according to punctuation, where would you come to a complete stop?
- ○ after lines 4 and 8
- ○ after lines 2 and 6
- ○ after lines 3, 6, and 7
- ○ at the end of every line

5 Which of these should the reader do in line 5?
- ○ Pause only after the end comma.
- ○ Pause only after the first comma.
- ○ Come to a stop after the end comma.
- ○ Pause briefly after each comma.

6 Which is the BEST paraphrase of the excerpt from Masefield's poem?
- ○ I love the wind and the salt spray when I am near the sea.
- ○ I cannot resist the call of the wild, free life on the seas.
- ○ I love to sail the sea on a clear, windy day.
- ○ I envy the wild, free life of seagulls and whales.

Read the following directions from a computer manual. Then answer questions 7–9.

Try these steps if your computer display goes blank or if your system freezes:
1. Unplug all external devices that are connected to your computer except the power adapter.
2. Simultaneously depress the Command and Control keys, as well as the Power button, to reactivate the system.
3. Allow the battery to charge at least ten percent before plugging in an external device.

Note: Look at the Battery Status icon to determine how much the battery has recharged

7 Which sentence is the BEST paraphrase of step 2?
- ○ Press the Command key, followed by the Control key.
- ○ Press the Command key, and then press the Control and Power buttons.
- ○ Press the Command, Control, and Power buttons, all at the same time.
- ○ Press the Power button, and then press the Command and Control keys.

8 Which of these is MOST IMPORTANT in reading the directions in order to perform the task?
- ○ understanding the order of the steps
- ○ memorizing the steps in order
- ○ drawing a diagram of the steps
- ○ skimming over the steps

9 Which paraphrase shows the steps described in the correct order?
   ○ Unplug the power adapter. Recharge the battery to ten percent. Then hold down the Command and Control keys. Press the Power button to restart your computer.
   ○ Plug in external devices to the computer. Then hold down the Command, Control, and Power buttons to turn off the computer. Let the battery recharge to ten percent.
   ○ Unplug all devices except the power adapter. Then restart the computer by holding down the Command, Control, and Power keys all at once. Let the battery charge to ten percent before plugging in external devices.
   ○ Hold down the Command and Control keys to shut down the computer. Then recharge the battery to ten percent. Restart the computer by pressing the Power key.

Literary Analysis

Read the following excerpts from two poems. Then answer questions 10–14.

Shall I compare thee to a summer's day?

Thou art more lovely and more temperate.

Rough winds do shake the darling buds of May,

And summer's lease hath all too short a date.

—from **"Sonnet 18"**
by **William Shakespeare**

The tide rises, the tide falls,

The twilight darkens, the curfew calls;

Along the sea-sands damp and brown

The traveller hastens toward the town,

And the tide rises, the tide falls.

—from **"The Tide Rises, the Tide Falls"**
by **Henry Wadsworth Longfellow**

10 What form of poetry are the lines by William Shakespeare?
   ○ lyric poetry   ○ concrete poetry
   ○ humorous poetry   ○ narrative poetry

11 Which of these BEST describes what the speaker is saying in Shakespeare's sonnet?
   ○ The speaker loves summer more than autumn.   ○ The speaker appreciates the different moods of summer.
   ○ The speaker is expressing tender love for someone. ○ The speaker feels that summer days pass too quickly.

12 Which of these BEST expresses the setting of Longfellow's poem?
   ○ a boat in the ocean   ○ a seashore near a town
   ○ a town near the sea   ○ a lonely road near town

13 What is the MAIN purpose of a narrative poem?
- ○ to express a feeling
- ○ to tell a story
- ○ to describe a character
- ○ to describe a setting

14 Which imagery from Longfellow's poem appeals to the senses of touch and sight?
- ○ the tide rises, the tide falls
- ○ the twilight darkens
- ○ the traveller hastens
- ○ the sea-sands damp and brown

Answer the questions below.

15 Which of these BEST defines imagery in poetry?
- ○ pictures that accompany poetry
- ○ comparison of one thing to another
- ○ language that appeals to the senses
- ○ imagination in poetry

16 Which of these BEST demonstrates the use of imagery?
- ○ The icy snow crunched underfoot.
- ○ Jack filled his plate with food.
- ○ Two chimneys rose from the house.
- ○ His mind was busily at work.

17 Which of these reflects the actual meaning of words?
- ○ a description using metaphor
- ○ a description using analogy
- ○ a figurative description
- ○ a literal description

18 Which of these BEST shows the use of analogy in a poem?
- ○ a description of a candle flame that can be compared to a life
- ○ a description of a storm using images that appeal to the senses
- ○ a description of a character who undergoes changes
- ○ a description of sights and sounds found in nature

Vocabulary: Word Origins

Answer the questions below.

19 In which of these would you MOST LIKELY find word origins?
- ○ a thesaurus
- ○ a dictionary
- ○ a history book
- ○ an almanac

20 If *aquatic* comes from the Latin word *aqua,* meaning "water," which word probably shares the same origin as *aquatic*?
- ○ aquarium
- ○ acquire
- ○ quart
- ○ quality

21 If *receive* comes from the Latin word *recipere,* meaning "to take," which word probably shares the same origin as *receive*?
- ○ reception
- ○ recipe
- ○ recite
- ○ respite

22 If *gratify* comes from the Latin word *gratus*, meaning "pleasing," which word probably shares the same origin as *gratify*?

- ○ graduate
- ○ congratulate
- ○ migrate
- ○ grating

Grammar

Answer the questions below.

23 What is the preposition in the following sentence?

The poet drew inspiration from nature.

- ○ poet
- ○ drew
- ○ from
- ○ nature

24 Which sentence contains a prepositional phrase?

- ○ Kip has composed a thoughtful essay.
- ○ Oates is a novelist and a poet.
- ○ Nature's poetry lies everywhere.
- ○ The last line of the poem is chilling.

25 What is the prepositional phrase in the following sentence?

Each day, White created both humorous and touching poetry in his attic room.

- ○ in his attic room
- ○ both humorous and touching poetry
- ○ each day
- ○ his attic room

26 What is the infinitive in the following sentence?

Elsa likes to read poetry that is composed by children.

- ○ likes to
- ○ to read
- ○ read poetry
- ○ by children

27 Which sentence contains an infinitive phrase?

- ○ To Jenny, the poem sounded false.
- ○ Eduardo recited the lines to me.
- ○ We hope to visit the poet's birthplace.
- ○ The writer paid tribute to his parents.

28 What is the infinitive phrase in the following sentence?

We must understand the poet's childhood to understand the poem's imagery.

- ○ We must understand
- ○ the poet's childhood
- ○ to understand the poem's imagery
- ○ the poem's imagery

29 Which is the BEST way to revise the following sentence to vary the sentence structure and to add descriptive details?

The cyclists pedaled to the top of the hill.

- ○ The cyclists pedaled quickly to the top of the hill.
- ○ The three cyclists pedaled to the top of the steep hill.
- ○ Huffing and chuffing, the cyclists pedaled slowly up the steep hill.
- ○ Several cyclists rode slowly up the steep hill.

30 Which of these BEST defines an appositive phrase?

- ○ a phrase that begins with a preposition and ends with a noun
- ○ a noun phrase that defines other words in a sentence
- ○ an infinitive with a modifier that acts as a single part of speech
- ○ a form of verb that follows the word *to* and acts as a noun, adjective, or adverb

Spelling

Answer the questions below.

31 In which sentence is the word in italics spelled correctly?

- ○ Phil's *absince* affected the project.
- ○ Her argument seemed *ilogical.*
- ○ We found an *affordable* vacation.
- ○ There was *resistence* to my idea.

32 Which word would correctly complete the following sentence?

Who is _____ for notifying the newspaper of our book sale?

- ○ responsable
- ○ responsible
- ○ responssible
- ○ responseable

33 Which word would correctly compete the following sentence?

An additional _____ of the play is scheduled for Sunday afternoon.

- ○ performance
- ○ performence
- ○ performmence
- ○ performince

ESSAY

Writing

1 Imagine that you want to write either a lyric or a narrative poem about a river. Decide whether you want to describe your impressions of the river or tell a story about it. On a separate sheet of paper, write the first line of a poem you might write. If you are writing a lyric poem, make sure to include at least two details about the river's qualities; if you are writing a narrative poem, include information about the setting and a character in the poem.

2 Choose one of the poems from this test and imagine that you have been asked to write a review of it. On a separate sheet of paper, write the headings "Word Choice" and "Imagery." Then write an example of each from the poem and tell whether you think the poet uses the word or words and images effectively. Give reasons for your opinions.

3 Imagine that you are given the following writing prompt. On a separate sheet of paper, list at least two similarities and two differences for each method of transportation. You may want to use a Venn diagram to show similarities and differences.

You are planning a summer trip to another state that is far from your home state. Should you travel by car or by plane? Write a comparison-and-contrast essay in which you examine the similarities and differences between the two methods of travel.

SHORT ANSWER

1 How would you restate lines 6–9 of Emerson's poem?

2 How would you paraphrase the excerpt from Masefield's poem on page 1?

3 What is the MAIN purpose of a narrative poem?

4 What is the definition of imagery in poetry?

Unit 5: Drama
Part 1 Benchmark Test 9

MULTIPLE CHOICE

Reading Skill

Answer the questions below.

1 Which of these is MOST IMPORTANT in drawing conclusions while reading?
   ○ identifying main ideas   ○ recognizing author's purpose
   ○ connecting important details   ○ identifying key details

2 Which of these BEST describes a conclusion?
   ○ a decision   ○ a reason   ○ a prediction   ○ an effect

3 Which of these BEST helps you draw conclusions about characters in a play?
   ○ deciding which characters are most   ○ observing characters' interactions with
     important in the play   each other
   ○ noting which characters have the most   ○ knowing whether the characters are
     dialogue in the play   based on real people

Read the dialogue below. Then answer questions 4–7.

THOMAS. Come on, Patrick, you'll have fun. You'll learn a lot, and you'll be helping a family have a home that they otherwise couldn't afford.

PATRICK. I don't know, Thomas. I've never built anything before, much less a house.

THOMAS. You don't have to build the whole thing by *yourself*. There are dozens of people donating their time. Someone will show you just what to do.

PATRICK. What if a piece of wood falls on me or I step on a nail . . .?

THOMAS. What if, what if. *What if* you just said "yes" to the project?

PATRICK. Well, I don't know . . .

THOMAS. Come for three hours on Saturday. If you're not having fun by then, you can leave. And I won't tease you like I did when you quit the baseball team.

4 Which of these can you conclude based on the following statement by Patrick?
   I've never built anything before, much less a house.
   ○ Patrick is not telling the truth.   ○ Patrick likes to tease Thomas.
   ○ Patrick is wary of new situations.   ○ Patrick enjoys challenges.

5 Which conclusion about the building project is supported by the dialogue?
   ○ It is for a company that builds houses.   ○ It is a volunteer project to help others.
   ○ It will be a good source of money.   ○ It was organized by Thomas.

6 Which conclusion is BEST supported by the dialogue?
- ○ Thomas knows that Patrick will not join the project.
- ○ Thomas feels that Patrick will benefit from helping on the project.
- ○ Patrick thinks that Thomas is trying to trick him.
- ○ Patrick is trying to appear braver than he really is.

7 Which conclusion is BEST supported by Thomas's statements and his interaction with Patrick?
- ○ Thomas and Patrick are not friends.
- ○ Thomas enjoys picking on others.
- ○ Thomas likes to help others.
- ○ Thomas can be pushy with Patrick.

Answer the questions below.

8 Which of these is an IMPORTANT characteristic of a generalization?
- ○ It applies to many examples.
- ○ It is difficult to prove.
- ○ It is a type of guess.
- ○ It is a narrow statement.

9 To make a generalization, which of these is important, in addition to using what you already know about a topic?
- ○ connecting causes and effects
- ○ previewing and reading ahead
- ○ summarizing the text
- ○ noting common elements as you read

10 Which of these is an example of a generalization?
- ○ Tonight's weather forecast is for rain.
- ○ The test will contain essay questions.
- ○ One of Dona's hamsters is missing.
- ○ Most supermarkets sell fresh fruit.

Literary Analysis

Answer the question below.

11 Which of these BEST defines stage directions in a play?
- ○ conversations among characters in a play
- ○ instructions for designing the props for a play
- ○ notes that tell how a play should be performed
- ○ directions for the order of events in a play

Read the following stage directions for a play. Then answer questions 12–15.

It is evening on the front porch of a small cabin in the woods. A lantern placed on a porch table gives off a soft glow. The buzzing of insects and croaking of frogs can be heard in the distance. Now and then there is the sound of water splashing, as if a fish has jumped in a pond. A gray-haired woman in her sixties rocks back and forth in a rocking chair on the porch. Her granddaughter, an 8-year-old girl, sits nearby, eating a cookie. It is obvious that there is great affection between the grandmother and girl in the way they speak to each other.

12 What information is included in these stage directions?
- ○ a description of sounds
- ○ the characters' lines
- ○ the central theme
- ○ the characters' costumes

13 What can you tell about the setting of the play from these stage directions?
- ○ The setting is afternoon, on a porch.
- ○ The setting is evening, in a kitchen.
- ○ The setting is night, on a cabin porch.
- ○ The setting is morning, near a pond.

14 What do you learn about the characters from these stage directions?
- ○ how they feel about each other
- ○ why they are at the cabin
- ○ what is important to them
- ○ how they will solve a problem

15 To whom might these stage directions be MOST USEFUL?
- ○ to a costume designer
- ○ to someone reading the play
- ○ to a reviewer of the play
- ○ to a viewer of the play

Answer the questions below.

16 Which of these BEST defines a literary adaptation?
- ○ a work to which dialogue is added
- ○ a work translated into another language
- ○ a work that is shortened
- ○ a work changed to fit a different form

17 Which of these is the BEST example of a literary adaptation?
- ○ a short story based on a real event
- ○ a film script rewritten to add a character
- ○ a novel made into a movie
- ○ a poem that is read on the radio

18 Which of these is important to keep in mind when comparing adaptations to originals?
- ○ differences between the literary forms
- ○ differences among main characters
- ○ differences in reviews of the works
- ○ differences in themes of the works

Vocabulary: Roots

Answer the questions below.

19 What is the meaning of the root shared by *consume* and *presume*?
- ○ to guess
- ○ to join
- ○ to go before
- ○ to take

20 Using your knowledge of the root -*sum*-, what is the MOST LIKELY meaning of the word *assume* in this sentence?

Nestor will assume responsibility for cooking the dinner.
- ○ to give to another
- ○ to become able
- ○ to take upon oneself
- ○ to put in charge

21   What is the meaning of the root shared by *invalid* and *valor*?

○   hopeful   ○   fearless   ○   strong   ○   smart

22   What is the MOST LIKELY meaning of *valiant* in the following sentence?

Rose made a valiant attempt to break her own swimming record.

○   strong and brave   ○   calm and confident
○   difficult and uncertain   ○   clever and daring

23   What is the MOST LIKELY meaning of *resume* in the following sentence?

After the rainstorm passes, the soccer game will resume.

○   be put on hold   ○   happen at another time
○   take place again   ○   start over again

24   What is the MOST LIKELY meaning of *devalued* in the following sentence?

Because the car had been slightly damaged, it was devalued.

○   easily repaired   ○   less attractive
○   lower in worth   ○   destroyed

Grammar

Answer the questions below.

25   Which of these BEST defines a participial phrase?

○   a phrase consisting of a verb form   ○   a verb form commonly ending in
    ending in *-ing* that acts as a noun   *-ing* or *-ed*
○   a phrase composed of a preposition   ○   a participle that, with its modifiers,
    and its object   acts as an adjective

26   What is the participle in the following sentence?

The bald eagle, spotting a fish in the river, plunged head-first into the water.

○   spotting   ○   in   ○   plunged   ○   into

27   What is the BEST way to combine these sentences using a participial phrase?

The crowd encouraged the team. The team scored ten points.

○   The crowd encouraged the team to   ○   The team scored ten points because
    score ten points.   they were encouraged by the crowd.
○   When the crowd encouraged the team,   ○   The team, encouraged by the crowd,
    they scored ten points.   scored ten points.

28 What is the BEST way to combine these sentences using a participial phrase?

The hiker whistled as he walked. The hiker thought he was on the right trail.

○ While the hiker thought he was on the right trail, he whistled as he walked.

○ As he walked, the hiker whistled and thought he was on the right trail.

○ Thinking he was on the right trail, the hiker whistled as he walked.

○ The hiker thought he was on the right trail, so he whistled as he walked.

29 Which of these is the BEST definition of a gerund?

○ a verb form ending in -ed that is used as an adjective

○ a verb form ending in -ing that is used as a direct object

○ a verb form ending in -ing that is used as a noun

○ a verb form ending in -ed that is used as a past participle

30 Which word in the following sentence is a gerund?

Tania prefers drinking filtered water.

○ prefers

○ drinking

○ filtered

○ water

31 What is the BEST way to combine the following sentences using a gerund or a participle?

Steve reached a conclusion. The conclusion was a surprise.

○ Steve reached a conclusion that was a surprise.

○ Steve reached a surprising conclusion.

○ Steve reached a conclusion, and it was surprising.

○ Steve reached a conclusion, a surprise.

32 What is the BEST way to combine these sentences using a gerund or participle?

Celina likes to read. She reads mysteries.

○ Celina likes reading mysteries.

○ Celina likes to read, and she enjoys mysteries.

○ Celina reads mysteries.

○ Mysteries are what Celina likes to read the most.

ESSAY

Writing

1 Imagine that you are preparing to write a scene with dialogue for a play. The scene will involve two characters speaking to each other. On a separate sheet of paper, write a sentence that describes the situation that will set up your scene, such as "Two friends who will enter projects in a school science fair discover that they are both preparing identical science projects." Then write the first few lines of dialogue for the scene.

2 Playwrights often borrow dialogue from real life to use in their plays. Think of a humorous situation that happened to you or to someone you know and that involved more than one person. Imagine that you are using this situation in a play you are writing. On a separate sheet of paper, write three lines of dialogue based on the humorous situation.

Name _____   Date _____

3 Imagine that you are writing a letter to a business to complain about a product that you ordered online. On a separate sheet of paper, write a sentence that might serve as your statement of purpose in the letter. Be specific about the problem you have with the product.

4 What is your ideal job? Imagine that you have a chance to apply for your "dream job." On a separate sheet of paper, name the job you are applying for. Then write a paragraph that you might use in a letter of application for the job, in which you give at least three reasons why you should be hired.

SHORT ANSWER

1 What is one thing that can help you draw conclusions about characters in a play?

2 What is an IMPORTANT characteristic of a generalization?

3 What are stage directions in a play?

4 What is a literary adaptation?

Unit 5: Drama
Part 2 Benchmark Test 10

MULTIPLE CHOICE

Reading Skill

Answer the question below.

1 Which of these BEST helps you link historical causes with their effects as you read a play?
  ○ knowing the author's purpose
  ○ reading similar plays
  ○ using background information
  ○ reading the stage directions

Read the following introduction to a play about a man who worked for justice in Guatemala. Then answer questions 2–3.

In the 1970s, after a period of calm and prosperity, demands for reform in Guatemala were increasing. A military dictatorship had been established and the popularly elected president was forced to leave. In addition, peasant cooperative farms were destroyed, and political parties and unions were crushed. Thousands of people were killed, and thousands fled Guatemala for their lives. Still, movements for reform continued to flourish, in spite of continued efforts to stamp them out. One man, a United States citizen and a priest, decided to put his life on the line for justice for the peasants and other oppressed people in the country.

2 The first scene of the play shows a priest speaking to a group of peasants deep in the woods of Guatemala. What information from the introduction BEST helps you understand what the priest is probably doing?
  ○ For a while, there was calm and prosperity in Guatemala.
  ○ The popularly elected president has been forced to leave.
  ○ The priest is determined to work for justice for the peasants.
  ○ Demands for reform in Guatemala are increasing.

3 The priest is most likely in danger because of his work. What background information in the introduction BEST helps you link this effect with a cause?
  ○ Thousands of people have fled the country.
  ○ People are being punished for working for reforms.
  ○ The man is a United States citizen as well as a priest.
  ○ Movements for reform continue to flourish.

Answer the questions below.

4 Which of these is an IMPORTANT question to ask when analyzing causes and effects in a literary work?
  ○ What happens to the main characters?
  ○ What is the central theme of the work?
  ○ Are two or more events really related?
  ○ How does the work affect the reader?

5 Which of these is true in analyzing causes and effects in a work?
   ○ One effect can have only one cause.   ○ Every cause has at least two effects.
   ○ An effect cannot become a cause.   ○ One cause can have multiple effects.

6 Which statement BEST describes the cause-and-effect relationship in the following situation?

   The endangered falcons eventually used the human-made nest boxes, which led to their raising
   young falcons in the nests; also because of the next boxes, the falcons began establishing their own
   nests on the nearby bluffs of the Mississippi.

   ○ One cause produced one effect.   ○ Two effects caused two more effects.
   ○ Two causes produced two effects.   ○ One cause produced two effects.

7 Which of these could you scan for in both printed documents and on Web sites?
   ○ section headings   ○ home pages
   ○ links to other sites   ○ navigation bars

8 Which of these might you expect to find on a historical Web site about the United States
   Civil War?
   ○ a table of contents for chapters   ○ information about major world wars
   ○ a timeline of major events   ○ a fictional account of the war

9 When you are scanning a historical Web site, which of these might you look for to view a
   list of topics covered by the site?
   ○ a home page   ○ key words
   ○ links to other sites   ○ the address window

Literary Analysis

Read the following excerpt from a play. Then answer questions 10–12.

CHURCHILL. [*growing more impatient*] We have *got* to try harder to come up with a solution, or
else England will fall to Hitler. I won't stand for having my country handed over to the Nazis.

MR. SOAMES. [*taking off his glasses and rubbing his weary eyes*] But, sir, it is nearly two in the
morning, and we've all been working since just after breakfast—

MR. WRIGHT. [*glaring at Churchill*] Except for the Prime Minister, who indulged in a nap—

CHURCHILL. [*drawing a deep breath and exhaling slowly before speaking*] All right, gentlemen. I
don't wish to deplete my finest resources. Let us end this meeting and resume tomorrow at nine.

10 Which of these BEST describes the passage?
    ○ dialogue   ○ narration
    ○ biography   ○ nonfiction

11 What does the passage reveal about the character of Churchill?
    ○ He does not appreciate the hard work   ○ He cares deeply about the safety of
       of his advisors.   his country.
    ○ He has difficulty tolerating criticism or ○ He expects others to work harder than
       disagreement.   he does.

12 What conflict is revealed in this passage?
- ○ a conflict between the United States and England
- ○ a conflict between England and the Nazis
- ○ a conflict between Churchill and Mr. Soames
- ○ a conflict between Mr. Wright and Mr. Soames

Read the dialogue below. Then answer questions 13–15.

> **LINDY.** [*approaches the new student, who is eating lunch at a table by himself in the cafeteria*] Hi there! My name is Lindy. Welcome to the United States and to Crockett School.
>
> **LUIS.** [*looks surprised and a little flustered; wipes his mouth with his napkin*] Hello. I . . . uh . . . my name is Luis. I—[*sighs deeply*] . . . well . . . It's a hard day. So much is new. Please excuse my English.
>
> **LINDY.** [*smiles warmly*] Your English is very good. You should hear my Spanish! [*she rolls her eyes*] My family has moved a lot, so I know how hard it is to be the new kid. You feel like a sore thumb at first!
>
> **LUIS.** [*looks a little baffled*] Did you say *sore thumb*? Now I am *really* confused.

13 Which of these BEST defines character motivation in a literary work?
- ○ the way a character relates to others
- ○ the way a writer develops a character
- ○ the personality of a character
- ○ the reason a character takes an action

14 Which of these MOST LIKELY motivates Lindy to approach Luis in the school cafeteria?
- ○ curiosity
- ○ compassion
- ○ loneliness
- ○ prejudice

15 Which of these MOST LIKELY motivates Luis to sit alone in the cafeteria?
- ○ anger
- ○ loneliness
- ○ discomfort
- ○ unfriendliness

Answer the questions below.

16 Which of these BEST defines a dramatization?
- ○ a play adapted from another work
- ○ a story that has a serious theme
- ○ a movie adapted from a novel
- ○ dialogue based on actual events

17 Which BEST shows an example of comparing a primary source with a dramatization?
- ○ comparing a biography and a novel based on the biography
- ○ comparing a novel and a movie script based on the novel
- ○ comparing a news account with a documentary based on the account
- ○ comparing a journal and a play based on the journal

Vocabulary: Roots

Answer the questions below.

18 What is the meaning of the root shared by *factory* and *manufacture*?
- ○ to complete
- ○ to make
- ○ to work
- ○ to arrange

19 What is the meaning of the root -*seq*- in *consequence*?
- ○ to make
- ○ to follow
- ○ to join
- ○ to appear

20 What is the MOST LIKELY meaning of *facilitates* in the following sentence?

The airport shuttle bus facilitates our getting to the gate quickly.

- ○ helps organize
- ○ adds to
- ○ goes faster
- ○ makes easier

21 What is the MOST LIKELY meaning of *sequence* in the following sentence?

Through a strange sequence of events, we ended up at an ancient castle.

- ○ one thing resembling another
- ○ one event following another
- ○ an unusual situation
- ○ a collection of events

22 What is the MOST LIKELY meaning of *benefactor* in the following sentence?

Because of a generous benefactor, we raised enough money to build a library.

- ○ one skilled in leading others
- ○ one who is wealthy
- ○ one who makes a contribution
- ○ one who organizes an event

23 What is the meaning of *sequel* in the following sentence?

In the sequel to *Thomas Jefferson: The Early Years*, we learn about the Jefferson presidency.

- ○ the part that comes before
- ○ an introduction
- ○ the part that follows
- ○ a type of summary

Grammar

Answer the questions below.

24 Which of these BEST defines a clause?
- ○ a group of words with its own subject and verb
- ○ a group of words that expresses a complete thought
- ○ a group of words that stands by itself as a complete sentence
- ○ a group of words that tells more about a noun

25 Which sentence contains a subordinate clause?

○ After the heavy meal, Gil took a long nap.

○ When Ian finished the book, he gave it to Sean.

○ You can reach me on my cell phone, if necessary.

○ Shortly before noon, the sky darkened and the air cooled.

26 Which of the following is a complete sentence?

○ When I write, I prefer pen and paper.

○ If the bicycle chain had not come off.

○ Because the stove was on fire.

○ In order to get to class on time.

27 Which of these contains BOTH an independent clause and a subordinate clause?

○ The children scrambled up the ladder and slid down the chute.

○ In less than an hour, Manny had cleaned his bedroom.

○ Coiled under a rock was a large rattlesnake.

○ Lijia kept yelling until someone finally rescued her.

28 Which of these BEST defines a subordinate clause?

○ a clause that stands alone as a complete sentence

○ a clause that has a verb but not a subject

○ a clause that has a subject but not a verb

○ a clause that cannot stand by itself as a sentence

29 What is one reason to use a subordinate clause to join two short sentences?

○ to show two important ideas

○ to complete an incomplete thought

○ to show connections between ideas

○ to express a complete thought

30 What is the BEST way to combine these sentences using a subordinate clause?

Ty spelled *cogent* correctly. *Cogent* was unfamiliar to him, though.

○ Ty spelled *cogent* correctly, but he was unfamiliar with the word.

○ Although *cogent* was unfamiliar to Ty, he spelled it correctly.

○ *Cogent* was unfamiliar to Ty, and he spelled it correctly.

○ Ty spelled *cogent* correctly; it was unfamiliar to him.

Spelling

Answer the questions below.

31 Which of these shows the correct spelling for the plural of *belief*?

○ beliefes

○ beliefs

○ believes

○ believs

32 In which sentence is the italized plural spelled correctly?

○ All the farmer's *sheeps* graze here.

○ Some of the *womans* were writers.

○ Two white *geese* honked as they flew.

○ One of Greg's *tooths* had a cavity.

33 Which sentence shows the correct spelling for the italicized plural?
- ○ Dad grows many *varietyes* of roses.
- ○ How many *varietys* of soap are there?
- ○ Some *varietis* of this plant are extinct.
- ○ The store carries five *varieties* of pears.

ESSAY

Writing

1 Think of an important event in history. Imagine that you experienced the event—either as a direct participant or as a witness—and are writing a diary entry about your experience. On a separate sheet of paper, write three sentences that you might include in your diary entry about the event. Make sure to name the historical event in one of the three sentences.

2 Imagine that you have written a play about a historical event in your town. Now you will write a letter to a well-known director to ask him or her to direct your play. On a separate sheet of paper, write the first two sentences of your letter, in which you describe the type of play you have written and tell why you want the director's help.

3 Think of a specific topic for a research report—one that is not too broad or too narrow. On a separate sheet of paper, write the topic. Then write four questions that you would like to answer about the topic.

SHORT ANSWER

Reading Skill

1 When scanning a historical Web site, what feature might you look for to view a list of topics covered by the site?

2 What is an IMPORTANT question to ask when analyzing causes and effects in a literary work?

Literary Analysis

3 What is character motivation in a literary work?

4 What is a dramatization?

Unit 6: Themes in American Short Stories
Part 1 Benchmark Test 11

MULTIPLE CHOICE

Reading Skill

Answer the questions below.

1 Which statement accurately describes a good summary?
- ○ A good summary presents all the details that appear in the original work.
- ○ A good summary is usually much longer than the original work.
- ○ A good summary uses precisely the same phrases as the original work.
- ○ A good summary restates a work's main ideas in as few words as possible.

2 In which of these ways can reading a summary be valuable?
- ○ It can easily replace the experience of reading the original work.
- ○ It can provide a quick way of previewing or reviewing the original work.
- ○ It can serve as a graphic aid in the original work.
- ○ It can provide an account far more interesting than the original work.

3 Which is the BEST one-sentence summary of this information about a Chicago museum?

Among the huge number of things you can see at the Art Institute of Chicago are the Harding collection of medieval armor and the Thorne collection of miniature rooms, handmade to the smallest detail. The museum's paintings, which go back to the thirteenth century, include a particularly fine collection of European impressionist and post-impressionist works. The museum is also known for its American art, including the famous paintings *Nighthawks* by Edward Hopper and *American Gothic* by Grant Wood.

- ○ The Art Institute of Chicago displays works going back to the thirteenth century.
- ○ Highlights at the Art Institute of Chicago include a collection of medieval armor and a collection of miniature rooms.
- ○ The Art Institute of Chicago has a huge collection of works from many cultures and eras.
- ○ At the Art Institute of Chicago you can find many famous works of art, including *American Gothic* by Grant Wood.

Read the story below. Then answer questions 4–6.

Janine and I were out collecting specimens for a science project, though we were finding very few items that we needed. Suddenly, the sky grew dark and the wind grew fierce. Realizing that a storm was coming, we turned and headed for home. We did not get far, however, when the downpour began. I ushered Janine into a cave on the side of the mountain to use as a shelter. Never having been in a cave, she was very frightened. The cave was damp and dark and smelled of decay. Luckily, we had a flashlight with us, though its light was rather dim. We remained there until the storm ended. Janine was glad to see the last of the cave—and frankly, so was I!

4 If you were writing a summary of this story, which of these details would you be MOST LIKELY to include?

- ○ We had not found very many science specimens.
- ○ During the storm, we found shelter in a cave.
- ○ The cave was damp and dark and smelled of decay.
- ○ Luckily we had a flashlight, though it was rather dim.

5 If you were writing a summary of this story, which of these details would you be LEAST LIKELY to include?

- ○ Janine and I were collecting specimens for a science project.
- ○ Janine and I had not found many specimens for our project.
- ○ We went into a cave to find shelter from the storm.
- ○ After the storm, we headed for home.

6 In preparing a summary of the story, which graphic aid would probably be MOST LIKELY in organizing the sequence of events?

- ○ a time line
- ○ a pie chart
- ○ a cluster diagram
- ○ a bar graph

Answer the question below.

7 Which of these types of writing is a good example of a summary?

- ○ a description of a TV show in a TV guide
- ○ a news story in a local or national newspaper
- ○ the instruction manual that comes with a new automobile
- ○ a story that appears in an anthology of short stories

Read the book review below. Then answer questions 8–10.

Wonders of Wonderland

(1) *Alice's Adventures in Wonderland* by Lewis Carroll is a delightful fantasy. (2) It tells of a young girl named Alice who follows a rabbit down a hole and winds up in a land of many wonders. (3) She drinks something that makes her very small and eats something that makes her a giant. (4) She has tea with a Mad Hatter, testifies at a trial for the King and Queen of Hearts, and meets dozens of other strange creatures. (5) The book's greatest charm is in its creative depiction of a world far from reality and in the gentle humor with which it pokes fun at our own world. (6) However, some readers may have problems with dated details and unfamiliar British customs—pocket watches and taking tea, for example. (7) Nevertheless, if you enjoy fantasy and humor, I strongly recommend this book.

8 Which two sentences in the book review give an overall opinion of the book's value?

- ○ sentences 1 and 2
- ○ sentences 2 and 5
- ○ sentences 5 and 6
- ○ sentences 1 and 7

9 Which three sentences in the book review give a summary of the book?

- ○ sentences 1, 2, and 3
- ○ sentences 2, 3, and 4
- ○ sentences 3, 4, and 5
- ○ sentences 4, 5, and 6

10 Which two sentences in the book review discuss the book's strengths and weaknesses?

- ○ sentences 1 and 3
- ○ sentences 3 and 5
- ○ sentences 5 and 6
- ○ sentences 1 and 7

Literary Analysis

Answer the question below.

11 For what MAIN purpose did ancient peoples create myths?

- ○ to create a body of literature that would stand the test of time
- ○ to explain natural occurrences or events in the peoples' history
- ○ to show that gods and goddesses are nothing like human beings
- ○ to give enduring fame to heroes and heroines who contributed to the society

Read the story below. Then answer questions 12–15.

Demeter, Greek goddess of agriculture, had a beautiful daughter named Proserpine. Proserpine caught the eye of the god known as Pluto, who wanted to marry her. He was god of the underworld, a dark, gloomy land where the ghosts of the dead flew around like bats. Demeter did not want her daughter to dwell in such an awful place. When she refused to allow the marriage, Pluto carried Proserpine off while she was picking flowers. After Pluto married Proserpine, Demeter was filled with grief at the loss of her daughter. Finally, Zeus, the brother of Pluto and ruler of the gods, ruled that Proserpine should spend only part of the year with her husband. The other part she would spend with Demeter, helping her with the growing season. Each year when Proserpine went below ground, winter would come. Each year when she rejoined her mother, the growing season would return.

12 What does the myth of Demeter and Proserpine show about the Greek gods and goddesses?

- ○ They often display human qualities.
- ○ They rarely display strong feelings or emotions.
- ○ They are all very beautiful.
- ○ They take little interest in human activities.

13 What does the myth of Demeter and Proserpine try to explain?

- ○ the best way to grow grain
- ○ the reason the underworld is dark
- ○ the origin of bats
- ○ the origin of the seasons

14 What does the behavior of Zeus in the myth suggest that the ancient Greeks valued?

- ○ wealth
- ○ unchecked power
- ○ power guided by compassion
- ○ respect for the dead

15 What does the myth of Demeter and Proserpine show about ancient Greek culture?

- ○ People lived longer than they do today.
- ○ Women had little influence over men.
- ○ People lived in tiny, dark homes.
- ○ Agriculture was an important activity.

Name _____ Date _____

Answer the questions below.

16 Which statement is true of literature composed in the oral tradition?
- ○ It shows little about the culture that produced it.
- ○ It is usually narrated in elegant formal English.
- ○ It includes legends, folk songs, folk tales, and tall tales.
- ○ It is usually written down soon after it is composed.

17 What is dialect?
- ○ the conversations that characters have in a work of literature
- ○ the language and grammar of a particular region or people
- ○ the customs and values of a particular region or people
- ○ works passed down by word of mouth before being written down

Read the story below. Then answer questions 18–21.

Hijos, let me tell you a story from our long ago. This was back when California was part of Spain. It was a time when the rich *hidalgos* were cruel to the poor farmers. They worked them very hard and gave them very little. But one man, *un hombre,* he was a champion of the poor. This man, he was known as Zorro—The Fox. He stole from the rich and gave to the poor. Not from all the rich— just the ones who had made their wealth on the backs of the poor. *El Señor* Zorro, he was bold and brave, and the finest swordsman in the world. He was clever like a fox, and quick—no one could catch him. No one even knew who he was! That was because he wore a black mask over his eyes to keep his real identity hidden. Now I will tell you a secret, *mis hijos.* The real identity of this Zorro— he was a rich *hidalgo* himself! He saw what other men like him did, and he was ashamed. That is why he became Zorro, to make up for what others did.

18 Which quality of this story MOST CLEARLY suggests that it comes from the oral tradition?
- ○ It uses formal, old-fashioned English.
- ○ It uses lots of modern slang.
- ○ It uses dialect and repetition.
- ○ It explains what the name Zorro means.

19 Which statement BEST describes Zorro?
- ○ He is a heroic character whose admirable qualities are exaggerated.
- ○ He is a weak character who pretends to be strong in the face of evil.
- ○ He is a selfish character who thinks very little about the feelings of others.
- ○ He is a villainous character who upsets the social order in old California.

20 What does the popularity of the legend of Zorro show about the Spanish-American culture that produced it?
- ○ It was a society with no economic or social classes.
- ○ It was a society where crime was virtually unknown.
- ○ It was a society where military might was deeply admired.
- ○ It was a society where compassion for the poor was deeply admired.

21 From the details in the legend of Zorro, what do you conclude that the Spanish word *hidalgos* probably means?
- ○ aristocrats   ○ mayors   ○ farmers   ○ explorers

Vocabulary

Answer the questions below.

22 Which statement is true about the prefixes *non-*, *dis-*, and *un-*?

- ○ They have opposite meanings.
- ○ They can change a word into its antonym.
- ○ They all mean the same thing.
- ○ *Non-* is used much more frequently than *dis-* or *un-*.

23 Based on your understanding of the prefix *dis-*, which of these paired items are the most *dissimilar*?

- ○ a legend and a folk tale
- ○ a god and a goddess
- ○ a baseball and a noodle
- ○ a stream and a river

24 Based on your understanding of the prefixes *non-* and *un-*, which word is a synonym of *nonessential*?

- ○ uncertain
- ○ unlimited
- ○ unnecessary
- ○ unthinkable

25 Which choice explains how the prefix *dis-* is part of the meaning of the italic word in this sentence?

Her jealous rivals did their best to *discredit* her achievements.

- ○ to *discredit* is to speak without thinking or to jump to conclusions
- ○ to *discredit* is to show the financial, moral, or other value of someone or something
- ○ to *discredit* is to perform activities that win you fame, honors, or social status
- ○ to *discredit* is to take away the credit, reputation, or believability of someone or something

26 From your knowledge of prefixes, what do you think you call someone who does not behave in a conventional way?

- ○ a nonresident
- ○ a dishonor
- ○ a uniform
- ○ a nonconformist

27 In which sentence does the italic word make use of the prefix *an-* or *a-*?

- ○ The World Series is an *annual* event in Major League Baseball.
- ○ The government collapsed and complete *anarchy* followed.
- ○ After she left public school, she enrolled in a private *academy*.
- ○ When will they *announce* the winner of the contest?

Grammar

Answer the questions below.

28 What type of sentence is this?

During the boat trip down the Nile, the people saw several crocodiles.

- ○ simple
- ○ compound
- ○ complex
- ○ compound-complex

29 Which of these sentences is a compound sentence?

- ○ For too long, Ms. Simmons paid little attention to the paperwork on her desk.
- ○ When she finally approached the task, the pile of paperwork was enormous.
- ○ She could do the work herself or hire a secretary.
- ○ She inquired about a temporary secretary, but the cost was far too high.

30 How should this sentence be rewritten so that it uses commas correctly?

Touring Spain we visited the cities of Madrid Granada, and Seville but never reached Barcelona.

- ○ Add a comma after *Spain*, *Madrid*, and *Seville* and keep the comma after *Granada*.
- ○ Add a comma after *Spain* and *Madrid* and remove the comma after *Granada*.
- ○ Add a comma after *Madrid* and *Seville* only and keep the comma after *Granada*.
- ○ Add a comma after *Spain* and *Madrid* and keep the comma after *Granada*.

31 How should you correct the punctuation in this sentence?

Owing to the rain the barbecue was canceled, our party was instead held indoors.

- ○ Add a comma after *rain* and remove the comma after *canceled*.
- ○ Add a comma after *rain* and change the comma after *canceled* to a semicolon.
- ○ Just change the comma after *canceled* to a period and capitalize the *o* in *our*.
- ○ No changes are necessary; the sentence is correct as is.

32 Which of these sentences is punctuated correctly?

- ○ The zoo which opens at ten stays open late on Thursdays, Saturdays, and Sundays.
- ○ Beautifully landscaped it is a large, impressive zoo with thousands of animals.
- ○ If you visit on a busy weekend, you will probably wait in line at opening time.
- ○ A visit usually costs seven dollars for adults but on Thursdays the zoo is free to all.

33 Which of these choices is a complete sentence?

- ○ The settlers building small cabins.
- ○ When they arrived in the New World.
- ○ Sailing for months across the Atlantic.
- ○ They traveled far.

ESSAY

Writing

1 Create a modern myth to explain something puzzling, annoying, or peculiar about modern life. For example, you might tell "Why the Bus Is Always Late" or "Why It Always Rains on Weekends." Use your imagination to come up with what you consider to be a suitable mythological explanation. If you do not have enough room on your paper, write your myth on a separate sheet.

2 On your paper or a separate sheet, write a critical analysis of a film or TV show that features a heroic character. In your analysis, focus on how effectively the character is portrayed.

3 Imagine that you are writing a multimedia report on a myth. It might be a report on a natural phenomenon that the myth tries to explain or a famous character or work from the world of mythology. On your paper or a separate sheet, jot down your ideas for the elements you might include in your multimedia report and the information sources you might use to gather your information.

SHORT ANSWER

Reading Skill

1 What does a good summary do?

2 Identify a type of writing that usually consists of a summary or contains a summary.

Literary Analysis

3 For what MAIN purpose did ancient peoples create myths?

4 What are three types of literature that are often composed in the oral tradition?

Unit 6: Themes in American Short Stories
Part 2 Benchmark Test 12

MULTIPLE CHOICE

Reading Skill

Answer the questions below.

1 When should you set a purpose for reading?
  ○ before you read
  ○ after you finish reading
  ○ only when you read to be entertained
  ○ only when you read to be informed

2 When you ask questions to set a purpose for reading, what should you put in the first column of a *K-W-L* chart?
  ○ what you already **k**now about the topic
  ○ what you want to **k**now about the topic
  ○ what you **k**eep reading about the topic
  ○ a **k**ey sentence about the topic

3 Once you set a purpose for reading, what should you do about your rate of reading?
  ○ Adjust your rate of reading to match your mood.
  ○ Read more slowly when you enjoy what you are reading.
  ○ Read more slowly when you are reading to learn new information.
  ○ Always read at the same speed, no matter what you are reading.

Read the following paragraph about the Wright brothers. Then answer questions 4–7.

(1) Today we associate the Wright brothers with the development of flying. (2) However, they were not the first to try to do it. (3) The person that the scientific community expected to perform the feat was a prominent scientist named Samuel Pierpont Langley. (4) Langley had a whole team of other scientists working with him as well as the financial backing of organizations, such as the Smithsonian Institute. (5) Working in the Washington, D.C., area, he built a series of experimental flying machines. (6) The only problem was, every time he launched one, it would crash. (7) Wilbur and Orville Wright, in contrast, had no formal scientific training. (8) To earn a living, they ran a bicycle shop in their hometown. (9) Intrigued by the possibility of flight, they studied aerodynamics, built their flying machine, and flew it successfully. (10) Even after their landmark success, it took years for them to get credit for the achievement.

4 Which of these is a likely purpose you might have for reading the paragraph?
  ○ to learn about the history of Washington, D.C.
  ○ to learn the history of Dayton, Ohio
  ○ to learn about the early history of flying
  ○ to learn the laws of aerodynamics

5 In addition to learning new information, what other purpose might you have for reading this selection?
  ○ to investigate products before buying them
  ○ to escape to an imaginary world of adventure
  ○ to be entertained with amusing historical anecdotes
  ○ to appreciate the poetry written about flying

6 Imagine that you were writing a paper on people other than the Wright Brothers who tried to develop early flying machines. What would you MOST LIKELY do?
- ○ Take notes on sentences 3–6 only.
- ○ Take notes on sentences 7–10 only.
- ○ Take notes on the whole paragraph.
- ○ Read the paragraph quickly.

7 In considering your purpose for reading this paragraph, which of these questions would you be MOST LIKELY to list in the middle column of a *K-W-L* chart?
- ○ What did the Wright Brothers' airplane look like?
- ○ Where is the Smithsonian Institute located?
- ○ How were airplanes important to military technology?
- ○ What was unusual about the Wright Brothers' achievement?

Answer the questions below.

8 What is a transcript?
- ○ a complete written record of a spoken event
- ○ a written summary of a spoken event
- ○ a paraphrase that restates people's words in simpler language
- ○ a commentary on a spoken event

9 For which of these events are people MOST likely to want transcripts?
- ○ a commercial on TV or radio
- ○ a public affairs program on TV
- ○ a live music concert
- ○ a birthday party

Literary Analysis

Read the story below. Then answer questions 10–13.

During the Great Depression, jobs were scarce. The small factory where Leah's father worked had to leave New York City's Garment Center for less costly operations in upstate New York. Leah's father, a skilled maker of wallets, had to move to keep his job, taking his family with him. It was a shocking change for the Kaminsky family, especially Leah's mother. Living in a Jewish immigrant community, Mrs. Kaminsky had gotten by with her poor English skills for nearly twenty years. Now, in the small upstate city, she was forced to rely on her daughter to help her with everyday tasks. For Leah, being a support to her mother was gratifying. And though she did not like moving away from her friends, she liked the looks of the new school. Most of all, she enjoyed living in a place where you could pass farms with cows and sheep and chickens.

10 What ethnic group is featured in the cultural context of this selection?
- ○ Jewish Americans
- ○ Mexican Americans
- ○ Italian Americans
- ○ African Americans

11 How is the Kaminsky family affected by the Great Depression of the 1930s?
- ○ The family is forced to immigrate to America.
- ○ The family must leave their immigrant community for an unfamiliar American city.
- ○ The parents have trouble putting food on the table to feed their children.
- ○ Mrs. Kaminsky is forced to find a job in order to supplement her husband's income.

12 How does Mrs. Kaminsky react to the cultural and historical events that change her life?

○ She is miserable about the loss of income and strives to regain her social status.

○ She is upset with the changes and relies more on her daughter.

○ She is glad to move to a place near farms like those she remembers from Europe.

○ She makes up her mind to learn English and to adopt American ways.

13 How does Leah react to the historical and cultural events that change her life?

○ She likes some of the changes but dislikes having to help her mother with everyday tasks.

○ She dislikes all the changes and especially hates the boredom of rural life.

○ She likes some of the changes but misses her friends from New York City.

○ She is so self absorbed that she barely notices the changes taking place around her.

Read the following biography of Agatha Christie. Then answer questions 14–16.

Born in England to an English mother and an American father, Agatha Christie grew up at a time when women from wealthy families did not work for a living. World War I, however, changed all that. During the war, Christie worked at a local hospital, helping to dispense medicines. Then, after the war, she decided to try writing mysteries. Soon she was creating stories featuring one of two popular detectives—Hercule Poirot, an eccentric former Belgian policeman working as a detective in London, and Miss Jane Marple, an elderly spinster who had an uncanny understanding of human nature. Christie's first marriage, to World War I pilot Archibald Christie, ended in divorce, but in 1930 she was remarried to the British archeologist Max Malloran, whom she sometimes accompanied on his digs in the Middle East.

14 Which aspect of Agatha Christie's novels was MOST CLEARLY affected by her cultural background?

○ her ability to create really puzzling mysteries

○ her portrayal of changing times in English society

○ her portrayal of Belgian detective Hercule Poirot

○ her detailed understanding of criminal procedures

15 How do you think Christie's World War I experiences MOST helped her in creating the plots of her mysteries?

○ She learned about the horrors men face in battle.

○ She learned how to make the likely person the guilty party.

○ She obtained knowledge of poisons to use as murder weapons.

○ She learned how the local police force worked.

16 Christie's *Death Comes as the End* is a historical mystery set in ancient Egypt. Which aspect of her background do you think probably had the MOST influence on this novel?

○ the fact that her father was American

○ the fact that she came from a wealthy family and was not expected to work for a living

○ the fact that she grew up in England

○ the fact that she married an archeologist and went on digs with him in the Middle East

Answer the question below.

17 What is a universal theme?

- ○ an insight, major idea, or underlying message specific to a work's setting
- ○ an insight, major idea, or underlying message about space exploration
- ○ an insight, major idea, or underlying message about God or the afterlife
- ○ an insight, major idea, or underlying message that appears in many cultures

Read the two story summaries below. Then answer questions 18–19.

Story A: A new headmaster comes to run the local school in a Nigerian village, hoping to improve the quality of life. The first thing he does is close the school to villagers who walk across the lawn to reach the local burial ground. The villagers are furious that they cannot visit their ancestors and complain to school authorities, who fire the headmaster.

Story B: A group of real-estate developers want to build a new sports stadium in an American city neighborhood. They say that the stadium will bring jobs and business opportunities to the neighborhood, and some politicians agree. People in the neighborhood, however, are furious, saying a stadium will change the quiet residential character of their neighborhood. When enough people turn against the idea, the politicians back out, and the stadium project is canceled.

18 Based on the summaries, what common theme do the two stories share?

- ○ Change is not always an improvement.
- ○ Love of money is the root of all evil.
- ○ You can't fight city hall.
- ○ It is important to respect one's ancestors.

19 What is different about the way the themes of the two stories are expressed?

- ○ The first story puts more emphasis on economic factors.
- ○ The first story puts more emphasis on political factors.
- ○ The first story puts more emphasis on social customs.
- ○ The second story puts more emphasis on education.

Vocabulary

Answer the questions below.

20 Which of these words comes to English from Spanish?

- ○ genre
- ○ boomerang
- ○ balcony
- ○ canyon

21 Which of these words related to cooking and food comes to English from French?

- ○ chef
- ○ pretzel
- ○ yam
- ○ bagel

22 Which English word for a wind storm do you think has its origins in the Chinese word *tai-fung*, which means "big wind"?

- ○ hurricane
- ○ blizzard
- ○ tornado
- ○ typhoon

23 In Persian, the word *khak* means "dust" or "earth." What color would you guess that *khaki* pants are?

- ○ white
- ○ yellow brown
- ○ violet blue
- ○ green

24 In Spanish, a *corro* is a circle or a ring. What part of a ranch do you think a *corral* is?

- ○ the farmhouse
- ○ the stable
- ○ the enclosure for holding the animals
- ○ the field where crops are grown

Grammar

Answer the questions below.

25 Which of these sentences is punctuated correctly?

- ○ My little brother lost his hat, I found it the next day.
- ○ I dressed him in: a hat, gloves, and a scarf.
- ○ The Lost and Found contains these items; an umbrella and five gloves.
- ○ I went to the Lost and Found; the hat was there.

26 How should you correct the punctuation in this sentence?

I looked up the word in the dictionary, the entry contained the following important information, the pronunciation, the origin, and the meaning.

- ○ Change the first comma to a semicolon and the second comma to a colon.
- ○ Change the first comma to a colon and the second comma to a semicolon.
- ○ Add a colon after *up* and remove the comma after *information*.
- ○ No changes are necessary; the sentence is correct as is.

27 Which of these sentences uses correct capitalization?

- ○ Last thanksgiving my parents and i visited the City of atlanta.
- ○ last thanksgiving my parents and I visited the city of atlanta.
- ○ Last Thanksgiving my Parents and I visited the City of Atlanta.
- ○ Last Thanksgiving my parents and I visited the city of Atlanta.

28 Which of these sentences uses correct capitalization?

- ○ Yesterday Miss Duncan asked the class, "How many of you like to read poetry?"
- ○ Yesterday Miss Duncan asked the class, "how many of you like to read poetry?"
- ○ Yesterday miss Duncan asked the class, "how many of you like to read poetry?"
- ○ Yesterday miss Duncan asked the class, "How many of you like to read poetry?"

29 When should you use quotation marks for quotations that you include in an essay or another paper?

- ○ for shorter quotations only
- ○ for longer quotations only
- ○ whenever you quote material exactly
- ○ whenever you introduce a quotation with a colon

30 What is a block quote?
- ○ any words within quotation marks
- ○ a longer quotation that is set off by indenting
- ○ any words that follow a colon
- ○ a quotation that does not use the exact words of the speaker or writer

Spelling

Answer the questions below.

31 Which word is spelled correctly?
- ○ sillable
- ○ udjoin
- ○ persue
- ○ pleasant

32 In which sentence is the italic word spelled correctly?
- ○ Mrs. Grant is the hospital's largest *benafactor.*
- ○ Did you read the *epalogue* at the end of the novel?
- ○ The 30 percent discount makes the bathing suit a real *bargain.*
- ○ Do not *hesatate* to phone me if you need me.

33 What should you do to spell the italic word in this sentence correctly?

The authors of many fine words are *unonymous.*

- ○ Change the first *u* to *a.*
- ○ Change the *u* to *a* and the *i* to *o.*
- ○ Change the *y* to *i* and drop the first *o.*
- ○ Leave the word alone; it is correct.

ESSAY

Writing

1 Think of a historical period in which you might like to set a story. On your paper or a separate sheet, jot down three questions that you would need to answer to learn more about the cultural context of the period. Then write a short proposal of the research you would do to answer your questions.

2 Imagine that you were a guest at the funeral of a historical figure that you admire. On your paper or a separate sheet, jot down your notes for a speech that you might have given at this person's funeral.

3 Think of something significant that has happened in the history of your region or nation or an event that was important to your heritage or ancestors. On your paper or a separate sheet, write a cause-and-effect essay explaining this historical event.

SHORT ANSWER

Reading Skill

1   Give an example of how your purpose for reading affects your rate of reading.

2   What is a transcript?

Literary Analysis

3   What is the cultural context of a literary work?

4   What is a universal theme?

Part 1
Outcome Test

Suppose that you are going to interview your town's mayor about her experiences as a middle-school student years ago. You will use the interview to write an article for the school newspaper. Answer questions 1–4.

1 What should you do before arriving at the mayor's office?
- ○ Wonder what the mayor is like.
- ○ Write a list of questions to ask.
- ○ Remember to bring your eighth-grade class picture with you.
- ○ Interview another person.

2 During the interview, how should you use a notebook?
- ○ Write the questions you want to ask in it.
- ○ Have the mayor autograph it for you.
- ○ Take notes in it as the mayor talks.
- ○ Begin writing your article for the newspaper in it.

3 What should you do when you quote the mayor in your article?
- ○ Try to write exactly what she says.
- ○ Use quotation marks.
- ○ Add to what she says to make it more interesting.
- ○ both A and B

4 Which of the following shows that you have asked good interview questions?
- ○ The mayor compliments you on them.
- ○ They yield information that helps you answer the questions "who," "what," "where," "when," "why," and "how."
- ○ You can use them to make up interesting stories about the mayor.
- ○ They are questions that many people have asked the mayor before.

Suppose that you and your classmates will work in small groups to write speeches about the importance of wearing seat belts while riding in an automobile. You will travel to elementary schools to deliver your speeches to fourth-grade students. Answer questions 5–10.

5 What should be the specific purpose of this speech?
- ○ to persuade listeners to wear their seat belts whenever they drive
- ○ to explain why listeners should buy only cars that have seat belts
- ○ to persuade listeners to wear seat belts whenever they ride in an automobile
- ○ to inform listeners of what to do in case they are in a car accident

6 What should be the tone of your speech?
- ○ serious and professional
- ○ serious and frightening
- ○ humorous and light-hearted
- ○ mysterious and vague

7 Which of the following should you do during your speech?
- ○ Use slang and a quick pace.
- ○ Make eye contact with the audience.
- ○ Mumble and say "um" a lot.
- ○ Slouch and keep your head down.

8 What is the point of letting the audience ask questions or make comments after you have finished your speech?
- ○ to provide more information and clarify your points
- ○ to fill time if your speech runs too short
- ○ to make the audience feel important
- ○ to demonstrate your listening skills

9 When you write your speech, which of the following should you do?
- ○ Include statistics and other facts that you aren't sure are accurate.
- ○ Use vocabulary and sentence structure that is above the heads of your listeners.
- ○ Include lots of jokes and humor.
- ○ Stay focused on your main idea.

10 What is the BEST way to help other groups improve on their presentation skills?
- ○ Read their speeches before they present them to the audience.
- ○ Observe their performances, taking notes on strengths and weaknesses.
- ○ Compare their speeches to your own group's speech.
- ○ Listen to the kinds of questions and comments the audience makes.

Read the advertisement below. Then answer questions 11–12.

SNEAKER SALE!

On sale this week only!

- The best sneakers money can buy—each pair is made especially to fit YOUR feet.
- Improve your performance in all sports: jump higher, run faster, kick harder. You'll feel as though you are flying!
- Sneakers come in 10 cool colors, for boys and girls.

Don't be the only kid in your school who wears old-fashioned sneakers.

Buy a new pair TODAY.

11 Which statement from the sneaker ad tries to appeal to your emotions?

- ○ Each pair is made especially to fit YOUR feet.
- ○ Improve your performance in all sports.
- ○ Don't be the only kid in your school who wears old-fashioned sneakers.
- ○ all of the above

12 What is the PRIMARY purpose of the sneaker ad?

- ○ to persuade
- ○ to entertain
- ○ to describe
- ○ to inform

Answer the question below.

13 Which of the following sentences contains a metaphor?

- ○ The long hall was dark, dreary, and frightening.
- ○ Sun shone through the south window of the little house.
- ○ The spotlight was a great eye looking down upon us.
- ○ Marlene flung her clothes carelessly over the furniture.

Read the following story about how the peacock got his feathers. Then answer questions 14–16.

The Price of Beauty

According to legend, the peacock did not always have such beautiful feathers. He was just an average bird who wanted to stand out. When the peacock's wish was granted, and he got his new feathers, he visited his old friends. The peacock presented himself grandly and called out, "Bonjour!" The pheasant, the swan, and the heron all admitted that the peacock was by far the most beautiful. On his way home, the peacock saw an eagle soaring overhead, as he used to do. Lifting his wings, the peacock tried to rise, but the weight of his new feathers held him down. He knew then that he would no longer fly up to greet the morning but instead walk the ground like a common beast.

14 Which of the following statements BEST expresses the theme of this story?

- ○ Do not give up freedom for something less important.
- ○ There is always someone less fortunate than you.
- ○ The most precious things in life can be bought.
- ○ Do not take credit for something you did not do.

15 Which of the following events is MOST likely to occur next in the passage above?

- ○ The peacock tries to adjust to his new limitations.
- ○ The eagle teaches the peacock to fly.
- ○ The peacock destroys his new feathers.
- ○ The heron requests new feathers as beautiful as the peacock's.

16 If you were using a reference book about peacocks to learn about their natural environment, which of the following chapters would probably be MOST useful?

- ○ A Colorful History
- ○ Bound to the Earth
- ○ Diet and Lifespan
- ○ Habitats

Read the three stories below. Then answer questions 17–20.

First Steps Concert

Jason watched with wide eyes as the four singers approached the stage. He had been looking forward to this moment for six weeks. When his choir director, Mr. Nelson, announced that the group First Steps would be performing for the school, Jason almost jumped out of his seat. He had all their CDs and dreamed of singing with the group someday. Mr. Nelson told the class that they could watch the group warm up before the performance, and Jason was the first one in the auditorium. He leaned forward, mesmerized, as they tuned to each other's voices. Suddenly they burst into an old spiritual. Jason had never heard anything so beautiful.

Lesson Plan

It was my favorite class of the day. Not only that, Ms. Peeler had asked *me* to come up with a lesson plan to teach the class! Today was the day I was supposed to present it. I could hardly wait to stand in front of the class and tell them what I had learned. I stayed up until 12 o'clock the night before preparing. When I walked into class, Ms. Peeler pulled me aside. She told me that the school was having a special assembly and that I would have to wait until next class time to present my lesson. I tried not to act disappointed, but I wanted to cry. As the class filed into the hall, I was the last to leave. I walked slowly to the auditorium and sat in the back row. Some group I'd never heard of called First Steps was going to sing. All I could think about was my lesson.

The Return

Chris, Randy, Mark, and Abel had never performed at a high school before. Abel's high school choir director called him after their last tour. Mr. Nelson suggested that they do a concert for Abel's school. Abel hadn't been back to his old school for ten years. When they arrived, Abel gave the guys a tour of the place. Memories from his past flooded back.

"This was my old locker. My friends and I would meet here after school every Wednesday to have jam sessions. Students would crowd around while we started to sing all kinds of fun stuff."

In the choir room, Abel hugged Mr. Nelson and said, "This is the man who made me fall in love with music." Abel and the guys followed Mr. Nelson into the auditorium where students were waiting to listen to the group warm up.

17 Which of the passages contains a special focus on classroom education?

- ○ "First Steps Concert"
- ○ "Lesson Plan"
- ○ "The Return"
- ○ all of the above

18 Which of the passages features a main character who experiences conflict?
○ "First Steps Concert"
○ "Lesson Plan"
○ "The Return"
○ all of the above

19 In "First Steps Concert," why is Jason excited about the concert?
○ He gets to go into the auditorium first.
○ He enjoys music and likes the group's work.
○ The group sings Jason's favorite spiritual.
○ The group wants to hear Jason sing.

20 Which of the following BEST describes the points of view in "Lesson Plan" and "The Return"?
○ "Lesson Plan" is in first person; "The Return" is in third person.
○ "Lesson Plan" is in third person; "The Return" is in first person.
○ "Lesson Plan" is in second person; "The Return" is in third person.
○ "Lesson Plan" is in first person; "The Return" is in second person.

Answer the question below.

21 Why does the poet repeat the word *knock* so often in these lines of poetry?

What was the constant knock,

knock, knocking

Waking me before dawn?

○ to show that the speaker is expecting a visitor
○ to show that the speaker has been asleep
○ to show that there is no doorbell
○ to show that the knocking is continuous

Read the two stories below. Then answer questions 22–23.

First Trip

I was happy to be taking my first long journey by wagon with my cousin, Beth, and her family. As the days passed, we covered dozens of miles. We crossed rivers and mountains, and by early June we stood on the shore of an ocean that neither of us had ever seen before.

Freedom

Freedom walked alongside my cousin Little Bear and me as we followed the wooded paths first marked by our ancestors. It was if these pathways were imprinted on our memories at birth, for though we had never seen these trees and hills and streams before, we never lost our way. After three moons, we stood on a flat red cliff, gazing at a shining golden face: the sea spread before us, a reward for our courage and an invitation to leave behind our youth.

22 Which of the following words helps you identify the time period of "First Trip"?

- ○ journey
- ○ rivers
- ○ shore
- ○ wagon

23 Which of the following statements about the two passages are true?

- ○ Each story concerns a journey to the sea.
- ○ The two narrators have different cultural backgrounds.
- ○ Unlike the author of "First Trip," the author of "Freedom" uses metaphors and symbolism.
- ○ all of the above

Answer the questions below.

24 Read the sentence that follows. Then choose the word that BEST expresses the meaning of the italicized word.

It was *unsettling* when the forks and spoons crashed to the floor.

- ○ confusing
- ○ terrifying
- ○ soothing
- ○ disturbing

25 Read the dictionary entry below. The word *bluff* can be used as how many parts of speech?

bluff *adj* **1.** frank and outspoken; *n* **1.** a high steep bank **2.** a cliff; *v* **1.** to deceive **2.** to deter or frighten by pretense or a mere show of strength

- ○ one
- ○ two
- ○ three
- ○ four

Part 2
Outcome Test

Read the story below. Then answer questions 1–7.

The Truth About "The Wizard Walks"

Recently, some parents tried to remove "The Wizard Walks" from the shelves of the local public library. These foolish people are entitled to decide for themselves what they will read, but "The Wizard Walks" should not be banned.

The people who object to "The Wizard Walks" believe that it is unsuitable for children. However, a poll showed that most people who want to ban "The Wizard Walks" haven't even read the book. They are mindlessly repeating what they have heard from others without taking the trouble to research the subject themselves.

The main argument for banning "The Wizard Walks" is that it is almost a textbook on magic. But anyone who has actually read the book knows that it does not teach witchcraft. Although the main character of "The Wizard Walks" has magical powers, the story is obviously fictional. Most children have no trouble figuring out that this book describes an imaginary world.

Perhaps "The Wizard Walks" is not good for every child, but banning it from the public library goes too far. If ignorant people start banning books, soon our libraries will be empty. Every book is offensive to someone for some reason.

Parents who do not want children to read "The Wizard Walks" can ban it from their homes. To ban it from the public library would take away the right of other parents to make that decision for their own children.

1 According to the speaker, what is the primary argument for banning "The Wizard Walks?"
- ○ The book contains excessive violence.
- ○ The book is not intended for a youthful audience.
- ○ The book functions as a kind of textbook on magic.
- ○ The book is not good for every child.

2 According to the speaker, what negative effect would result from banning the book from the public library?
- ○ Public libraries would be empty.
- ○ Parents would reserve the right to decide what their children should read.
- ○ The people who say that the book is unsuitable for children would not have to read the book.
- ○ It would take away the right of parents to decide what their children should read.

3 Which of the following is the BEST summary of the speaker's views?
- ○ Books on magic are enjoyable for children, despite the fact that some adults are not interested in the subject.
- ○ The main character of "The Wizard Walks" has magical powers, and the book is a work of fiction.
- ○ Public libraries are one of the most valuable resources in a free society.
- ○ Informed people will agree that "The Wizard Walks" poses no threat to children and should not be banned from the public library.

4 For what purpose is the speaker using oral language?
   ○ to persuade the audience by comparing and contrasting different viewpoints
   ○ to entertain the audience
   ○ to inform the audience about the novel
   ○ to analyze a literary text

5 Which of the following would be an effective way for the speaker to support his or her ideas and enhance the oral presentation?
   ○ Read a chapter from "The Wizard Walks."
   ○ Show a copy of "The Wizard Walks" along with several classic works of literature that have been banned in the past.
   ○ Show a broomstick and a witch's hat.
   ○ all of the above

6 Based on the evidence in this essay, what can you infer that the speaker believes?
   ○ Only a few books should ever be banned from the library.
   ○ All children should be required to read "The Wizard Walks."
   ○ "The Wizard Walks" is the best children's book of our time.
   ○ Public libraries should not have a wide variety of books.

7 How does the speaker make the argument effective?
   ○ The speaker says negative things about the people who ban books.
   ○ The speaker states the issues, gives examples, and presents a solution.
   ○ The speaker agrees that the book may not be good for every child.
   ○ The speaker says that those who ban books are wrong.

Read the following directions for operating a hand mixer. Then answer questions 8–11.

Using Your Chef's Gourmet Hand Mixer

Before using your mixer for the first time, wash and dry the beaters and the mixing bowl. Make sure that the speed control is in the OFF position and the mixer is not plugged in. Insert the beaters into the openings on the bottom of the mixer. Push until each beater clicks into position. Then plug the cord into a standard household electrical outlet (120 volt, 60 Hz AC).

8 What should you do just before inserting the beaters?
   ○ Plug the mixer into an outlet.
   ○ Check that the mixer is turned off and unplugged.
   ○ Set the speed control to "1."
   ○ Rock the mixer back onto its base.

9 What should you do before using the mixer for the first time?
   ○ Wash and dry the beaters and mixing bowl.
   ○ Wash and dry the electrical outlet.
   ○ Wash and dry the cord.
   ○ Wash and dry the speed control.

10 Which of the following is the BEST explanation of the purpose of this passage?

○ The passage describes how to buy The Chef's Gourmet Hand Mixer.

○ The passage informs how to use The Chef's Gourmet Hand Mixer.

○ The passage informs how to plug in The Chef's Gourmet Hand Mixer.

○ The passage describes how to wash The Chef's Gourmet Hand Mixer.

11 Based on the information in this passage, what you can conclude?

○ The mixer should be operated without the beaters.

○ The mixer should be operated by professional chefs.

○ The mixer should be operated near an electrical outlet.

○ The mixer should be operated outdoors.

Read the following description of Lake Louise, a lake in Canada. Then answer questions 12–14.

Lake Louise

Lake Louise is part of Banff National Park in southern Alberta, Canada. Visitors find it quiet and peaceful at Lake Louise. The smooth waters mirror the surrounding mountains, creating breathtaking views. Often the lake water is too cold for swimming. More people visit Lake Louise than anywhere else in the Canadian Rockies.

12 Which of the following sentences is MOST effective as a supporting sentence in the paragraph?

○ Often the lake water is too cold for swimming.

○ Lake Louise is part of Banff National Park.

○ More people visit Lake Louise than anywhere else in the Canadian Rockies.

○ Lake Louise is located in southern Alberta, Canada.

13 Which of these statements can be inferred from the paragraph?

○ Lake Louise is close to the United States.

○ People enjoy the spectacular scenery at Lake Louise.

○ Lake Louise is the largest lake in Canada.

○ The Canadian Rockies have many beautiful lakes.

14 Which of the following would be a useful way for the writer to find additional information to use in this essay?

○ Use the Internet to find out more about Banff National Park.

○ Read a magazine article on the popularity of fishing and water sports.

○ Create an outline to organize writing ideas.

○ Write an email to a friend about vacation destinations.

Name _____ Date _____

Read the story below. Then answer questions 15–17.

Modern Bandage

Although many people don't even know his name, Earle Dickson was responsible for creating one of today's most common household items. Dickson was the genius behind Band-Aids®.

In 1917, Dickson was a newly married man and a cotton buyer for a successful bandage company in New Jersey called Johnson & Johnson.

As the story goes, Dickson's wife, Frances, was accident-prone. She often cut herself or nicked her fingers doing various household tasks. The regular bandages were too big and clumsy for Frances, so Dickson devised something better.

He folded pads of cotton gauze and placed them on long strips of surgical tape. He covered this with a material called crinoline. This prevented the tape from sticking to itself when it was rolled back together. Frances could unroll the bandage and cut off as much as she needed.

One day, Dickson mentioned his creation to a friend at work. Soon, Dickson was before the Johnsons, showing them what he had come up with. The Johnsons were especially impressed with the fact that you could put the new bandage on yourself. Up until that point, bandages had been difficult to apply without help.

Johnson & Johnson began producing Band-Aids®, but the bandages didn't take off until the mid-1920s when the company gave thousands of samples to the Boy Scouts. After that, Band-Aids® were a hit. Dickson was made vice president of Johnson & Johnson, and when he died in 1961, the company was selling $30,000,000 dollars' worth of Band-Aids® a year.

15 Which answer would fit BEST in the blank in the outline below?

The Invention of Band-Aids®

I.   Who Earle Dickson was
II. _____
III. How Dickson made his own bandage
IV. What happened at Johnson & Johnson
V.   The success of Band-Aids®

○ Where Johnson & Johnson was
○ What Dickson's wife's name was
○ Why Dickson made his own bandage
○ How Dickson met with Johnson & Johnson

16 If you were taking notes about this passage, which of these ideas should you omit?
○ Dickson became vice president.
○ Band-Aids® were popular right away.
○ Early bandages were difficult to put on.
○ Dickson worked for Johnson & Johnson.

17 Which of these statements gives the BEST summary of the passage?
○ The Boy Scouts make Band-Aids® more popular.
○ A housewife is finally able to bandage herself.
○ A cotton inventor becomes head of a company.
○ One man's homemade bandages become Band-Aids®.

Read the following article about tennis. Then answer questions 18–20.

The Growing Popularity of Tennis

<u>The sport of tennis is becoming more popular with children and teenagers.</u> <u>Young</u>

Part 1

<u>stars such as Andy Roddick and Serena Williams to look up to.</u> <u>Many schools are adding</u>

Part 2

<u>tennis.</u> <u>To their physical education programs.</u> <u>Community centers have recognized the</u>

Part 3

<u>growing popularity of tennis.</u> <u>Added tennis courts to their existing facilities.</u>

18 Which is the BEST way to revise Part 1?
- ○ The sport of tennis is becoming more popular with children and teenagers; young stars such as Andy Roddick and Serena Williams to look up to.
- ○ With young stars such as Andy Roddick and Serena Williams to look up to, the sport of tennis is becoming more popular with children and teenagers.
- ○ Young stars such as Andy Roddick and Serena Williams have made the sport of tennis more popular with children and teenagers.
- ○ Young stars such as Andy Roddick and Serena Williams. Have made the sport of tennis more popular with children and teenagers.

19 Suppose that the writer wanted to use the material in this passage to write two paragraphs, with Part 2 appearing at the beginning of the second paragraph. Which of the following would be the BEST transition to the second paragraph?
- ○ For instance,
- ○ After all,
- ○ As a result,
- ○ On the contrary,

20 If you were typing this paragraph into a computer's word-processing program, which of the following would be helpful?
- ○ The computer can automatically add additional research for you.
- ○ You can make corrections easily.
- ○ You can move text around easily.
- ○ both B and C

Name _____ Date _____

Read the story below. Then answer questions 21–23.

Techniques of Fiction Writers

   Fiction writers use a variety of techniques to _____1_____ their characters seem like real people. One such technique is to have characters use dialects when they speak. Some writers use first-person narration so that the reader knows how one of the characters feels, as well as what _____2_____ says.

21 Suppose you were to make a web showing the sentence that contains the main idea in the center and the sentences that contain details in circles that connect to the center. Which sentence would you place in the center?
   ○ the first sentence
   ○ the second sentence
   ○ the third sentence
   ○ This paragraph does not contain a main idea.

22 Which of the following words belongs in space 1?
   ○ makes
   ○ made
   ○ make
   ○ making

23 Which word or group of words belongs in space 2?
   ○ he or she
   ○ they
   ○ the narrator
   ○ the author

Answer the questions below.

24 Which word BEST completes the analogy below?

   "Rebellion" is to "dissent" as _____.

   ○ "corridor" is to "isle."
   ○ "tragedy" is to "misfortune."
   ○ "path" is to "track."
   ○ "congregation" is to "worship."

25 Which word or group of words BEST completes the sentence below?

   The newspapers in my town and your city _____ the championship games.

   ○ covers
   ○ covering
   ○ cover
   ○ has covered

Writing Prompt 1

Imagine that the community center in your town will soon be adding something new. It may be a new piece of equipment, a new club, or a new class that you would like to take. Write a letter to convince the director of the community center that your idea is the one that should be added. Be specific in your descriptions of the new element and explain your reasons for selecting it.

Writing Prompt 2

If you had three wishes, what would they be? Write an essay in which you explain what you wish for and why. Support your ideas with examples and details.

ISTEP+ Practice Test

"Shut Off Television" Week

Read the writing prompt below and complete the writing activity.

> The student council at your school is promoting a "Shut Off Television" Week. At the end of the week, it is hoped that students will be encouraged to continue not watching or at least to watch less television than they did previously.
>
> Write a persuasive essay to be submitted for the next edition of your school newspaper in which you agree or disagree with "Shut Off Television" Week.

Be sure to include

- a clear statement of your opinion on the topic
- sound, thoughtful reasons that support your opinion and persuade others to agree
- good examples that support each reason you give
- an introduction, a body, and a conclusion to your essay

Go On ➡

Use the Pre-Writing/Planning space or additional paper for notes, lists, webs, outlines, or anything else that might help you plan your writing. Then write you essay on the lined pages. Be sure to write neatly. Using the Editing Checklist on page 139, check your writing for correct paragraphing, grammar, spelling, punctuation, and the use of Standard English.

NOTE: Only your writing on the lined pages in this book will be scored.

Pre-Writing/Planning

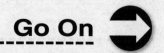

Name _____ Date _____

Pre-Writing/Planning

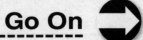

Essay

Title: _____

_____

_____

_____

_____

_____

_____

_____

_____

_____

_____

_____

_____

_____

_____

_____

_____

_____

_____

_____

_____

_____

_____

_____

_____

Go On

Go On ➡

Name _____ Date _____

_____

_____

_____

_____

_____

_____

_____

_____

_____

_____

_____

_____

_____

_____

_____

_____

_____

_____

Now check your writing using this Editing Checklist.

Editing Checklist

1 Check your capitalization and punctuation.

2 Spell all words correctly.

3 Check for sentence fragments or run-on sentences.

4 Keep verb tense consistent.

5 Make sure subject and verb agree.

6 Use words according to the rules of Standard English.

7 Remember to paragraph correctly.

STOP! _ _ _ _ STOP! _ _ _ _ STOP! _ _ _ _ STOP! _ _ _ _ STOP! _ _ _ _

STOP

You now will read a poem and an article. You will answer questions based on each passage. Then you will write an essay on a related topic.

Have you ever wondered how people make the decisions that determine their lives? The poem "The Road Not Taken" deals with this important issue in a very unique way.

Now read "The Road Not Taken" and do Numbers 1 through 6. You may look back at the poem as often as you like.

Go On

The Road Not Taken

by Robert Frost

Two roads diverged in a yellow wood,
And sorry I could not travel both
And be one traveler, long I stood
And looked down one as far as I could
To where it bent in the undergrowth;

Then took the other, as just as fair,
And having perhaps the better claim,
Because it was grassy and wanted wear;
Though as for that, the passing there
Had worn them really about the same,

And both that morning equally lay
In leaves no step had trodden black.
Oh, I kept the first for another day!
Yet knowing how way leads on to way,
I doubted if I should ever come back.

I shall be telling this with a sigh
Somewhere ages and ages hence:
Two roads diverged in a yellow wood,
and I—
I took the one less traveled by,
And that has made all the difference.

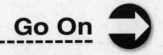
Go On

1 What is the tone of "The Road Not Taken"?

○ humorous

○ thoughtful

○ unhappy

○ lighthearted

2 What do the images in "The Road Not Taken" symbolize?

○ the joy of hiking

○ the beauty of nature

○ the process of making decisions

○ the importance of safety

3 Give TWO different phrases or lines from the poem that support the idea that the poet is satisfied with the choice he made.

1) _____

_____

2) _____

_____

Go On

4 Complete the chart below to explain ONE reason why the poet took the less traveled road. Then provide ONE example from the poem to support your explanation.

Reason	Example

5 What does the line "In leaves no step had trodden black" MOST LIKELY mean?

○ Where no evidence of travel was visible

○ Where no leaves had fallen from the trees

○ Where there was no path

○ Where leaves on the trees were all black

Go On ➡

6 Based on what the reader says at the end of the poem, it is clear that

○ the thought of the trees have haunted him for many years

○ he returned to the spot in the woods many times

○ he will never again choose the road less traveled

○ taking the less traveled road made a difference in his life

Go On ➡

Name _____ Date _____

Many people love this time of year with the beautiful colors of the leaves, but few of us understand what process changes the leaves colors. Have you ever wondered how leaves change colors in the autumn and why?

You will now read "Why Leaves Turn Color in the Fall," an article that mixes the author's personal feelings for autumn with scientific information about the subject. After you read this article, you will answer some questions and write an essay on a related topic.

Read "Why Leaves Turn Color in the Fall" and do Numbers 7 through 13. You may look back at the article as often as you like.

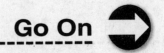

Go On

from "Why Leaves Turn Color in the Fall"

by Diane Ackerman

The stealth of autumn catches one unaware. Was that a goldfinch perching in the early September woods, or just the first turning leaf? A red-winged blackbird or a sugar maple closing up shop for the winter? Keen-eyed as leopards, we stand still and squint hard, looking for signs of movement. Early-morning frost sits heavily on the grass, and turns barbed wire into a string of stars. On a distant hill, a small square of yellow appears to be a lighted stage. At last the truth dawns on us: Fall is staggering in, right on schedule, with its baggage of chilly nights, macabre holidays, and spectacular, heart-stoppingly beautiful leaves. Soon the leaves will start cringing on the trees, and roll up in clenched fists before they actually fall off. Dry seedpods will rattle like tiny gourds. But first there will be weeks of gushing color so bright, so pastel. So confettilike, that people will travel up and down the East Coast just to stare at it—a whole season of leaves.

Where do the colors come from? Sunlight rules most living things with its golden *edicts.* When the days begin to shorten, soon after the summer solstice on June 21, a tree reconsiders its leaves. All summer if feeds them so they can process sunlight, but in the dog days of summer the tree begins pulling nutrients back into its trunk and roots, pares down, and gradually chokes off its leaves. A corky layer of cells forms at the leaves' slender petioles, then scars over. Undernourished, the leaves stop producing the pigment chlorophyll, and photosynthesis ceases. Animals can migrate, hibernate, or store food to prepare for winter. But where can a tree go? It survives by dropping its leaves, and by the end of autumn only a few fragile threads of fluid-carrying xylem hold leaves to their stems.

A turning leaf stays partly green at first, then reveals splotches of yellow and red as the chlorophyll gradually breaks down. Dark green seems to stay longest in the veins, outlining and defining them. During the summer, chlorophyll dissolves in the heat and light, but it also being steadily replaced. In the fall, on the other hand, no new pigment is produced, and so we notice the other colors that were always there, right in the leaf, although chlorophyll's shocking green hid them from view. With their camouflage gone, we see these colors for the first time all year, and marvel, but they were always there, hidden like a vivid secret beneath the hot glowing greens of summer. . . .

An odd feature of the colors is that they don't seem to have any special purpose. We are *predisposed* to respond to their beauty, of course. They shimmer with the colors of sunset, spring Bowers, the tawny buff of a colt's pretty rump, the shuddering pink of a blush. Animals and Bowers color for a reason—adaptation to their environment—but there is no adaptive reason for leaves to color so beautifully in the fall any more than there is for the sky or ocean to be blue. It's just one of the haphazard marvels the planet *bestows* every year. We find the sizzling colors thrilling, and in a sense they dupe us. Colored like living things, they signal death and disintegration. In time, they will become fragile and, like the body, return to dust. They are as we hope our fate will be when we die; not to vanish, just to sublime from one beautiful state into another. Though leaves lose their green life, they bloom with urgent colors, as the woods grow mummified day by day, and Nature becomes more carnal, mute, and radiant.

Go On ➡

7 Which feature of the selection MOST suggests it is nonfiction?

○ It contains colorful descriptions.

○ It takes place outdoors in the world of nature.

○ It presents a scientific explanation.

○ It tells a story about the narrator's experiences.

8 This selection would be MOST useful for a reader wanting to

○ study a cyclical process of nature

○ enjoy a good short story about trees

○ compare the ways trees are planted

○ learn how to prevent tree disease

9 Give TWO different examples from the article that show that, although the autumn leaves have no real purpose, they are meaningful to people.

1) _____

_____

2) _____

_____

Go On ➡

10 Which of the following statements BEST describes what happens to the yellow pigments in a leaf during the summer months?

○ They are concealed.

○ They are dissolved.

○ They are replaced.

○ They are nonexistent.

11 Read this sentence from the article.

Early-morning frost sits heavily on the grass, and turns barbed wire into a string of stars.

1) What kind of poetic device is this an example of?

_____

_____

2) What do the two things being compared have in common that makes the image come alive?

_____

_____

Go On

12 The word *disposed* means "inclined to like something." Based on this definition and how it is used in the passage, what does *predisposed* mean?

○ inclined to like something later

○ inclined to like something in advance

○ inclined to like something again

○ inclined to never like something

Go On ➡

13

Author Diane Ackerman obviously loves the autumn, as her article makes clear. Her persuasive prose makes her readers have similar feelings. What is your favorite season? Using the article you have just read as a model, write a persuasive essay in which you give reasons why your favorite season is the best time of the year. **Be sure to use some aspect of science that helps make your season unique. It might be describing snowflakes for winter or the way flowers and plants bloom in the spring.**

You may use the space below to plan your writing. Using the Editing Checklist on page 152, check your writing for correct paragraphing, grammar, spelling, punctuation, and the use of Standard English. **Remember, your essay should be well organized and have an introduction, a body, and a conclusion.**

NOTE: Only your writing on the lined pages in this book will be scored.

Pre-Writing/Planning

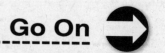

Go On

Name _____ Date _____

Essay

_____
_____
_____
_____
_____
_____
_____
_____
_____
_____
_____
_____
_____
_____
_____
_____
_____
_____
_____
_____
_____
_____
_____
_____
_____
_____

Go On ➡

Name _____ Date _____

_____

_____

_____

_____

_____

_____

_____

_____

_____

_____

_____

_____

_____

_____

_____

_____

Now check your writing using this Editing Checklist.

Editing Checklist

1   Check your capitalization and punctuation.

2   Spell all words correctly.

3   Check for sentence fragments or run-on sentences.

4   Keep verb tense consistent.

5   Make sure subject and verb agree.

6   Use words according to the rules of Standard English.

7   Remember to paragraph correctly.

STOP! ____ **STOP!** ____ **STOP!** ____ **STOP!** ____ **STOP!** ____ STOP

ITBS PRACTICE TEST

Vocabulary

DIRECTIONS

This is a test about words and their meanings.

■ For each question, you are to decide which one of the four answers has most nearly the same meaning as the underlined word above it.

■ Then, on your answer folder, find the row of answer spaces numbered the same as the question. Fill in the answer space that has the same letter as the answer you picked.

The sample on this page shows you what the questions are like and how to mark your answers.

SAMPLE

S1 Getting enough **exercise**

   A excitement
   B work finished
   C enjoyment of life
   D movement of the body

ANSWER

S1 A B C **D**

Name _____ Date _____

Vocabulary

1 To <u>cease</u> fighting

  A enjoy
  B avoid
  C receive
  D halt

2 To tell an <u>anecdote</u>

  J funny story
  K strong argument
  L riddle
  M untruth

3 Discovered a <u>rarity</u>

  A something underground
  B anything difficult
  C something uncommon
  D anything remembered

4 A <u>genteel</u> officer

  J polite
  K well-trained
  L well-armed
  M gruff

5 The <u>nimble</u> mouse

  A hungry
  B quick
  C tame
  D naughty

6 He showed great <u>valor</u>.

  J dancing skill
  K courage
  L sense of adventure
  M understanding

7 A <u>petite</u> girl

  A having good manners
  B dressing with style
  C short and thin
  D long and lean

8 An <u>oath</u> given

  J promise
  K gift
  L support
  M alarm

9 <u>Genuine</u> leather

  A tough
  B real
  C new
  D sold

10 The police <u>relented</u>.

  J patrolled
  K softened
  L continued
  M chased

11 To <u>wreak</u> destruction

  A break
  B escape
  C add to
  D carry out

12 The glasses <u>cascaded</u>.

  J broke into pieces
  K slid across
  L were cleaned
  M fell like water

13 Full of <u>mirth</u>

  A mixture
  B danger
  C happiness
  D togetherness

14 An <u>outstanding</u> job

  J difficult
  K long waited for
  L high quality
  M serious

Reading Comprehension

DIRECTIONS

This is a test of how well you understand what you read.

- This test consists of reading passages followed by questions.

- Read each passage and then answer the questions.

- Four answers are given for each question. You are to choose the answer that you think is better than the others.

- Then, on your answer folder, find the row of answer spaces numbered the same as the question. Fill in the answer space for the best answer.

The sample on this page shows you what the questions are like and how to mark your answers.

SAMPLE

> Demi watched her new treasure sink beneath the surface of the lake. She was not in a hurry to get home because she knew she would have to tell her father what happened. He had spent quite a bit of money on that disk.

S1 **Why is Demi not in a hurry to get home?**

A She wants to go and buy another doll.
B She is afraid her father will be angry.
C She is having a lot of fun at the lake.
D She wants to look for her doll in the lake.

ANSWER

S1 A B **C** D

Name _____ Date _____

This is an excerpt from an adaptation of a speech by American Indian speaker and diplomat, Chief Seattle. Originally delivered in the 1850s, Chief Seattle's message was modified by screenwriter Ted Perry for use in a 1972 film about ecology.

¶1   The President in Washington sends word that he wishes to buy our land. But how can you buy or sell the sky? The land? The idea is strange to us. If we do not own the freshness of the air and the sparkle of the water, how can you buy them?

¶2   Every part of the earth is sacred to my people. Every shining pine needle, every sandy shore, every mist in the dark woods, every meadow, every humming insect. All are holy in the memory and experience of my people. . . .

¶3   The shining water that moves in the streams and rivers is not just water, but the blood of our ancestors. If we sell you our land, you must remember that it is sacred. Each ghostly reflection in the clear water of the lake tells of events and memories in the life of my people. The water's murmur is the voice of my father's father.

¶4   The rivers are our brothers. They quench our thirst. They carry our canoes and feed our children. So you must give the rivers the kindness you would give any brother.

¶5   If we sell you our land, remember that the air is precious to us, that the air shares its spirit with all the life it supports. The wind that gave our grandfather his first breath also receives his last sigh. The wind also gives our children the spirit of life. So if we sell you our land, you must keep it apart and sacred, as a place where man can go to taste the wind that is sweetened by the meadow flowers. . . .

¶6   This we know: The earth does not belong to man, man belongs to the earth. All things are connected like the blood which unites us all. Man did not weave the web of life, he is merely a strand in it. Whatever he does to the web, he does to himself. . . .

¶7   Your destiny is a mystery to us. What will happen when the buffalo are all slaughtered? The wild horses tamed? What will happen when the secret corners of the forest are heavy with the scent of many men and the view of the ripe hills is blotted by talking wires? Where will the thicket be? Gone! Where will the eagle be? Gone! And what is it to say goodbye to the swift pony and the hunt? The end of living and the beginning of survival.

¶8   When the last Red Man has vanished with his wilderness and his memory is only the shadow of a cloud moving across the prairie, will these shores and forests still be here? Will there be any of the spirit of my people left?

1 **What is the main idea of this essay?**

A The memories of people are connected to their homeland.

B People should never try to sell land that belongs to their family.

C The spirits of Native Americans live on in the water and air.

D People should respect the land because it gives them life.

2 **What is the effect of the writer asking questions in paragraphs 1, 7, and 8?**

J It forces the reader to think more carefully about the ideas in the passage.

K It makes the reader wonder how much the writer knows about his subject.

L It challenges the reader to look for the answers somewhere in the paragraph.

M It persuades the reader to agree with the ideas in the passage.

3 **What prompts the narrator to discuss how important the earth is to his people?**

A Determination not to sell his land

B Appreciation for the beauty of the dark woods

C Concern for what whites will do to it

D Hope that his father's spirit will remain

4 **Why does the narrator think the idea of buying land is so strange?**

J The narrator has inherited land, not bought it.

K It is too hard to set a price on water and air.

L The narrator does not understand money.

M You cannot buy what is not owned.

5 **How does the author of this essay feel about the earth?**

A He is puzzled by its mysteries.

B He believes that it is sacred.

C He is worried that it will vanish.

D He wishes that he owned it.

6 **What does the narrator think the white people will do after they have bought the land?**

J Sell it

K Ruin it

L Work it

M Worship it

7 **How does the author feel about white people?**

A He does not know any of them.

B He does not believe them.

C He does not understand them.

D He does not like them.

8 **In paragraph 7, what does "talking wires" mean?**

J Television cables

K Clothes lines

L Telephone wires

M Radio wires

9 **The tone of this essay is one of**

A anger.

B melancholy.

C humor.

D mystery.

Reading Comprehension

Identity

Let them be as flowers,
always watered, fed, guarded, and
    admired,
but harnessed to a pot of dirt.

I'd rather be a tall, ugly weed,
clinging on cliffs, like an eagle
wind-wavering above high, jagged rocks.

To have broken through the surface
    of stone,
to live, to feel exposed to the madness
of the vast, eternal sky.
To be swayed by the breezes of an
    ancient sea,
carrying my soul, my seed, beyond
    the mountains of time
or into the abyss of the bizarre.

I'd rather be unseen, and if
then shunned by everyone,
than to be a pleasant-smelling flower,
growing in clusters in the fertile valley,
where they're praised, handled, and
    plucked
by greedy, human hands.

I'd rather smell of musty, green stench
than of sweet, fragrant lilac.
If I could stand alone, strong and free,
I'd rather be a tall, ugly weed.

— *Julio Noboa Polanco*

10 **What point is the author of this poem attempting to make?**

J To be beautiful is to be admired.
K Beauty and comfort are nothing without freedom.
L Breaking free from the everyday can make one crazy.
M To stand up for something sets a person free.

11 **With which statement about the importance of friends would the author most likely agree?**

A Real friends allow a person to be an individual.
B Good friends will join a person who stands alone.
C The best friends like the same things their friends do.
D True friends admire a friend who acts as they do.

12 **The tone of this poem is one of**

J bitterness.
K revolution.
L hope.
M defiance.

13 **What does breaking through stone prove about the author?**

A That he is destructive
B That he is stubborn
C That he is admired
D That he is strong

14 **If the weed hanging on the cliff were a person, it would be**

J noble.
K intelligent.
L independent.
M friendly.

Reading Comprehension

This passage is from a 1973 speech by Alice Walker in which she remembers what seeing Dr. Martin Luther King, Jr., for the first time meant to her.

¶1   In 1960, my mother bought a television set . . . And then, one day, there appeared the face of Dr. Martin Luther King, Jr. What a funny name, I thought. At the moment I first saw him, he was being handcuffed and shoved into a police truck. He had dared to claim his rights as a native son, and had been arrested. He displayed no fear, but seemed calm and serene, unaware of his own extraordinary courage. His whole body, like his conscience, was at peace. . . .

¶2   He was The One, The Hero, The One Fearless Person for whom we had waited. I hadn't even realized before that we *had* been waiting for Martin Luther King, Jr., but we had. And I knew it for sure when my mother added his name to the list of people she prayed for every night.

¶3   I sometimes think that it was literally the prayers of people like my mother and father, who had bowed down in the struggle for such a long time, that kept Dr. King alive until five years ago. For years we went to bed praying for his life, and awoke with the question "Is the 'Lord' still here?"

¶4   The public acts of Dr. King you know. They are visible all around you. His voice you would recognize sooner than any other voice you have heard in this century—this in spite of the fact that certain municipal libraries, like the one in downtown Jackson, do not carry recordings of his speeches, and the librarians chuckle cruelly when asked why they do not.

¶5   You know, if you have read his books, that his is a complex and revolutionary philosophy that few people are capable of understanding fully or have the patience to embody in themselves. Which is our weakness, which is our loss. . . .

¶6   You know of the prizes and awards that he tended to think very little of. And you know of his concern for the disinherited: the American Indian, the Mexican-American, and the poor American white—for whom he cared very much. . . .

¶7   But add to all of these things the one thing that seems to me second to none in importance: He gave us back our heritage. He gave us back our homeland; the bones and dust of our ancestors, who may now sleep within our caring *and* our hearing. . . . He gave us full-time use of our woods, and restored our memories to those of us who were forced to run away, as realities we might each day enjoy and leave for our children.

¶8   He gave us continuity of place, without which community is ephemeral. He gave us home.

15 In paragraph 5, what does the word "embody" mean?

A Wait one's turn
B Provide an example
C Discuss intelligently
D Invest wisely

16 To whom is the narrator referring when she says that "we had waited"?

J Native Americans
K African Americans
L The Walker Family
M The King Family

17 From the author's description of the librarians in downtown Jackson, they are most likely

A black.
B misunderstood.
C rich.
D white.

18 When did the narrator realize that Dr. Martin Luther King, Jr., was such an important person?

J When he began to receive his awards
K When her mother started praying for him
L When she first saw him on television
M When his first book was published

19 In paragraph 6, what does the word "disinherited" mean?

A Loss of property
B Not having a family
C Those without money
D Those deprived of rights

20 Why would King's conscience have been "at peace"?

J His conscience was part of his body, which was at peace.
K He felt hope that he would achieve what he fought for.
L He believed what he was fighting for was just.
M He believed in equality through peaceful means.

21 In paragraph 7, what does the narrator mean when she says that King "gave us back our heritage"?

A He made African Americans proud of where they came from.
B He took in African Americans who were homeless.
C He brought African traditions to blacks in America.
D He reminded them that their ancestors had been slaves.

22 What was it about seeing King on television that the narrator thought was funny?

J His name
K His courage
L His face
M His son

Reading Comprehension

This piece comes from the story *The Dinner Party* by Mona Gardner.

¶1   . . . A large dinner party is being given in an up-country station by a colonial official and his wife. . . .

¶2   At one side of the long table a spirited discussion springs up between a young girl and a colonel. The girl insists women have long outgrown the jumping-on-a-chair-at-sight-of-a-mouse era, that they are not as fluttery as their grandmothers. The colonel says they are, explaining that women haven't the actual nerve control of men. . . .

¶3   "A woman's unfailing reaction in any crisis," the colonel says, "is to scream. And while a man may feel like it, yet he has that ounce more of control than a woman has. And that last ounce is what counts!"

¶4   The American scientist does not join in the argument, but sits watching the faces of the other guests. As he looks, he sees a strange expression come over the face of the hostess. She is staring straight ahead, the muscles of her face contracting slightly. With a small gesture she summons the native boy standing behind her chair. She whispers to him. The boy's eyes widen: he turns quickly and leaves the room. No one else sees this, nor the boy when he puts a bowl of milk on the verandah . . .

¶5   The American comes to with a start. In India, milk in a bowl means only one thing. It is bait for a snake. . . .

¶6   He looks up at the rafters . . . and sees they are bare. Three corners of the room, which he can see by shifting only slightly, are empty. In the fourth corner a group of servants stand . . . The American realizes there is only one place left—under the table.

¶7   His first impulse is to jump back and warn the others. But he knows the commotion will frighten the cobra and it will strike. He speaks quickly, the quality of his voice so arresting that it sobers everyone.

¶8   "I want to know just what control everyone at this table has. I will count three hundred . . . and not one of you is to move a single muscle. . . ."

¶9   The 20 people sit like stone images while he counts. . . . [H]e sees the cobra emerge and make for the bowl of milk. Four or five screams ring out as he jumps to slam shut the verandah doors.

¶10   "You certainly were right, Colonel!" the host says. "A man has just shown us an example of real control."

¶11   "Just a minute," the American says, turning to his hostess, "there's one thing I'd like to know. Mrs. Whynnes, how did you know that cobra was in the room?"

¶12   A faint smile lights up the woman's face as she replies. "Because it was lying across my foot."

23 The American scientist appears to be the type of person who likes to

   A relax.
   B investigate.
   C take orders.
   D take risks.

24 In paragraph 7, what does the phrase "so arresting that it sobers everyone" mean?

   J So serious-sounding that it makes everyone laugh
   K So beautiful-sounding that it makes everyone melancholy
   L So legal-sounding that everyone gets frightened
   M So important-sounding that everyone pays attention

25 What is the effect of putting the argument about self-control at the beginning of the story?

   A It provides ideas for the reader to consider while reading the rest of the story.
   B It causes surprise when it is revealed that a woman had such self-control.
   C It creates more sympathy for the American, who is not allowed to participate.
   D It distracts everyone in the story so that the cobra may sneak into the room.

26 Why does the hostess call to the boy waiting behind her chair?

   J There is a cobra on her foot.
   K The next course of the meal is ready.
   L She wants another bowl of milk for her guests.
   M She wants him to check on the American.

27 How does the American know the milk is for a cobra when he has not yet seen the snake?

   A There are no other pets in the house.
   B He could smell the poison cobras have.
   C Milk is used as cobra bait in India.
   D He asks the serving boy.

28 What is the author's view of the American scientist?

   J He has more respect for women than most men.
   K He has more self-control than most men.
   L His great heroism saves everyone at the party.
   M His training as a scientist makes him a valuable guest.

29 Which character in the story is named Whynnes?

   A The American
   B The hostess
   C The serving boy
   D The young girl

30 In paragraph 9, what does "sit like stone images" mean?

   J Pose for pictures
   K Remain very still
   L Sit very straight
   M Wait for dessert

Spelling

DIRECTIONS

This test will show how well you can spell.

■ Many of the questions in this test contain mistakes in spelling. Some do not have any mistakes at all.

■ You should look for mistakes in spelling.

■ When you find a mistake, fill in the answer space on your answer folder that has the same letter as the **line** containing the mistake.

■ If there is no mistake, fill in the last answer space.

The samples on this page show you what the questions are like and how to mark your answers.

SAMPLES

S1
A crisp
B bright
C washed
D appel
E (No mistakes)

S2
J silver
K copper
L bronze
M nickel
N *(No mistakes)*

ANSWERS

S1 A B C **D** E

S2 J K L M **N**

Name _____ Date _____

Spelling

1
  A ligten
  B glitch
  C thorough
  D borrow
  E *(No mistakes)*

2
  J stallion
  K oriental
  L accidentel
  M tournament
  N *(No mistakes)*

3
  A trophy
  B ability
  C catastrophe
  D commitee
  E *(No mistakes)*

4
  J reproduce
  K proportion
  L installation
  M lettuce
  N *(No mistakes)*

5
  A indignant
  B severance
  C preparation
  D allowense
  E *(No mistakes)*

6
  J tremendous
  K torrential
  L pourous
  M emperor
  N *(No mistakes)*

7
  A tremble
  B tenous
  C extend
  D delirious
  E *(No mistakes)*

8
  J incidental
  K practicing
  L galactic
  M significant
  N *(No mistakes)*

9
  A gaget
  B rocket
  C hatchet
  D college
  E *(No mistakes)*

10
  J invisible
  K fairy
  L totalety
  M entirety
  N *(No mistakes)*

11
  A nibbled
  B antelope
  C cantalope
  D builder
  E *(No mistakes)*

12
  J energize
  K anesthesia
  L gypsy
  M incapible
  N *(No mistakes)*

13
  A dabbling
  B gossiped
  C irresistible
  D graple
  E *(No mistakes)*

14
  J hereditary
  K ordinery
  L intrigue
  M boredom
  N *(No mistakes)*

Name _____ Date _____

Capitalization

DIRECTIONS

This is a test on capitalization. It will show how well you can use capital letters in sentences.

■ You should look for mistakes in capitalization in the sentences on this test.

■ When you find a mistake, fill in the answer space on your answer folder that has the same letter as the **line** containing the mistake.

■ Some sentences do not have any mistakes at all. If there is no mistake, fill in the last answer space.

The samples on this page show you what the questions are like and how to mark your answers.

SAMPLES

S1
  A My birthday is on
  B june 25, and I am
  C having a party.
  D *(No mistakes)*

S2
  J My Aunt asked
  K my cousin to bring
  L his pet horse.
  M *(No mistakes)*

S3
  A The horse's name
  B is Lightfoot, and he
  C is an Arabian.
  D *(No mistakes)*

ANSWERS

S1 A B C D
S2 J K L M
S3 A B C D

Capitalization

1
A Although Mark Twain traveled
B widely, his boyhood experiences
C on the Mississippi river affected
   him most.
D *(No mistakes)*

2
J The Congress avenue bridge
K is home to the largest urban colony
   of bats.
L I have tried but never suceeded in
   seeing them.
M *(No mistakes)*

3
A Every Saturday night, more than
   two million
B listeners tune in to Garrison
   Keillor's
C radio show, "A Prairie Home
   Companion."
D *(No mistakes)*

4
J For years, astronauts have
   conducted
K experiments to learn about
   living in
L space, maybe even on the Moon.
M *(No mistakes)*

5
A The underground Railroad was a
   network
B of people who helped slaves escape
   from
C the South in the mid-1800s.
D *(No mistakes)*

6
J Many of the Pilgrims who first
   came to
K America were members of the
   puritan
L sect, who were unpopular in
   England.
M *(No mistakes)*

7
A I find some of the strangest people
B enjoy listening to AM radio.
   stranger
C ones still listen to the FM stuff.
D *(No mistakes)*

8
J The Yukon Territory is in the
K northwestern corner of Canada,
L just beside alaska.
M *(No mistakes)*

9
A History's largest gold rush took
   place
B in august of 1896 near a river
C called Dawson's Creek.
D *(No mistakes)*

10
J Taiwan has been occupied by
   Portugal,
K China, Holland, and Japan. Today,
   it is
L home to many who fled Mainland
   China.
M *(No mistakes)*

11
A Langston Hughes published his
   first
B collection of poetry, *The Weary
   blues,*
C in 1926. By 1930, he was famous.
D *(No mistakes)*

12
J One of Russia's, and perhaps the
   world's,
K greatest writers, Leo Tolstoy, died
L seven years before the Russian
   revolution.
M *(No mistakes)*

Punctuation

DIRECTIONS

This is a test on punctuation. It will show how well you can use periods, question marks, commas, and other kinds of punctuation marks.

■ You should look for mistakes in punctuation in the sentences on this test.

■ When you find a mistake, fill in the answer space on your answer folder that has the same letter as the **line** containing the mistake.

■ Some sentences do not have any mistakes at all. If there is no mistake, fill in the last answer space.

The samples on this page show you what the questions are like and how to mark your answers.

SAMPLES

S1 A When he spotted the
    B water fountain, Bill
    C said, "Finally!"
    D *(No mistakes)*

S2 J How long had he been
    K running? He was too
    L tired to remember?
    M *(No mistakes)*

S3 A He knew he had started
    B at 8:00 A.M, but what
    C time was it now?
    D *(No mistakes)*

ANSWERS

S1 A B C **D**
S2 J K L **M**
S3 A **B** C D

Punctuation

1 A Carved into a peak, Mount Rushmore has the
B heads of four U.S. presidents Washington,
C Jefferson, Lincoln, and Teddy Roosevelt.
D *(No mistakes)*

2 J In 1936, the United States was in
K the middle of the Great Depression a time
L of economic struggle.
M *(No mistakes)*

3 A Between 1892 and 1924 more than
B 12,000,000 immigrants entered the
C United States through Ellis Island.
D *(No mistakes)*

4 J Carl Sandburg said of Americans
K during the Great Depression "The people
L will live on . . . and come back."
M *(No mistakes)*

5 A On a trip from California to New York,
B John Steinbeck passed through the Mojave
C Desert; Texas; and the Deep South.
D *(No mistakes)*

6 J Carhenge is a replica of Stonehenge.
K It is built entirely out of American
L cars stacked on top of each other
M *(No mistakes)*

7 A Dear Allan and Julia Stiles.
B I am very sorry for your loss,
C and I know things will be better soon.
D *(No mistakes)*

8 J "Tell them I hope the funeral is just
K beautiful, was what Mom said, and
L then she just started crying again.
M *(No mistakes)*

9 A Skippy was a good friend and a loyal
B companion. so full of life and love that
C it seemed he would live forever.
D *(No mistakes)*

10 J Can you ever love another dog
K I certainly hope so because
L I'm sending along a new friend for you.
M *(No mistakes)*

11 A The puppy's name is Winston, and he
B licks your face just the way Skippy did.
C He eats puppy food now, but he's growing.
D *(No mistakes)*

12 J Try to write back and tell me what you think.
K With much love
L Wendy Jackson
M *(No mistakes)*

Name _____ Date _____

Usage and Expression

PART 1 DIRECTIONS

This is a test on the use of words. It will show how well you can use words according to the standards of correctly written English.

■ You should look for mistakes in the sentences on this test.

■ When you find a mistake, fill in the answer space on your answer folder that has the same letter as the **line** containing the mistake.

■ Some sentences do not have any mistakes at all. If there is no mistake, fill in the last answer space.

The samples on this page show you what the questions are like and how to mark your answers.

SAMPLES

S1 **A** If dogs are called man's
       B best friend, shouldn't
       C it be nice to men?
       D *(No mistakes)*

S2 **J** I have had three dogs
       K in my life, and not one
       L of them has liked me.
       M *(No mistakes)*

ANSWERS
S1 A B C **D**
S2 J K L **M**

Usage

1 **A** A symbolic shadow fell across the country
B when war breaks out between the northern
C and southern states in 1861.
D *(No mistakes)*

2 **J** The couple stopped to look at
K the flock of gooses rising from the pond
L in one tremendous swoop.
M *(No mistakes)*

3 **A** Eated for hours made Edward so
B thirsty that he drank four sodas,
C three milkshakes, and a gallon of milk.
D *(No mistakes)*

4 **J** Mushrooms are a type of fungus. As long as
K much needed minerals, climate, and moisture
L are provided, mushrooms can live for years.
M *(No mistakes)*

5 **A** Whenever I make a mistake, I try to get
B the grip on where was it I went wrong.
C This helps me figure out how to fix it.
D *(No mistakes)*

6 **J** Alice was very tired after she bringed
K fifteen bags of groceries back from the
L store and put them all away.
M *(No mistakes)*

7 **A** The recipe called for two cups of Swiss
B cheese, so Maria searched in the top
C cupboard for her cheese grater.
D *(No mistakes)*

8 **J** "Try not to eat them tomatoes," Gary's
K father warned him. "They've been sitting
L in the chicken coop for hours."
M *(No mistakes)*

9 **A** A bat is a mammal, meaning that its
B young are born live, not hatched, and get
C its milk from its mothers.
D *(No mistakes)*

10 **J** Evan was being made tired and cranky
K by the constant spinning and whirling
L of the empty clothes dryer.
M *(No mistakes)*

11 **A** Creative more than a hundred years ago,
B Sherlock Holmes is as popular as ever,
C appearing in countless films and plays.
D *(No mistakes)*

12 **J** One of those brand new gelatin machines
K are being delivered to my parents' house,
L and they said I get to try it first.
M *(No mistakes)*

Expression

PART 2 DIRECTIONS

This is Part 2 of the test about the use of words. It will show how well you can express ideas correctly and effectively. There are several sections to this part of the test. Read the directions to each section carefully. Then mark your answers on your answer folder.

Directions: In questions 13–19, choose the best way to express the idea.

13 **A** The two boys hunted through the entire toy store without finding the dolls.
  B The two boys through the entire toy store hunted without finding the dolls.
  C The two boys hunted, without finding, through the entire toy store the dolls.
  D The two boys, without finding the dolls, hunted through the entire toy store.

14 **J** Before going to bed, he finished his sandwich.
  K He finished his sandwich, and then he decided to go to bed.
  L Even though he was going to bed, he felt like he needed to finish his sandwich.
  M Before going to bed, his sandwich was finished.

15 **A** Beth saw a woman looking at her mother, who was too good for this world.
  B Beth saw a woman looking at her mother who was too good for this world.
  C Looking at her mother, Beth saw a woman too good for this world.
  D Too good for this world, Beth's mother saw a woman looking.

16 **J** Going on a hike and bike riding are Joan's favorite outdoor activities.
  K Hiking and bike riding are Joan's favorite outdoor activities.
  L Joan's favorite outdoor activities are hiking and a ride on her bike.
  M Joan's favorite outdoor activities are a hike and a bike.

17
  A The door shut with a crash. The door squeaked loudly.
  B The door shut with a crash, loudly squeaking.
  C Crashing loudly, the door squeaked shut.
  D The door squeaked loudly and then shut with a crash.

18
  J Running in the park, Dave's son saw a squirrel, and he chased him.
  K Dave's son saw a squirrel, and Dave chased him in the park.
  L Running in the park, Dave's son chased him and a squirrel.
  M Dave chased his son running after a squirrel in the park.

19
  A Clowns that don't have big noses, usually has huge feet.
  B Clowns without big noses usually have huge feet.
  C Clowns that had huge feet usually end up not having big noses.
  D Clowns without big noses were clowns without having huge feet.

20 Which of these is the best advertisement for a big shoe sale?
  J All sneakers, pumps, and boots in the store are up to 75% off.

  K Up to 75 shoes are on sale, from sneakers to boots to pumps.

  L If you go one place to buy shoes, come to the place where they are cheap.

  M A 75% off sale is going on this weekend only; everything must go.

TERRANOVA PRACTICE TEST

Reading and Language Arts

Sample Passage

Volunteers

In communities across the nation, people volunteer and improve the lives of others. Some volunteering opportunities can be found through organizations—serving food in a soup kitchen, working with a group to teach adults to read, or joining others to build houses for those who might not otherwise be able to afford them. In contrast, some volunteering opportunities are not organized. People may take groceries to their elderly neighbors, or a few adults might get together to help a mother of triplets manage her newborns.

Sample A

This passage is mostly about

(A) why people volunteer

(B) how people can volunteer

(C) how people benefit from volunteering

(D) why volunteer programs save money

Directions

A student wrote a paragraph about volunteering at a local nursing home. There are some mistakes that need correcting.

> ¹Last summer I volunteered one day a week at the Sunshine Retirement Center. ²Some days I helped change sheets and deliver meals, and other days I just spending time talking to the residents. ³Even though the summer volunteer program is over and I'm back in school, I still stop by to spend time with the people there.

Sample B

Choose the best way to write Sentence 2.

Ⓕ Some days I helped change sheets and deliver meals, and other days I just spent time talking to the residents.

Ⓖ Some days I helped change sheets and delivered meals, and other days I just spending time talking to the residents.

Ⓗ Some days I helping change sheets and delivering meals, and other days I just spending time talking to the residents.

Ⓙ Best as it is

Sample C

Which sentence would best follow Sentence 2?

Ⓐ It took a lot of my time.

Ⓑ It was more rewarding than I could have ever imagined.

Ⓒ I don't like doing that much work if I'm not being graded.

Ⓓ I think that next year I'll do some other kind of volunteering.

The Wonders of Technology

When you talk on the telephone, watch television, send e-mail, or use a computer, you depend on technology to perform your task. *Technology* is the application of human skill. Technology can be as simple as a pen and paper or as complicated as the inner workings of a computer. Technology is continually changing. New and better ways of doing things are developed every day.

In this theme, you will read about some ways technology is used—and overused. Start reading and begin to learn more about **The Wonders of Technology.**

from E-Mail from Bill Gates *by* John Seabrook

Directions

In this excerpt, John Seabrook describes how he corresponded with Bill Gates via e-mail while gathering information for a magazine article. Ongoing correspondence between the two reveals Gates's philosophy about technology. Read the excerpt. Then do numbers 1 through 6.

At the moment, the best way to communicate with another person on the information highway[1] is to exchange electronic mail: to write a message on a computer and send it through the telephone lines into someone else's computer. In the future, people will send each other sound and pictures as well as text, and do it in real time,[2] and improved technology will make it possible to have rich, human electronic exchanges, but at present E-mail is the closest thing we have to that. Even now, E-mail allows you to meet and communicate with people in a way that would be impossible on the phone, through the regular mail, or face to face, as I discovered while I was working on this story. Sitting at my computer one day, I realized that I could try to communicate with Bill Gates, the chairman and co-founder of the software giant Microsoft, on the information highway. At least, I could send E-mail to his electronic address, which is widely available, not tell anyone at Microsoft I was doing it, and see what happened. I wrote:

Dear Bill,

I am the guy who is writing the article about you for The New Yorker. It occurs to me that we ought to be

able to do some of the work through e-mail. Which raises the fascinating question—What kind of understanding of another person can e-mail give you? . . .

You could begin by telling me what you think is unique about e-mail as a form of communication.

John

I hit "return," and the computer said, "mail sent." I walked out to the kitchen to get a drink of water and played with the cat for a while, then came back and sat at my computer. Thinking that I was probably wasting money, I nevertheless logged on again and entered my password. "You have mail," the computer said.

I typed "get mail," and the computer got the following:

From: Bill Gates
<billg@microsoft.com>
Ok, let me know if you get this email.

According to my computer, eighteen minutes had passed between the time I E-mailed Bill and he E-mailed me back. His message said:

E-mail is a unique communication vehicle for a lot of reasons. However, email is not a substitute for direct interaction. . . .

There are people who I have corresponded with on email for months before actually meeting them—people at work and otherwise. If someone isn't saying something of interest its easier to not respond to their mail than it is not to answer the phone. In fact I give out my home phone number to almost no one but my email address is known very broadly. I am the only person who reads my email so no one has to worry about embarrassing themselves or going around people when they send a message. Our email is completely secure. . . .

Email helps out with other types of communication. It allows you to exchange a lot of information in advance of a meeting and make the meeting far more valuable. . . .

Email is not a good way to get mad at someone since you can't interact. You can send friendly messages very easily since those are harder to misinterpret.

We began to E-mail each other three or four times a week. I would have a question about something and say to myself, "I'm going to E-mail Bill about that," and I'd write him a message and get a one- or two-page message back within twenty-four hours, sometimes much sooner. At the beginning of our electronic relationship, I would wake up in the middle of the night and lie in bed wondering if I had E-mail from Bill. Generally, he seemed to write messages at night, sleep (maybe), then send them the next morning. We were intimate in a curious way, in the sense of being wired into each other's minds, but our contact was elaborately stylized, like ballroom dancing.

[1]**Information highway:** Network of computers and file servers that allows for the rapid exchange of electronic information.

[2]**real time:** Accessing of information or exchange of data that requires no downloading of files.

Here is a time line of what happens in the passage.

Author asks Bill Gates a question by e-mail.	Author checks his e-mail.	?	Author and Bill Gates e-mail each other regularly.

1 Which of these should go in the empty box in the time line?

Ⓐ Author wakes up in the middle of the night.

Ⓑ Author decides not to tell Microsoft that he e-mails Bill Gates.

Ⓒ Author reads answer from Bill Gates.

Ⓓ Author decides to write article for *The New Yorker.*

Name _____ **Date** _____

2 **Choose the sentence that best describes what the passage is mainly about.**

Ⓝ E-mail is a great way to gather research for an article.

Ⓡ E-mail allows you to communicate with people in a special way.

ⓔ While e-mail is a great way to communicate, it has its limitations.

Ⓧ Even very busy people like Bill Gates enjoy sending and receiving e-mail.

3 **From evidence in the passage, which of these descriptions best fits Bill Gates?**

Ⓐ He tries to help the author.

Ⓑ He is nervous about being interviewed.

Ⓒ He wishes the author would call him on the phone.

Ⓓ He expects the author to be intimidated by his success.

4 **According to the passage, e-mail is helpful for business meetings because it**

Ⓝ eliminates the need to meet in person

Ⓡ helps you take notes during the meeting

ⓔ helps you process requests more quickly

Ⓧ allows you to exchange information beforehand

5 **According to the passage, Bill Gates responds to the author's e-mail**

Ⓐ sometimes

Ⓑ very quickly

Ⓒ after a long wait

Ⓓ before the author is ready

6 **In the passage, Bill Gates says, "email is not a substitute for direct interaction." The word *interaction* means**

Ⓝ contact

Ⓡ leisure time

ⓔ private thought

Ⓧ telephone conversation

Name _____ Date _____

The Internet

Directions

Mrs. Anderson's class is writing about different kinds of technology. Josh wrote about the Internet, a worldwide computer network. There are several mistakes that need correcting. Here is the first part of his report.

---

[1]What is the Internet? [2]I have to admit that before I started writing this report. [3]I really wasn't sure. [4]The Internet is the largest computer network on the planet. [5]A network is a group of computers linked together to share information. [6]The network of computers grouped together to make up the Internet connects over 20 million computers!

---

7 Sentence 2 is not a complete sentence. Which of these best combines it with Sentence 3?

- Ⓐ Before I started writing this report, I really wasn't sure I have to admit.

- Ⓑ Before I started writing this report, I have to admit that I really wasn't sure of that.

- Ⓒ I have to admit that before I started writing this report, I really wasn't sure.

- Ⓓ I have to admit that I really wasn't sure and that's why I started writing this report.

8 Which is the best way to write Sentence 6?

- Ⓕ The computer network that makes up the Internet connects over 20 million computers!

- Ⓖ The Internet connects over 20 million computers with the computers that make up its network.

- Ⓗ The network of computers that are grouped together to form the Internet connects over 20 million computers!

- Ⓙ Best as it is

Name _____ Date _____

Now read the second part of the report.

---

¹The United States Department of Defense started the Internet in the 1960s so that researchers in different parts of the country could communicate and exchange information. ²In addition to work, these researchers discussed all kinds of things on the Internet. ³It wasn't long before their friends started using the Internet. ⁴Some of their families used it too. ⁵By the 1990s, the Internet was huge and real popular. ⁶Today, anyone with a computer and a modem can access the Internet.

---

9 **Where would this sentence best fit in the paragraph?**

They talked about the Rolling Stones, flying kites, friends, and other things that interested them.

   Ⓐ after Sentence 1

   Ⓑ after Sentence 2

   Ⓒ after Sentence 3

   Ⓓ after Sentence 5

10 **Which is the best way to write Sentence 5?**

   Ⓕ Huge and popular the Internet was by the 1990s.

   Ⓖ By the 1990s, the huge Internet was real popular.

   Ⓗ By the 1990s, the Internet was huge and really popular.

   Ⓙ Best as it is

Here is the last part of the report.

---

¹Today, you can use the Internet for all kinds of things. ²I used it to research this report. ³I also used it to help me with a science project. ⁴The Internet is like having a gigantic library at your fingertips—all you have to do to enter it is click your mouse! ⁵Researchers believe that in the future every single house on the planet has a computer and will have access to the Internet.

---

11 **Which is the best way to combine Sentences 2 and 3 into one?**

   Ⓐ I used the Internet to research this report and help me with a science project.

   Ⓑ I used the Internet to research this report, I also used it to help me with a science project.

   Ⓒ I used the Internet to research this report, but I also used it to help me with a science project.

   Ⓓ While I used the Internet to research this report, I also used it to help me with a science project.

12 **The best way to write Sentence 5 is**

   Ⓕ Researchers believe that in the future every house on the planet will have a computer and access to the Internet.

   Ⓖ Researchers believe that in the future every house on the planet, having a computer and access to the Internet.

   Ⓗ Researchers believe that, on the planet, most houses in the future will have a computer and will have access to the Internet.

   Ⓙ Best as it is

from The Trouble with Television
by Robert MacNeil

Directions

Here is an excerpt from an essay by Robert MacNeil, a former broadcast journalist. In the essay, MacNeil explains why he believes TV threatens the development of our language, literacy, and imagination.

The trouble with television is that it discourages concentration. Almost anything interesting and rewarding in life requires some constructive, consistently applied effort. The dullest, the least gifted of us can achieve things that seem miraculous to those who never concentrate on anything. But television encourages us to apply no effort. It sells us instant gratification. It diverts us only to divert, to make the time pass without pain.

Television's variety becomes a narcotic,[1] not a stimulus.[2] Its serial, kaleidoscopic[3] exposures force us to follow its lead. The viewer is on a perpetual guided tour: thirty minutes at the museum, thirty at the cathedral, then back on the bus to the next attraction—except on television, typically, the spans allotted are on the order of minutes or seconds, and the chosen delights are more often car crashes and people killing one another. In short, a lot of television usurps one of the most precious of all human gifts, the ability to focus your attention yourself, rather than just passively surrendering it.

Capturing your attention—and holding it—is the prime motive of most television programming and enhances its role as a profitable advertising vehicle. Programmers live in constant fear of losing anyone's attention—anyone's. The surest way to avoid doing so is to keep everything brief, not to strain the attention of anyone but instead to provide constant stimulation through variety, novelty, action and movement. Quite simply, television operates on the appeal to the short attention span. . . .

. . . In its place that is fine. Who can quarrel with a medium that so brilliantly packages escapist entertainment as a mass-marketing tool? But I see its values now pervading this nation and its life. It has become fashionable to think that, like fast food, fast ideas are the way to get to a fast-moving, impatient public.

In the case of news, this practice, in my view, results in inefficient communication. I question how much of television's nightly news effort is really absorbable and understandable. Much of it is what has been aptly described as "machine gunning with scraps." I think its technique fights coherence.[4] I think it tends to make things ultimately boring and dismissable (unless they are accompanied by horrifying pictures) because almost anything is boring and dismissable if you know almost nothing about it.

I believe that TV's appeal to the short attention span is not only inefficient communication but decivilizing as well. Consider the casual assumptions that television tends to cultivate: that complexity must be avoided, that visual stimulation is a substitute for thought, that verbal precision is an anachronism.[5] It may be old-fashioned, but I was taught that thought is words, arranged in grammatically precise ways.

[1] **narcotic** (när kät´ ik) *n.:* Something that has a soothing effect.

[2] **stimulus** (stim´ yə ləs) *n.:* Something that rouses to action.

[3] **kaleidoscopic** (kə li´ də skäp´ ik) *adj.:* Constantly changing.

[4] **coherence** (kō hir´ əns) *n.:* The quality of being connected in an intelligible way.

[5] **anachronism** (ə nak´ rə niz´ əm) *n.:* Anything that seems to be out of its proper place in history.

13 **What is the major purpose of this essay?**

Ⓐ to reveal little-known facts about television

Ⓑ to persuade readers that television is harmful

Ⓒ to teach readers how to live without television

Ⓓ to entertain readers with stories about television

14 **In the passage, the author says that television "sells us instant gratification." The word *gratification* probably means**

Ⓕ information

Ⓖ interpretation

Ⓗ observation

Ⓙ satisfaction

15 **The author believes television news may be difficult to understand because**

Ⓐ too much violence is shown

Ⓑ too much advertising is on the news

Ⓒ the news is shown too quickly

Ⓓ the anchors use complicated language

16 **In the passage, the author says that television "diverts us only to divert, to make the time pass without pain." The word *divert* means**

Ⓕ inform

Ⓖ dismiss

Ⓗ distract

Ⓙ instruct

17 **The author of this passage would probably agree that**

Ⓐ people are generally very patient

Ⓑ television enhances concentration

Ⓒ television helps us focus on ourselves

Ⓓ people should spend more time reading

from How to be Polite Online *by* Virginia Shea

Directions

Here is an excerpt from "How to be Polite Online," an essay by Virginia Shea. In the excerpt, Shea offers tips and guidelines to help computer users communicate more effectively and courteously online.

The truth is that computer networking is still in its infancy. Probably nothing illustrates this more clearly than the "ASCII[1] jail": 90 percent of network communications are still limited to plain old ASCII text—that is, the characters of the alphabet, the numerals 0 through 9, and the most basic punctuation marks. It's bad enough that multimedia communications have not been implemented in most of cyberspace.[2] Most of the time you can't even put a word in bold or italics!

Because people cannot see or hear you in cyberspace, you need to pay close attention to the style of your electronic communications if you hope to make a good impression there. The style of electronic communications encompasses everything about your correspondence except its content, from your use of network conventions like "smileys" and "sigs" to the number of characters per line in your email messages.

Style considerations are influenced by several of the rules of Netiquette, especially Rule 4, Respect other people's time, and Rule 5, Make yourself look good online. It doesn't matter how brilliant your messages are if they're formatted in such a way that no one can read them.

Tone of voice online

The fact that most network interactions are limited to written words can be the source of misunderstandings. Fortunately, clever network users have had years to deal with this. They've created a shorthand to help communicate the tone that you'd otherwise get from the other person's voice, facial expressions, and gestures. These shorthand expressions are known as smileys or emoticons. They're easy to figure out once you get the hang of it. Just remember that they're all sideways faces.

See Table 1 for a list of the most commonly used emoticons. There are whole books about smileys for those who are interested, including the enjoyable *Smiley Dictionary* by Seth Godin.

People also use abbreviations to express emotional states or to qualify what they're saying. See Table 2 for a list of common abbreviations.

The "FLAME ON/FLAME OFF" notifier

When you really want to run off at the keyboard—but you want your readers to know that that you're not expressing yourself in your usual measured, reasoned manner—you need to let them know that you know that you're flaming.[3] So before you begin your rant, simply enter the words FLAME ON. Then rant away. When you're done, write FLAME OFF and resume normal discourse.

[1]**ASCII:** Abbreviation of American Standard Code for Information Interchange, a standard computer code used to assist the interchange of information among various types of data-processing equipment.

[2]**cyberspace:** Global communication performed through the use of computer technology.

[3]**flaming:** Slang for "ranting."

Name _____ Date _____

Table 1: Emoticons	
:-)	Smile; laugh; "I'm joking"
:-(	Frown; sadness; "Bummer"
:)	Variant of :-) or "Have a nice day"
:(	Variant of :-(
;-)	Wink; denotes a pun or sly joke
:-O	Yelling or screaming; or completely shocked
:-()	Can't (or won't) stop talking
:-D	Big, delighted grin
:-P	Sticking out your tongue
:-] or :-)	Sarcastic smile
%-)	Confused but happy
%-(	Confused and unhappy
:'-(	Crying
:'-)	Crying happy tears
:-l	Can't decide how to feel; no feelings either way
:-\	Mixed but mostly happy
:-/	Mixed but mostly sad
*	Kiss
{} or [ ]	Hug
{{{***}}}	Hugs and kisses

Table 2: Abbreviations	
BTW	By the way
IMHO	In my humble opinion
IMNSHO	In my not so humble opinion
IOW	In other words
IRL	In real life
ITRW	In the real world
LOL	Laughing out loud
OTF	On the floor (laughing)
ROTFL	Rolling on the floor laughing
WRT	With regard to
YMMV	Your mileage may vary
<g> or <G>	Grin
<bg>	Big grin

18 Look over the passage again. Choose the sentence that gives a clue that email sometimes causes confusion. Write the sentence on the lines below.

_____

_____

Now write the sentence in your own words.

_____

_____

Write a message to a friend on the lines below. Use at least two emoticons and two abbreviations.

_____

_____

_____

_____

19 A student used the Internet to research and write this paragraph about volcanoes. She made <u>five</u> mistakes in grammar, capitalization, and punctuation. Draw a line through each part that has a mistake, and write the correction above it.

A volcano is a vent in the surface of the earth through which hot gases and ashes sometimes flows. When the gases and ashes flow out of the top of a volcano. It's said to be active. When this activity stops, the Volcano is considered dormant. One of the most famousest volcanoes is Mt. St. Helen's in Washington. After being dormant for over 120 years, the volcano erupted on May 18, 1980. While the major activity has stop, Mt. St. Helen's is still considered active.

---

20 Look back at the essay "The Trouble with Television" and think about how watching too much TV can be harmful. Now think about "E-Mail from Bill Gates." When can sending and receiving e-mail be harmful? Write a paragraph explaining your answer. Be sure to support your opinion with examples from either "The Trouble with Television" or "E-Mail from Bill Gates."

For this answer, make sure you use complete sentences and check your work for correct spelling, capitalization, and punctuation.

_____

_____

_____

_____

_____

_____

_____

_____

SAT 10 PRACTICE TEST

Vocabulary

Directions:

Look at each underlined word. Choose the word or group of words that means about the same thing.

1 A <u>volume</u> is a—

A bottle

B book

C storm

D map

2 To <u>remain</u> is to—

F stay

G keep

H travel

J buy

3 <u>Circumference</u> refers to—

A how tall

B how long

C how far around

D how heavy

4 <u>Speedily</u> means—

F quickly

G recently

H accurately

J carefully

Directions:

Read each boxed sentence. Then read the sentences that follow. Choose the sentence that uses the underlined word in the same way as in the box.

5

> Steel contains <u>iron</u> and carbon.

In which sentence does the word <u>iron</u> mean the same thing as in the sentence above?

A Use an <u>iron</u> to press your skirt.

B <u>Iron</u> is a metallic element.

C Greg was stubborn and had an <u>iron</u> will.

D The ranchers marked the cattle with a branding <u>iron</u>.

6

> The playground is in a bad <u>state</u> of repair.

In which sentence does the word <u>state</u> mean the same thing as in the sentence above?

F Alabama was the 22nd <u>state</u> to join the union.

G Please <u>state</u> your name and age.

H Keiko was in a <u>state</u> of excitement on her birthday.

J You should <u>state</u> your intentions.

Name _____ Date _____

Reading Comprehension

from "Shooting Stars" by Hal Borland

Directions:

Read this excerpt from "Shooting Stars" by Hal Borland. Then complete numbers 1 through 3 by choosing the best answer.

Most clear, dark nights you can see a shooting star, as we call it, if you keep looking. Those shooting stars are meteors. They are points of light that suddenly appear in the sky, like distant stars, race across the darkness, usually toward the horizon, and disappear.

For a long time nobody knew what a meteor was. But finally those who study stars and the sky decided that a meteor is a piece of a comet that exploded long ago. Those pieces are still wandering about the universe in huge, looping paths that follow the original comet's orbit. There are uncounted pieces of such comets out there in the depths of space. Periodically clusters of them come close to the earth's orbit, or path around the sun. Most meteors are small, probably only a few inches in diameter, but when they enter the earth's atmosphere the friction makes them white hot. Then they look big as stars streaking across the darkness.

There are half a dozen meteor showers each year. Each is named after the constellation from which it appears to come. The biggest of all, the Perseids, named for the constellation of Perseus, occurs on the 10th, 11th, and 12th of August. The next largest, the Leonids, named for the constellation of Leo, comes on the nights of November 14, 15, and 16. . . .

1 Which of the following is the best description of a shooting star?

A an aging star that explodes in the night sky

B a distant comet that shoots across the sky

C the sun's rays when seen in the night sky

D a white-hot meteor that streaks across the sky

2 If scientists observe a new meteor shower, it will most likely be named after

F a comet

G an astronomer

H an orbit

J a constellation

3 Why did the author write this passage?

A to contrast shooting stars with meteors

B to give readers basic information about meteors

C to entertain readers with a story about comets

D to make predictions of future meteor showers

Name _____ Date _____

Reading Comprehension
from "Up the Slide" by Jack London

Directions:

Read this excerpt from "Up the Slide" by Jack London. Then complete numbers 4 through 7 by choosing the best answer.

When Clay Dilham left the tent to get a sled-load of firewood, he expected to be back in half an hour. So he told Swanson, who was cooking the dinner. Swanson and he belonged to different outfits, located about twenty miles apart on the Stewart River, but they had become traveling partners on a trip down the Yukon to Dawson to get the mail.

Swanson had laughed when Clay said he would be back in half an hour. It stood to reason, Swanson said, that good, dry firewood could not be found so close to Dawson; that whatever firewood there was originally had long since been gathered in; that firewood would not be selling at forty dollars a cord if any man could go out and get a sled-load and be back in the time Clay expected to make it.

Then it was Clay's turn to laugh, as he sprang on the sled and *mushed* the dogs on the river-trail. For, coming up from the Siwash village the previous day, he had noticed a small dead pine in an out-of-the-way place, which had defied discovery by eyes less sharp than his. And his eyes were both young and sharp, for his seventeenth birthday was just cleared.

4 Why does Swanson laugh at Clay?

F Swanson thinks that Clay is trying to trick him.

G Swanson believes that firewood should be cheaper.

H Swanson thinks Clay's trip will be much longer.

J Swanson thinks that Clay is being lazy.

5 Why does Clay laugh at Swanson?

A Clay is nervous about traveling on the ice alone.

B Clay knows where to find a dead tree for firewood.

C Clay thinks Swanson is too old to be camping.

D Clay thinks Swanson is too easily worried.

6 From what literary point of view is this passage told?

F first-person limited

G first-person omniscient

H third-person limited

J third-person omniscient

7 Which of the following is the best evidence that this passage is a work of fiction?

A The places described exist in the real world.

B It describes events that took place in the past.

C It does not contain extensive dialogue.

D The thoughts of a main character are revealed.

Name _____ Date _____

Reading Comprehension
from *Travels with Charley* by John Steinbeck

Directions:

In this excerpt from *Travels with Charley*, John Steinbeck discusses his need to get back in touch with something that means a great deal to him. Read the excerpt. Then complete numbers 8 and 9 by choosing the best answer.

My plan was clear, concise, and reasonable, I think. For many years I have traveled in many parts of the world. In America I live in New York, or dip into Chicago or San Francisco. But New York is no more America than Paris is France or London is England. Thus I discovered that I did not know my own country. I, an American writer, writing about America, was working from memory, and the memory is at best a faulty, warpy reservoir. I had not heard the speech of America, smelled the grass and trees and sewage, seen its hills and water, its color and quality of light. I knew the changes only from books and newspapers. But more than this, I had not felt the country for twenty-five years. In short, I was writing of something I did not know about, and it seems to me that in a so-called writer this is criminal. My memories were distorted by twenty-five intervening years.

8 Which of the following statements best summarizes the passage?

F The author does not believe that his memories are accurate.

G The author feels he has been writing about America without knowing it.

H The author wants to be concise in what he writes about America.

J The author feels that New York is to America as Paris is to France.

9 What does the author mean when he says, "New York is no more America than Paris is France"?

A New York does not represent the truth about America.

B New York and Paris are approximately the same size.

C New York is more like France than Paris is like America.

D New York is more French than American.

Reading Comprehension

from *The Story-Teller* by Saki

Directions:

Read this excerpt from "The Story-Teller" by Saki. Then complete numbers 10 and 11 by choosing the best answer.

It was a hot afternoon, and the railway carriage was correspondingly sultry, and the next stop was at Templecombe, nearly an hour ahead. The occupants of the carriage were a small girl, and a smaller girl, and a small boy. An aunt belonging to the children occupied one corner seat, and the further corner seat on the opposite side was occupied by a bachelor who was a stranger to their party, but the small girls and the small boy emphatically occupied the compartment. Both the aunt and the children were conversational in a limited, persistent way, reminding one of the attentions of a housefly that refused to be discouraged. Most of the aunt's remarks seemed to begin with "Don't," and nearly all of the children's remarks began with "Why?" The bachelor said nothing out loud.

10 **What in this excerpt indicates that the remainder of the story is most likely to be about the bachelor?**

F The story is told from his point of view.

G The aunt and the children are soon leaving the carriage.

H He gets the other characters to react to him.

J He is the most mysterious character.

11 **Which characteristic is the narrator referring to when he compares the conversation of the aunt and children to a housefly?**

A the housefly's buzzing sound

B the housefly's circular flight

C the housefly's persistent nature

D the housefly's small size

Reading Comprehension

Directions:

Read this excerpt from a brochure. Then, complete number 12 by choosing the best answer.

In communities across the nation, people volunteer and improve the lives of others. Some volunteering opportunities can be found through organizations—serving food in a soup kitchen, working with a group to teach adults to read, or joining others to build houses for those who might not otherwise be able to afford them. In contrast, some volunteering opportunities are not organized. People may take groceries to their elderly neighbors, or a few might get together to help a mother of triplets manage her newborns.

---

12 What is this passage mostly about?

F why people volunteer

G how people can volunteer

H how people benefit from volunteering

J why volunteer programs save money

Directions:

Read the following announcement. Then, complete number 13 by choosing the best answer.

JOIN THE EIGHTH GRADE DRAMA CLUB!

Whatever talent you have, the Drama Club has a part for you in its upcoming production of Mark Twain's *Tom Sawyer and Huckleberry Finn.*

The Drama Club is searching for the following members:

Actors
Cast members must memorize script and attend all rehearsals and performances.

Set Designers, Artists, and Assistants
Design scenery and props. Attend mandatory meetings. Design and produce stage props and scrim layouts. Drawing and painting skills are required.

Backstage Crew
Members set up and change scenes; construct props; and manage the voice system, curtains, and lighting.

Writers, Editors, and Clerical Staff
Members produce the playbill, posters, newspaper stories, and advertising brochures. Research in encyclopedias and other sources is a required activity.

Please attend our meeting in the auditorium on Friday, March 19, at 3:00 P.M.

Reading Comprehension

13 Why are writers and editors required to research information in encyclopedias and other sources?

    A These members help the people who sell advertisements.

    B These members have to persuade the audience to see the play.

    C These members must report on how the audience liked the play.

    D These members need to create factual materials.

Directions:

Read the following passage. Then, complete number 14 by choosing the best answer.

> The recently proposed plan to create a curbside recycling program for the community of Summerstown is a bad idea. It will be very expensive to hire a recycling company to pick up and sort the recyclable materials. As a result, citizens of Summerstown will be required to pay more taxes. In addition, the program may be unnecessary. People who want to recycle may already do so by taking recyclable materials to a local recycling center.

14 The main argument of this passage is that—

    F the curbside recycling program is too expensive

    G the curbside recycling program is necessary

    H the curbside recycling program needs to be stopped

    J the curbside recycling program is a good idea

Name _____ Date _____

Spelling

Directions:

Read each group of sentences. For each item on the answer sheet, fill in the bubble for the answer that has a mistake in spelling. If there is no mistake, fill in the last answer choice.

1 A The magazine had an <u>advertisement</u> for skates.

   B Two <u>buses</u> go to the stadium.

   C Cut the paper with <u>scissors</u>.

   D No mistake

2 F Add that <u>colum</u> of numbers.

   G Ling tripped over the door's <u>threshold</u>.

   H The traffic noise is a <u>nuisance</u>.

   J No mistake

3 A <u>Nickel</u> is a metallic element.

   B I like watermelon for <u>desert</u>.

   C You can use the computers in the <u>library</u>.

   D No mistake

4 F <u>Rehersals</u> for the play start today.

   G A holiday is a happy <u>occasion</u>.

   H Liars try to <u>deceive</u> people.

   J No mistake

5 A Things you own are your <u>possessions</u>.

   B Murray <u>usualy</u> eats peanut butter and jelly for lunch.

   C The race was <u>canceled</u> because of rain.

   D No mistake

6 F Jack and Jill had a wedding <u>banquet</u>.

   G Please <u>answer</u> the phone.

   H The month on the <u>calander</u> is June.

   J No mistake

7 A It is said that "<u>beggars</u> can't be choosers."

   B The baby sleeps in her <u>carriage</u>.

   C What is the <u>explanation</u> for an eclipse?

   D No mistake

8 F There are <u>various</u> toppings on the pizza.

   G Carla's <u>bycicle</u> has ten speeds.

   H That kite is <u>guaranteed</u> to fly.

   J No mistake

9 A Choose a <u>catagory</u>: fiction or nonfiction.

   B Be sure your answer is <u>accurate</u>.

   C Tony got a <u>bruise</u> when he fell.

   D No mistake

10 F The new student is <u>likeable</u>.

   G Sunset will <u>occur</u> at 7:30.

   H Jerry plays the <u>bass</u>.

   J No mistake

11 A Acid rain has a bad <u>effect</u> on the environment.

   B Mr. Kelly is <u>chief</u> of police.

   C I do not <u>beleive</u> in UFOs.

   D No mistake

Spelling

12 F Dental <u>hygiene</u> keeps teeth healthy.

G It is <u>necessary</u> to brush and floss every day

H A dentist is a <u>physician</u> who fixes teeth.

J No mistake

13 A The fallen tree was an <u>obstacle</u> to drivers.

B <u>Nucular</u> accidents are very rare.

C She did not <u>recognize</u> the stranger.

D No mistake

14 F A <u>cilinder</u> is a solid figure.

G The flood was <u>disastrous</u>.

H Display your graph on the <u>bulletin</u> board.

J No mistake

15 A The quarterback has <u>athletic</u> ability.

B The <u>comittee</u> chose the music for the dance.

C A <u>census</u> takes place every ten years.

D No mistake

16 F *Pride and Prejudis* is a book by Jane Austen.

G 100¢ is <u>equivalent</u> to $1.00.

H It takes <u>patience</u> to learn to play piano.

J No mistake

17 A The project is easier if you <u>cooperate</u>.

B Are the lines <u>parallel</u> or perpendicular?

C Oak <u>Bulevard</u> is two blocks north.

D No mistake

18 F Diamonds are <u>valuable</u> stones.

G Betsy moved to a new <u>nieghborhood</u>.

H The <u>previous</u> month was April.

J No mistake

19 A Thomas Jefferson wrote the Declaration of <u>Independance</u>.

B You can return the CD if you have the <u>receipt</u>.

C Heat and humidity make me <u>irritable</u>.

D No mistake

20 F The muffins have a <u>pleasant</u> aroma.

G The meeting is <u>scheduled</u> for Friday.

H The movie <u>theatre</u> sells popcorn.

J No mistake

21 A Bryce's cold turned into <u>pneumonia</u>.

B Practice will improve your <u>pronounciation</u>.

C Is that a <u>genuine</u> moon rock?

D No mistake

22 F Carmen was a <u>defendant</u> in court.

G The flashlight needs a new <u>battery</u>.

H I <u>apologize</u> for interrupting you.

J No mistake

Language

Directions:

Read the passage. Then, choose the word or group of words that belongs in each space. For each item on the answer sheet, fill in the bubble for the answer that you think is correct.

One of the greatest American artists was Charles M. Russell, ___(1)___ was born in St. Louis in 1866. Russell ___(2)___ to Montana at the age of 15 to become a cowboy, and he never left. By the age of 29, Russell ___(3)___ his living as an artist. During the course of ___(4)___ career, Russell created more than 3,000 paintings, drawings, and sculptures that captured the splendor of the American West. Art critics ___(5)___ Frederic Remington and him to be the most authentic of the western painters. Today, his works ___(6)___ in galleries throughout the world, displayed in the same galleries as works by the world's greatest painters. This is quite an achievement for a Montana cowboy!

---

1 A which
   B that
   C he
   D who

2 F moved
   G will move
   H had been moving
   J is moving

3 A was making
   B will make
   C makes
   D can make

4 F its
   G their
   H his
   J your

5 A considering
   B considers
   C consider
   D will be considering

6 F hangs
   G hang
   H were hanging
   J will hang

Language

Directions:

Read the passage. Then, decide which type of error, if any, appears in each underlined section. For each item on the answer sheet, fill in the bubble for the answer that you think is correct. If there is no error, fill in the last answer choice.

<u>Dear Aunt Jen</u>
7

    I am really looking forward to your visit this summer. We always have so much fun when

you are here. Are you ready to go on another <u>picnic down by the creek. I found</u> a great spot!
                                    8

    I have a question to ask you. When I was looking at a box of <u>your childhood toys in</u>
                                           9

<u>the attic,</u> I found an antique skeleton key. It looks so mysterious; I'm dying to know what

<u>it's for. My Mother said she</u> had never seen it before. When you visit, will you <u>tell me the</u>
10   11

<u>storey of the key?</u>

    I guess I had better go now, since I have so much homework to do. I just wanted to

let you know that <u>I'm looking foreword to your visit.</u>
                      12

                                        Love,

                                        Patricia

---

7 **A** Spelling error

    B Capitalization error

    C Punctuation error

    D No error

8 **F** Spelling error

    G Capitalization error

    H Punctuation error

    J No error

9 **A** Spelling error

    B Capitalization error

    C Punctuation error

    D No error

10 **F** Spelling error

    G Capitalization error

    H Punctuation error

    J No error

11 **A** Spelling error

    B Capitalization error

    C Punctuation error

    D No error

12 **F** Spelling error

    G Capitalization error

    H Punctuation error

    J No error

Language

Many people have fond memories of <u>childhood games. What some people may not</u>
<u>13</u>

<u>realize, however, is</u> how old these games actually are. Follow-the-leader dates back to the

twelfth century. Others, <u>especially those involveing rhyme,</u> have long histories as well.
<u>14</u>

The rhyme chanted for ring-around-the-rosey, for example, dates back to at least the

sixteenth century. Not only do games remain popular over the centuries, passed down

from generation to <u>generation, but they also cross National and cultural</u> boundaries.
<u>15</u>

Marbles, hide-and-seek, and spinning tops are <u>only a few of the games, that are played</u>
<u>16</u>

<u>around the world.</u>

Although some games go out of fashion and new ones are constantly <u>emerging, there</u>
<u>17</u>

<u>appeal is timeless.</u> It seems likely that the games that will still be played four <u>centuries</u>
<u>18</u>

<u>from now are the ones that have entertained kids'</u> for the past four centuries.

---

13 A Spelling error

  B Capitalization error

  C Punctuation error

  D No error

14 F Spelling error

  G Capitalization error

  H Punctuation error

  J No error

15 A Spelling error

  B Capitalization error

  C Punctuation error

  D No error

16 F Spelling error

  G Capitalization error

  H Punctuation error

  J No error

17 A Spelling error

  B Capitalization error

  C Punctuation error

  D No error

18 F Spelling error

  G Capitalization error

  H Punctuation error

  J No error

Language

Directions:

Read each passage. Some sections are underlined. The underlined sections may be one of the following:

- **Incomplete sentences**
- **Run-on sentences**
- **Correctly written sentences that should be combined**
- **Correctly written sentences that do not need to be rewritten**

Choose the best way to write each underlined section and mark the letter for your answer. If the underlined section needs no change, mark the choice "Correct as is."

If you are afraid of spiders, it may comfort you to learn that only two spiders in the

United States can be truly dangerous to humans. <u>One is the brown recluse spider. Also</u>
                                                     19

<u>called the violin spider. It is a shy creature. Often found among rocks or in unused</u>
                                 20

<u>corners of houses. If you want to avoid this unfriendly little creature, you should know</u>
                            21

<u>that it is easily identified by a distinct violin-shaped patch on its head and body.</u>

---

19 A One is the brown recluse spider, also called the violin spider.

   B One is the brown recluse spider: also called the violin spider.

   C One is the brown recluse spider; also called the violin spider.

   D Correct as is

20 F It is a shy creature, often found among rocks or in unused corners of houses.

   G It is a shy creature, often found. Among rocks or in unused corners of houses.

   H It is a shy creature. This creature is often found among rocks or in unused corners of houses.

   J Correct as is

21 A If you want to avoid this unfriendly little creature. You should know that it is easily identified by a distinct violin-shaped patch on its head and body.

   B If you want to avoid this unfriendly little creature you should know that it is easily identified. By a distinct violin-shaped patch on its head and body.

   C You should know, if you want to avoid this unfriendly little creature. That it is easily identified by a distinct violin-shaped patch on its head and body.

   D Correct as is

Language

Almost everyone has heard of the unlucky dodo bird. Which has been extinct for a
22

long time. It was first reported in 1598 by Dutch colonizers on the island of Mauritius.

The dodo received its name from the Portuguese word *duodo,* meaning "silly" or "stupid."
23

There are drawings and even engravings of the dodo, so we have a pretty good idea of

what it looked like. It was quite large. It had short legs. It also had a large, curved beak.
24

However, not much is known of its habits, except that it was flightless. Apparently a

dodo would make a nest on the ground, out in the open. In the nest, it laid a single large
25

egg, the egg was at the mercy of whatever might walk by. The last dodo was observed in

1681. They were the victims of careless hunters. They were also the victims of imported
26

domestic animals that destroyed their unprotected eggs.

22 F Almost everyone has heard of the unlucky dodo bird. The dodo bird has been extinct for a long time.

  G Almost everyone has heard of the unlucky dodo bird, of which it has been extinct for a long time.

  H Almost everyone has heard of the unlucky dodo bird, which has been extinct for a long time.

  J Correct as is

23 A The dodo received its name. From the Portuguese word *duodo,* meaning "silly" or "stupid."

  B Meaning "silly or stupid." The dodo received its name from the Portuguese word *duodo.*

  C The dodo received its name from the Portuguese word. *Duodo* means "silly" or "stupid."

  D Correct as is

Language

24 F It was quite large, it had short legs, it also had a large, curved beak.

   G It was quite large, with short legs and a large, curved beak.

   H It was quite large and it had short legs and had a large, curved beak.

   J Correct as is

25 A In the nest, it laid a single large egg and it was at the mercy of whatever might walk by.

   B In the nest, it laid a single large egg that was at the mercy of whatever might walk by.

   C At the mercy of whatever might walk by, the dodo laid a single large egg. The egg was in the nest.

   D Correct as is

26 F They were the victims of careless hunters and imported domestic animals that destroyed their unprotected eggs.

   G They were the victims of careless hunters and they were also the victims of imported domestic animals that destroyed their unprotected eggs.

   H They were the victims of careless hunters, and victims of imported domestic animals that destroyed their unprotected eggs.

   J Correct as is

Language

Directions:

Complete number 27 by choosing the best answer.

27 Which of the following would be the most appropriate tool to help you plan an essay?

    A a graphic organizer

    B a sentence diagram

    C a scoring rubric

    D a bibliography

Directions:

The following report contains several mistakes. Read the following passage. Then, complete numbers 28 through 30 by choosing the best answer.

---

^{1}Poets use language imaginatively to create images, tell stories, explore feelings, and suggest meanings. ^{2}The greatest poets have never made much money from their work. ^{3}They choose and combine words carefully to enable you to see your world in a fresh, new way. ^{4}To appreciate and enjoy poetry fully, use the following reading strategies.

^{5}Read the lines according to punctuation. ^{6}Punctuation marks are like traffic signals to a reader of poetry. ^{7}Then, identify the speaker in the poem. ^{8}The speaker was the voice that the poet creates to communicate his or her message. ^{9}Finally, you should try to use your senses as fully as possible when you read a poem. ^{10}Identify the images that appeal to your senses; and pause to experience and appreciate them.

---

28 Which sentence does not support the main idea of the passage?

    F Sentence 2

    G Sentence 3

    H Sentence 4

    J Sentence 6

29 What is the best way to write Sentence 8?

    A The speaker had been the voice that the poet creates to communicate his or her message.

    B The speaker had the voice that the poet creates to communicate his or her message.

    C The speaker is the voice that the poet creates to communicate his or her message.

    D best as it is

30 Which transition best fits at the beginning of Sentence 5?

    F However,

    G Next,

    H Then,

    J First,

Name _____ Date _____

Listening

Directions:

Suppose that the following poem is being read aloud. Read the poem. Then, complete numbers 1 through 3 by choosing the best answer.

Dark hills at evening in the west,
Where sunset <u>hovers</u> like a sound
Of golden horns that sang to rest
Old bones of warriors under ground,
Far now from all the bannered ways
Where flash the legions of the sun,
You fade—as if the last of days
Were fading, and all wars were done.
—"The Dark Hills" by Edwin Arlington Robinson

---

1 You can tell from the poem that the word <u>hovers</u> means—

A glows

B sinks

C hangs

D flashes

2 What do the "golden horns" sing "to rest"?

F the bannered ways

G the old bones of warriors

H the dark hills

J the legions of the sun

3 What is the mood of this poem?

A joyful

B humorous

C anxious

D serious

Listening

Directions:

Read the following passage from an oral report. Then, complete number 4 by choosing the best answer.

> Wetlands are areas of land on which the water level remains near or above the surface of the ground for most of the year. Types of wetlands include bogs, fens, marshes, and swamps. Wetlands are home to many types of plants and animals, including several endangered species. They also help control flooding by retaining large amounts of water. Although wetlands in the United States are protected by the Federal Clean Water Act and by various state and local laws, many environmentalists are asking for stronger laws to preserve these important water features.

4 This passage is mostly about—

    F the Federal Clean Water Act

    G the importance of wetlands

    H endangered plants and animals

    J the importance of controlling flooding

Directions:

Read the following message left on Mr. Jackson's answering machine. Then, complete number 5 by choosing the best answer.

> Hello, Mr. Jackson, this is Carla calling from Dr. Avery's office. I just wanted to confirm your appointment with Dr. Avery on September 9 at 8:00 A.M. You should not eat or drink anything for eight hours before your exam. When you arrive at the office, you'll need to give your insurance card to the receptionist. Please call me at 555-1926 if you have any questions. Thank you.

5 In order to dictate this message for Mr. Jackson, you would—

    A wait for Carla to call back

    B listen only for names you know

    C ignore the information that you think is unimportant

    D listen carefully to the entire message

Indiana Benchmark Test 1: Unit 1, Part 1

Indiana Academic Standards		Test Item(s)
STANDARD 1		
READING: Word Recognition, Fluency, and Vocabulary Development		
8.1.3	Verify the meaning of a word in its context, even when its meaning is not directly stated, through the use of definition, restatement, example, comparison, or contrast.	21, 22, 23, 24, 25
STANDARD 2		
READING: Comprehension (Focus on Informational Materials)		
8.2.1	Compare and contrast the features and elements of consumer materials to gain meaning from documents.	8
8.2.5	Use information from a variety of consumer and public documents to explain a situation or decision and to solve a problem.	9, 10, SA-2
STANDARD 3		
READING: Literary Response and Analysis		
8.3.2	Evaluate the structural elements of the plot, such as subplots, parallel episodes, and climax; the plot's development; and the way in which conflicts are (or are not) addressed and resolved.	1, 2, 3, 4, 5, 6, 7, 11, 12, 13, 14, 15, 16, 17, 18, 19, 20, SA-1, SA-3, SA-4
STANDARD 5		
WRITING: Applications (Different Types of Writing and Their Characteristics)		
8.5.1	Write biographies, autobiographies, and short stories that: • tell about an incident, event, or situation, using well-chosen details. • reveal the significance of, or the writer's attitude about, the subject. • use narrative and descriptive strategies, including relevant dialogue, specific action, physical description, background description, and comparison or contrast of characters.	E-1, E-2

Name _____ Date _____

Indiana Academic Standards		Test Item(s)
8.5.4	Write persuasive compositions that: • include a well-defined thesis that makes a clear and knowledgeable appeal. • present detailed evidence, examples, and reasoning to emotional appeals. • provide details, reasons, and examples, arranging them effectively by anticipating and answering reader concerns and counterarguments.	E-3
8.5.6	Write using precise word choices to make writing interesting and exact.	E-1, E-2, E-3
8.5.7	Write for different purposes and to a specific audience or person, adjusting tone and style as necessary.	E-1, E-2, E-3
STANDARD 6		
WRITING: English Language Conventions		
8.6.4	Edit written manuscripts to ensure that correct grammar is used.	26, 27, 30, 31, 32, 33
8.6.6	Use correct capitalization.	28
8.6.7	Use correct spelling conventions.	29

Teacher Comments: _____

_____

Parent Comments: _____

_____

Student Comments: _____

_____

Indiana Benchmark Test 2: Unit 1, Part 2

Indiana Academic Standards		Test Item(s)
STANDARD 1		
READING: Word Recognition, Fluency, and Vocabulary Development		
8.1.3	Verify the meaning of a word in its context, even when its meaning is not directly stated, through the use of definition, restatement, example, comparison, or contrast.	22, 23, 24
STANDARD 2		
READING: Comprehension (Focus on Informational Materials)		
8.2.2	Analyze text that uses proposition (statement of argument) and support patterns.	8, 9, 10
8.2.6	Evaluate the logic, internal consistency, and structural patterns of text.	19, 21, SA-1, SA-2
STANDARD 3		
READING: Literary Response and Analysis		
8.3.2	Evaluate the structural elements of the plot, such as subplots, parallel episodes, and climax; the plot's development; and the way in which conflicts are (or are not) addressed and resolved.	18, SA-4
8.3.4	Analyze the importance of the setting to the mood, tone, and meaning of the text.	13, 14, 15, 16, SA-3
8.3.7	Analyze a work of literature, showing how it reflects the heritage, traditions, attitudes, and beliefs of its author.	1, 2, 3, 4, 5, 6, 7, 11, 12, 17, 20
STANDARD 5		
WRITING: Applications (Different Types of Writing and Their Characteristics)		
8.5.1	Write biographies, autobiographies, and short stories that: • tell about an incident, event, or situation, using well-chosen details. • reveal the significance of, or the writer's attitude about, the subject. • use narrative and descriptive strategies, including relevant dialogue, specific action, physical description, background description, and comparison or contrast of characters.	E-1, E-3

Name _____ Date _____

Indiana Academic Standards		Test Item(s)
8.5.4	Write persuasive compositions that: • include a well-defined thesis that makes a clear and knowledgeable appeal. • present detailed evidence, examples, and reasoning to emotional appeals. • provide details, reasons, and examples, arranging them effectively by anticipating and answering reader concerns and counterarguments.	E-2
8.5.7	Write for different purposes and to a specific audience or person, adjusting tone and style as necessary.	E-1, E-2, E-3
STANDARD 6		
WRITING: English Language Conventions		
8.6.4	Edit written manuscripts to ensure that correct grammar is used.	25, 26, 27, 28, 29, 30
8.6.7	Use correct spelling conventions.	31, 32, 33

Teacher Comments: _____

_____

Parent Comments: _____

_____

Student Comments: _____

_____

Name _____ Date _____

Indiana Benchmark Test 3: Unit 2, Part 1

Indiana Academic Standards		Test Item(s)
STANDARD 1		
READING: Word Recognition, Fluency, and Vocabulary Development		
8.1.3	Verify the meaning of a word in its context, even when its meaning is not directly stated, through the use of definition, restatement, example, comparison, or contrast.	21, 22, 23, 24, 25
STANDARD 2		
READING: Comprehension (Focus on Informational Materials)		
8.2.4	Compare the original text to a summary to determine whether the summary accurately describes the main ideas, includes important details, and conveys the underlying meaning.	9, 10
8.2.6	Evaluate the logic, internal consistency, and structural patterns of text.	1, 2, 3, 5, 6, SA-1, SA-2
STANDARD 3		
READING: Literary Response and Analysis		
8.3.3	Compare and contrast the motivations and reactions of literary characters from different historical eras confronting either similar situations and conflicts or similar hypothetical situations.	7, 8
8.3.4	Analyze the importance of the setting to the mood, tone, and meaning of the text.	11, 12, 13, 14, SA-3
8.3.7	Analyze a work of literature, showing how it reflects the heritage, traditions, attitudes, and beliefs of its author.	3, 4, 6
STANDARD 4		
WRITING: Process		
8.4.1	Discuss ideas for writing, keep a list or notebook of ideas, and use graphic organizers to plan writing.	E-3

Indiana Academic Standards		Test Item(s)
STANDARD 5		
WRITING: Applications (Different Types of Writing and Their Characteristics)		
8.5.1	Write biographies, autobiographies, and short stories that: • tell about an incident, event, or situation, using well-chosen details. • reveal the significance of, or the writer's attitude about, the subject. • use narrative and descriptive strategies, including relevant dialogue, specific action, physical description, background description, and comparison or contrast of characters.	E-1
8.5.2	Write responses to literature that: • demonstrate careful reading and insight into interpretations. • connect response to the writer's techniques and to specific textual references. • make supported inferences about the effects of a literary work on its audience. • support judgments through references to the text, other works, other authors, or to personal knowledge.	15, 16, 17, 18, 19, 20, SA-4
8.5.4	Write persuasive compositions that: • include a well-defined thesis that makes a clear and knowledgeable appeal. • present detailed evidence, examples, and reasoning to emotional appeals. • provide details, reasons, and examples, arranging them effectively by anticipating and answering reader concerns and counterarguments.	E-3
8.5.6	Write using precise word choices to make writing interesting and exact.	E-1, E-2
8.5.7	Write for different purposes and to a specific audience or person, adjusting tone and style as necessary.	E-1, E-2, E-3

Name _____ Date _____

Indiana Academic Standards		Test Item(s)
STANDARD 6		
WRITING: English Language Conventions		
8.6.4	Edit written manuscripts to ensure that correct grammar is used.	26, 27, 28, 29, 30, 31, 32, 33

Teacher Comments: _____

_____

Parent Comments: _____

_____

Student Comments: _____

_____

Indiana Benchmark Test 4: Unit 2, Part 2

Indiana Academic Standards		Test Item(s)
STANDARD 1		
READING: Word Recognition, Fluency, and Vocabulary Development		
8.1.3	Verify the meaning of a word in its context, even when its meaning is not directly stated, through the use of definition, restatement, example, comparison, or contrast.	21, 22, 23, 24
STANDARD 2		
READING: Comprehension (Focus on Informational Materials)		
8.2.1	Compare and contrast the features and elements of consumer materials to gain meaning from documents.	7, 8, 9, 10
STANDARD 3		
READING: Literary Response and Analysis		
8.3.5	Identify and analyze recurring themes (such as good versus evil) that appear frequently across traditional and contemporary works.	15, 16, 17, 18, 19, 20, SA-4
STANDARD 4		
WRITING: Process		
8.4.1	Discuss ideas for writing, keep a list or notebook of ideas, and use graphic organizers to plan writing.	E-3
STANDARD 5		
WRITING: Applications (Different Types of Writing and Their Characteristics)		
8.5.1	Write biographies, autobiographies, and short stories that: • tell about an incident, event, or situation, using well-chosen details. • reveal the significance of, or the writer's attitude about, the subject. • use narrative and descriptive strategies, including relevant dialogue, specific action, physical description, background description, and comparison or contrast of characters.	E-1, E-2, E-3

Name _____ Date _____

Indiana Academic Standards		Test Item(s)
8.5.2	Write responses to literature that: • demonstrate careful reading and insight into interpretations. • connect response to the writer's techniques and to specific textual references. • make supported inferences about the effects of a literary work on its audience. • support judgments through references to the text, other works, other authors, or to personal knowledge.	1, 2, 3, 4, 5, 6, 11, 12, 13, 14, SA-1, SA-2, SA-3
8.5.6	Write using precise word choices to make writing interesting and exact.	E-1, E-2
8.5.7	Write for different purposes and to a specific audience or person, adjusting tone and style as necessary.	E-1, E-2
STANDARD 6		
WRITING: English Language Conventions		
8.6.4	Edit written manuscripts to ensure that correct grammar is used.	25, 26, 27, 28, 29, 30
8.6.7	Use correct spelling conventions.	31, 32, 33

Teacher Comments: _____

_____

Parent Comments: _____

_____

Student Comments: _____

_____

Indiana Benchmark Test 5: Unit 3, Part 1

Indiana Academic Standards		Test Item(s)
STANDARD 1		
READING: Word Recognition, Fluency, and Vocabulary Development		
8.1.3	Verify the meaning of a word in its context, even when its meaning is not directly stated, through the use of definition, restatement, example, comparison, or contrast.	21, 22, 23, 24
STANDARD 2		
READING: Comprehension (Focus on Informational Materials)		
8.2.6	Evaluate the logic, internal consistency, and structural patterns of text.	1, 2, 3, 4, 5, 6, 7, 8, 9, 10, 17, 18, 19, 20, SA-1, SA-3, SA-4
STANDARD 3		
READING: Literary Response and Analysis		
8.3.2	Evaluate the structural elements of the plot, such as subplots, parallel episodes, and climax; the plot's development; and the way in which conflicts are (or are not) addressed and resolved.	11
STANDARD 5		
WRITING: Applications (Different Types of Writing and Their Characteristics)		
8.5.2	Write responses to literature that: • demonstrate careful reading and insight into interpretations. • connect response to the writer's techniques and to specific textual references. • make supported inferences about the effects of a literary work on its audience. • support judgments through references to the text, other works, other authors, or to personal knowledge.	11, 12, 13, 14, 15, 16, SA-2
8.5.4	Write persuasive compositions that: • include a well-defined thesis that makes a clear and knowledgeable appeal. • present detailed evidence, examples, and reasoning to emotional appeals. • provide details, reasons, and examples, arranging them effectively by anticipating and answering reader concerns and counterarguments.	E-2, E-3

Indiana Academic Standards		Test Item(s)
8.5.5	Write technical documents that: • identify the sequence of activities needed to design a system, operate a tool, or explain the bylaws of an organization's constitution or guidelines. • include all the factors and variables that need to be considered. • use formatting techniques, including headings and changing the fonts (typeface) to aid comprehension.	E-1
8.5.6	Write using precise word choices to make writing interesting and exact.	E-1, E-2, E-3
8.5.7	Write for different purposes and to a specific audience or person, adjusting tone and style as necessary.	E-1, E-2, E-3
STANDARD 6		
WRITING: English Language Conventions		
8.6.4	Edit written manuscripts to ensure that correct grammar is used.	25, 26, 27, 28, 29, 30, 31, 32, 33

Teacher Comments: _____

_____

Parent Comments: _____

_____

Student Comments: _____

_____

Indiana Benchmark Test 6: Unit 3, Part 2

Indiana Academic Standards		Test Item(s)
STANDARD 1		
READING: Word Recognition, Fluency, and Vocabulary Development		
8.1.3	Verify the meaning of a word in its context, even when its meaning is not directly stated, through the use of definition, restatement, example, comparison, or contrast.	19, 20, 21, 22, 23, 24, 31, 32, 33
STANDARD 2		
READING: Comprehension (Focus on Informational Materials)		
8.2.1	Compare and contrast the features and elements of consumer materials to gain meaning from documents.	E-3
8.2.6	Evaluate the logic, internal consistency, and structural patterns of text.	9, 10
STANDARD 3		
READING: Literary Response and Analysis		
8.3.7	Analyze a work of literature, showing how it reflects the heritage, traditions, attitudes, and beliefs of its author.	17, 18, SA-4
STANDARD 5		
WRITING: Applications (Different Types of Writing and Their Characteristics)		
8.5.2	Write responses to literature that: • demonstrate careful reading and insight into interpretations. • connect response to the writer's techniques and to specific textual references. • make supported inferences about the effects of a literary work on its audience. • support judgments through references to the text, other works, other authors, or to personal knowledge.	1, 2, 3, 4, 5, 6, 7, 8, SA-1, SA-2
8.5.4	Write persuasive compositions that: • include a well-defined thesis that makes a clear and knowledgeable appeal. • present detailed evidence, examples, and reasoning to emotional appeals. • provide details, reasons, and examples, arranging them effectively by anticipating and answering reader concerns and counterarguments.	11, 12, 13, E-1, E-2, SA-3

Indiana Academic Standards		Test Item(s)
8.5.6	Write using precise word choices to make writing interesting and exact.	14, 15, 16, E-1, E-2, E-3
8.5.7	Write for different purposes and to a specific audience or person, adjusting tone and style as necessary.	E-1, E-2, E-3
STANDARD 6		
WRITING: English Language Conventions		
8.6.3	Use subordination, coordination, noun phrases that function as adjectives (*These gestures—acts of friendship—were noticed but not appreciated.*), and other devices to indicate clearly the relationship between ideas.	29, 30
8.6.4	Edit written manuscripts to ensure that correct grammar is used.	25, 26, 27, 28, 29, 30
8.6.7	Use correct spelling conventions.	31, 32, 33
STANDARD 7		
LISTENING AND SPEAKING: Skills, Strategies, and Applications		
8.7.8	Evaluate the credibility of a speaker, including whether the speaker has hidden agendas or presents slanted or biased material.	E-3

Teacher Comments: _____

_____

Parent Comments: _____

_____

Student Comments: _____

_____

Indiana Benchmark Test 7: Unit 4, Part 1

Indiana Academic Standards		Test Item(s)
STANDARD 1		
READING: Word Recognition, Fluency, and Vocabulary Development		
8.1.1	Analyze idioms and comparisons—such as analogies, metaphors, and similes—to infer the literal and figurative meanings of phrases. • Idioms: expressions that cannot be understood just by knowing the meanings of the words in the expression, such as *to be an old hand at something* or *to get one's feet wet* • Analogies: comparisons of the similar aspects of two different things • Metaphors: implied comparisons, such as *The stars were brilliant diamonds in the night sky.* • Similes: comparisons that use *like* or *as*, such as *The stars were like a million diamonds in the sky.*	15, 16, 17, E-2
8.1.3	Verify the meaning of a word in its context, even when its meaning is not directly stated, through the use of definition, restatement, example, comparison, or contrast.	1, 2, 3, 4, 5, 6, 7, 8, 9, 10, 25, SA-1, SA-2
STANDARD 2		
READING: Comprehension (Focus on Informational Materials)		
8.2.6	Evaluate the logic, internal consistency, and structural patterns of text.	E-3
STANDARD 3		
READING: Literary Response and Analysis		
8.3.1	Determine and articulate the relationship between the purposes and characteristics of different forms of poetry (including ballads, lyrics, couplets, epics, elegies, odes, and sonnets). • Ballad: a poem that tells a story • Lyric: words set to music • Couplet: two successive lines of verse that rhyme • Epic: a long poem that describes heroic deeds or adventures • Elegy: a mournful poem for the dead • Ode: a poem of praise • Sonnet: a rhymed poem of 14 lines	11, 12, 13, E-1, SA-3

Name _____ Date _____

Indiana Academic Standards		Test Item(s)
8.3.6	Identify significant literary devices, such as metaphor, symbolism, dialect or quotations, and irony, which define a writer's style and use those elements to interpret the work. • Metaphor: an implied comparison in which a word or phrase is used in place of another, such as *He was drowning in money.* • Symbolism: the use of an object to represent something else; for example, a dove might symbolize peace • Dialect: the vocabulary, grammar, and pronunciation used by people in different regions • Irony: the use of words to express the opposite of the literal meaning of the words, often to be humorous	16, 17, 18, 19, SA-4
STANDARD 4		
WRITING: Process		
8.4.1	Discuss ideas for writing, keep a list or notebook of ideas, and use graphic organizers to plan writing.	E-2
STANDARD 5		
WRITING: Applications (Different Types of Writing and Their Characteristics)		
8.5.4	Write persuasive compositions that: • include a well-defined thesis that makes a clear and knowledgeable appeal. • present detailed evidence, examples, and reasoning to emotional appeals. • provide details, reasons, and examples, arranging them effectively by anticipating and answering reader concerns and counterarguments.	E-1
8.5.6	Write using precise word choices to make writing interesting and exact.	14, 16, 17, E-1, E-2, E-3
8.5.7	Write for different purposes and to a specific audience or person, adjusting tone and style as necessary.	E-1, E-2, E-3

Name _____ Date _____

Indiana Academic Standards	Test Item(s)
STANDARD 6	
WRITING: English Language Conventions	
8.6.4 Edit written manuscripts to ensure that correct grammar is used.	26, 27, 28, 29, 30, 31, 32, 33

Teacher Comments: _____

_____

Parent Comments: _____

_____

Student Comments: _____

_____

Indiana Benchmark Test 8: Unit 4, Part 2

Indiana Academic Standards		Test Item(s)
STANDARD 1		
READING: Word Recognition, Fluency, and Vocabulary Development		
8.1.1	Analyze idioms and comparisons—such as analogies, metaphors, and similes—to infer the literal and figurative meanings of phrases. • Idioms: expressions that cannot be understood just by knowing the meanings of the words in the expression, such as *to be an old hand at something* or *to get one's feet wet* • Analogies: comparisons of the similar aspects of two different things • Metaphors: implied comparisons, such as *The stars were brilliant diamonds in the night sky.* • Similes: comparisons that use *like* or *as*, such as *The stars were like a million diamonds in the sky.*	18
8.1.3	Verify the meaning of a word in its context, even when its meaning is not directly stated, through the use of definition, restatement, example, comparison, or contrast.	19, 20, 21, 22
STANDARD 2		
READING: Comprehension (Focus on Informational Materials)		
8.2.4	Compare the original text to a summary to determine whether the summary accurately describes the main ideas, includes important details, and conveys the underlying meaning.	1, 2, 3, 6, 7, 9, 11, SA-1, SA-2
8.2.6	Evaluate the logic, internal consistency, and structural patterns of text.	8
STANDARD 3		
READING: Literary Response and Analysis		
8.3.1	Determine and articulate the relationship between the purposes and characteristics of different forms of poetry (including ballads, lyrics, couplets, epics, elegies, odes, and sonnets). • Ballad: a poem that tells a story • Lyric: words set to music • Couplet: two successive lines of verse that rhyme • Epic: a long poem that describes heroic deeds or adventures • Elegy: a mournful poem for the dead • Ode: a poem of praise • Sonnet: a rhymed poem of 14 lines	4, 5, 10, 13, 15, E-1, E-2, SA-3, SA-4

Indiana Academic Standards		Test Item(s)
8.3.4	Analyze the importance of the setting to the mood, tone, and meaning of the text.	12, E-1
8.3.6	Identify significant literary devices, such as metaphor, symbolism, dialect or quotations, and irony, which define a writer's style and use those elements to interpret the work. • Metaphor: an implied comparison in which a word or phrase is used in place of another, such as *He was drowning in money.* • Symbolism: the use of an object to represent something else; for example, a dove might symbolize peace • Dialect: the vocabulary, grammar, and pronunciation used by people in different regions • Irony: the use of words to express the opposite of the literal meaning of the words, often to be humorous	14, 16, 17
STANDARD 4		
WRITING: Process		
8.4.1	Discuss ideas for writing, keep a list or notebook of ideas, and use graphic organizers to plan writing.	E-3
STANDARD 5		
WRITING: Applications (Different Types of Writing and Their Characteristics)		
8.5.4	Write persuasive compositions that: • include a well-defined thesis that makes a clear and knowledgeable appeal. • present detailed evidence, examples, and reasoning to emotional appeals. • provide details, reasons, and examples, arranging them effectively by anticipating and answering reader concerns and counterarguments.	E-2
8.5.6	Write using precise word choices to make writing interesting and exact.	29, E-1, E-2, E-3
8.5.7	Write for different purposes and to a specific audience or person, adjusting tone and style as necessary.	E-1, E-2, E-3

Name _____ Date _____

Indiana Academic Standards		Test Item(s)
STANDARD 6		
WRITING: English Language Conventions		
8.6.1	Use correct and varied sentence types (simple, compound, complex, and compound-complex) and sentence openings to present a lively and effective personal style.	29
8.6.4	Edit written manuscripts to ensure that correct grammar is used.	23, 24, 25, 26, 27, 28, 30
8.6.7	Use correct spelling conventions.	31, 32, 33

Teacher Comments: _____

_____

Parent Comments: _____

_____

Student Comments: _____

_____

Indiana Benchmark Test 9: Unit 5, Part 1

Indiana Academic Standards		Test Item(s)
STANDARD 1		
READING: Word Recognition, Fluency, and Vocabulary Development		
8.1.2	Understand the influence of historical events on English word meaning and vocabulary expansion.	19, 21
8.1.3	Verify the meaning of a word in its context, even when its meaning is not directly stated, through the use of definition, restatement, example, comparison, or contrast.	20, 22, 23, 24
STANDARD 2		
READING: Comprehension (Focus on Informational Materials)		
8.2.3	Find similarities and differences between texts in the treatment, amount of coverage, or organization of ideas.	16, 17, 18, SA-4
8.2.4	Compare the original text to a summary to determine whether the summary accurately describes the main ideas, includes important details, and conveys the underlying meaning.	16, 17, 18, SA-4
8.2.6	Evaluate the logic, internal consistency, and structural patterns of text.	1, 2, 3, 9, 10, 11, 12, 13, 14, 15, SA-3
STANDARD 3		
READING: Literary Response and Analysis		
8.3.2	Evaluate the structural elements of the plot, such as subplots, parallel episodes, and climax; the plot's development; and the way in which conflicts are (or are not) addressed and resolved.	5, 6, 7, 8, SA-2
8.3.4	Analyze the importance of the setting to the mood, tone, and meaning of the text.	4, 12, 13
STANDARD 4		
WRITING: Process		
8.4.3	Support theses or conclusions with analogies (comparisons), paraphrases, quotations, opinions from experts, and similar devices.	1, 2, 3, SA-1

Name _____ Date _____

Indiana Academic Standards	Test Item(s)
STANDARD 5	
WRITING: Applications (Different Types of Writing and Their Characteristics)	
8.5.1	Write biographies, autobiographies, and short stories that: • tell about an incident, event, or situation, using well-chosen details. • reveal the significance of, or the writer's attitude about, the subject. • use narrative and descriptive strategies, including relevant dialogue, specific action, physical description, background description, and comparison or contrast of characters.	E-1, E-2
8.5.4	Write persuasive compositions that: • include a well-defined thesis that makes a clear and knowledgeable appeal. • present detailed evidence, examples, and reasoning to emotional appeals. • provide details, reasons, and examples, arranging them effectively by anticipating and answering reader concerns and counterarguments.	E-3, E-4
STANDARD 6	
WRITING: English Language Conventions	
8.6.1	Use correct and varied sentence types (simple, compound, complex, and compound-complex) and sentence openings to present a lively and effective personal style.	25, 26, 27, 28, 29, 30, 31, 32

Teacher Comments: _____

_____

Parent Comments: _____

_____

Student Comments: _____

_____

Indiana Benchmark Test 10: Unit 5, Part 2

Indiana Academic Standards		Test Item(s)
STANDARD 1		
READING: Word Recognition, Fluency, and Vocabulary Development		
8.1.3	Verify the meaning of a word in its context, even when its meaning is not directly stated, through the use of definition, restatement, example, comparison, or contrast.	18, 19, 20, 21, 22, 23
STANDARD 2		
READING: Comprehension (Focus on Informational Materials)		
8.2.4	Compare the original text to a summary to determine whether the summary accurately describes the main ideas, includes important details, and conveys the underlying meaning.	16, 17, SA-4
8.2.6	Evaluate the logic, internal consistency, and structural patterns of text.	10
STANDARD 3		
READING: Literary Response and Analysis		
8.3.2	Evaluate the structural elements of the plot, such as subplots, parallel episodes, and climax; the plot's development; and the way in which conflicts are (or are not) addressed and resolved.	12
8.3.7	Analyze a work of literature, showing how it reflects the heritage, traditions, attitudes, and beliefs of its author.	1
STANDARD 4		
WRITING: Process		
8.4.1	Discuss ideas for writing, keep a list or notebook of ideas, and use graphic organizers to plan writing.	E-3
8.4.4	Plan and conduct multiple-step information searches using computer networks.	7, 8, 9, SA-1

Indiana Academic Standards		Test Item(s)
STANDARD 5		
WRITING: Applications (Different Types of Writing and Their Characteristics)		
8.5.1	Write biographies, autobiographies, and short stories that: • tell about an incident, event, or situation, using well-chosen details. • reveal the significance of, or the writer's attitude about, the subject. • use narrative and descriptive strategies, including relevant dialogue, specific action, physical description, background description, and comparison or contrast of characters.	E-1
8.5.2	Write responses to literature that: • demonstrate careful reading and insight into interpretations. • connect response to the writer's techniques and to specific textual references. • make supported inferences about the effects of a literary work on its audience. • support judgments through references to the text, other works, other authors, or to personal knowledge.	2, 3, 4, 5, 6, 11, 13, 14, 15, SA-2, SA-3
8.5.4	Write persuasive compositions that: • include a well-defined thesis that makes a clear and knowledgeable appeal. • present detailed evidence, examples, and reasoning to emotional appeals. • provide details, reasons, and examples, arranging them effectively by anticipating and answering reader concerns and counterarguments.	E-2
8.5.6	Write using precise word choices to make writing interesting and exact.	E-1, E-2, E-3
8.5.7	Write for different purposes and to a specific audience or person, adjusting tone and style as necessary.	E-1, E-2, E-3
STANDARD 6		
WRITING: English Language Conventions		
8.6.1	Use correct and varied sentence types (simple, compound, complex, and compound-complex) and sentence openings to present a lively and effective personal style.	26

Name _____ Date _____

Indiana Academic Standards		Test Item(s)
8.6.3	Use subordination, coordination, noun phrases that function as adjectives (*These gestures—acts of friendship— were noticed but not appreciated.*), and other devices to indicate clearly the relationship between ideas.	25, 27, 28, 29, 30
8.6.4	Edit written manuscripts to ensure that correct grammar is used.	24
8.6.7	Use correct spelling conventions.	31, 32, 33

Teacher Comments: _____

_____

Parent Comments: _____

_____

Student Comments: _____

_____

Indiana Benchmark Test 11: Unit 6, Part 1

Indiana Academic Standards		Test Item(s)
STANDARD 1		
READING: Word Recognition, Fluency, and Vocabulary Development		
8.1.3	Verify the meaning of a word in its context, even when its meaning is not directly stated, through the use of definition, restatement, example, comparison, or contrast.	21, 22, 23, 24, 25, 26, 27
STANDARD 2		
READING: Comprehension (Focus on Informational Materials)		
8.2.4	Compare the original text to a summary to determine whether the summary accurately describes the main ideas, includes important details, and conveys the underlying meaning.	1, 2, 3, 4, 5, 6, 7, 9, SA-1, SA-2
STANDARD 3		
READING: Literary Response and Analysis		
8.3.6	Identify significant literary devices, such as metaphor, symbolism, dialect or quotations, and irony, which define a writer's style and use those elements to interpret the work. • Metaphor: an implied comparison in which a word or phrase is used in place of another, such as *He was drowning in money.* • Symbolism: the use of an object to represent something else; for example, a dove might symbolize peace • Dialect: the vocabulary, grammar, and pronunciation used by people in different regions • Irony: the use of words to express the opposite of the literal meaning of the words, often to be humorous	17
Literary Criticism		
8.3.7	Analyze a work of literature, showing how it reflects the heritage, traditions, attitudes, and beliefs of its author.	11, 12, 13, 14, 15, 16, 18, 20, SA-3, SA-4
STANDARD 4		
WRITING: Process		
8.4.1	Discuss ideas for writing, keep a list or notebook of ideas, and use graphic organizers to plan writing.	6, E-3
8.4.4	Plan and conduct multiple-step information searches using computer networks.	E-3

Indiana Academic Standards		Test Item(s)
STANDARD 5		
WRITING: Applications (Different Types of Writing and Their Characteristics)		
8.5.1	Write biographies, autobiographies, and short stories that: • tell about an incident, event, or situation, using well-chosen details. • reveal the significance of, or the writer's attitude about, the subject. • use narrative and descriptive strategies, including relevant dialogue, specific action, physical description, background description, and comparison or contrast of characters.	E-1
8.5.2	Write responses to literature that: • demonstrate careful reading and insight into interpretations. • connect response to the writer's techniques and to specific textual references. • make supported inferences about the effects of a literary work on its audience. • support judgments through references to the text, other works, other authors, or to personal knowledge.	8, 10, 11, 12, 13, 14, 15, 19
8.5.4	Write persuasive compositions that: • include a well-defined thesis that makes a clear and knowledgeable appeal. • present detailed evidence, examples, and reasoning to emotional appeals. • provide details, reasons, and examples, arranging them effectively by anticipating and answering reader concerns and counterarguments.	E-2
8.5.6	Write using precise word choices to make writing interesting and exact.	E-1, E-2, E-3
8.5.7	Write for different purposes and to a specific audience or person, adjusting tone and style as necessary.	E-1, E-2, E-3
STANDARD 6		
WRITING: English Language Conventions		
8.6.1	Use correct and varied sentence types (simple, compound, complex, and compound-complex) and sentence openings to present a lively and effective personal style.	28, 29, 33
8.6.5	Use correct punctuation.	30, 31, 32

Name _____ Date _____

Indiana Academic Standards	Test Item(s)
STANDARD 7	
LISTENING AND SPEAKING: Skills, Strategies, and Applications	
8.7.12 Deliver research presentations that: • define a thesis • research important ideas, concepts, and direct quotations from significant information sources and paraphrase and summarize important perspectives on the topic • use a variety of research sources and distinguish the nature and value of each • present information in charts, maps, and graphs	E-3

Teacher Comments: _____

_____

Parent Comments: _____

_____

Student Comments: _____

_____

Indiana Benchmark Test 12: Unit 6, Part 2

Indiana Academic Standards		Test Item(s)
STANDARD 1		
READING: Word Recognition, Fluency, and Vocabulary Development		
8.1.3	Verify the meaning of a word in its context, even when its meaning is not directly stated, through the use of definition, restatement, example, comparison, or contrast.	20, 21, 22, 23, 24
STANDARD 2		
READING: Comprehension (Focus on Informational Materials)		
8.2.6	Evaluate the logic, internal consistency, and structural patterns of text.	8, 9, SA-2
STANDARD 3		
READING: Literary Response and Analysis		
8.3.5	Identify and analyze recurring themes (such as good versus evil) that appear frequently across traditional and contemporary works.	17, 18, 19, SA-4
8.3.7	Analyze a work of literature, showing how it reflects the heritage, traditions, attitudes, and beliefs of its author.	14, 15, 16
STANDARD 4		
WRITING: Process		
8.4.1	Discuss ideas for writing, keep a list or notebook of ideas, and use graphic organizers to plan writing.	E-1, E-2
8.4.4	Plan and conduct multiple-step information searches using computer networks.	E-1
STANDARD 5		
WRITING: Applications (Different Types of Writing and Their Characteristics)		
8.5.2	Write responses to literature that: • demonstrate careful reading and insight into interpretations. • connect response to the writer's techniques and to specific textual references. • make supported inferences about the effects of a literary work on its audience. • support judgments through references to the text, other works, other authors, or to personal knowledge.	1, 2, 3, 4, 5, 7, 10, 11, 12, 13, SA-1, SA-3

Indiana Academic Standards		Test Item(s)
8.5.3	Write research reports that: • define a thesis (a statement of position on the topic). • include important ideas, concepts, and direct quotations from significant information sources, including print reference materials and the Internet, and paraphrase and summarize all perspectives on the topic, as appropriate. • use a variety of primary and secondary sources and distinguish the nature and value of each. • organize and display information on charts, tables, maps, and graphs. • document sources with reference notes and a bibliography.	6
8.5.4	Write persuasive compositions that: • include a well-defined thesis that makes a clear and knowledgeable appeal. • present detailed evidence, examples, and reasoning to emotional appeals. • provide details, reasons, and examples, arranging them effectively by anticipating and answering reader concerns and counterarguments.	E-3
8.5.6	Write using precise word choices to make writing interesting and exact.	E-2, E-3
8.5.7	Write for different purposes and to a specific audience or person, adjusting tone and style as necessary.	E-1, E-2, E-3
STANDARD 6		
WRITING: English Language Conventions		
8.6.5	Use correct punctuation.	25, 26, 29, 30
8.6.6	Use correct capitalization.	27, 28
8.6.7	Use correct spelling conventions.	31, 32, 33

Name _____ Date _____

Indiana Academic Standards	Test Item(s)
STANDARD 7	
LISTENING AND SPEAKING: Skills, Strategies, and Applications	
8.7.12 Deliver research presentations that: • define a thesis • research important ideas, concepts, and direct quotations from significant information sources and paraphrase and summarize important perspectives on the topic • use a variety of research sources and distinguish the nature and value of each • present information in charts, maps, and graphs	E-3

Teacher Comments: _____

_____

Parent Comments: _____

_____

Student Comments: _____

_____

Name _____ Date _____

Indiana Outcome Test

Indiana Academic Standards		Part 1	Part 2
STANDARD 1			
READING: Word Recognition, Fluency, and Vocabulary Development			
8.1.1	Analyze idioms and comparisons—such as analogies, metaphors, and similes—to infer the literal and figurative meanings of phrases. • Idioms: expressions that cannot be understood just by knowing the meanings of the words in the expression, such as *to be an old hand at something* or *to get one's feet wet* • Analogies: comparisons of the similar aspects of two different things • Metaphors: implied comparisons, such as *The stars were brilliant diamonds in the night sky.* • Similes: comparisons that use *like* or *as*, such as *The stars were like a million diamonds in the sky.*	13	24
8.1.2	Understand the influence of historical events on English word meaning and vocabulary expansion.	22	
8.1.3	Verify the meaning of a word in its context, even when its meaning is not directly stated, through the use of definition, restatement, example, comparison, or contrast.	24, 25	
STANDARD 2			
READING: Comprehension (Focus on Informational Materials)			
8.2.1	Compare and contrast the features and elements of consumer materials to gain meaning from documents.	11, 12	8, 9, 10, 11
8.2.2	Analyze text that uses proposition (statement of argument) and support patterns.		1, 2, 6
8.2.4	Compare the original text to a summary to determine whether the summary accurately describes the main ideas, includes important details, and conveys the underlying meaning.		3
8.2.6	Evaluate the logic, internal consistency, and structural patterns of text.	16	

Indiana Academic Standards		Part 1	Part 2
STANDARD 3			
READING: Literary Response and Analysis			
8.3.1	Determine and articulate the relationship between the purposes and characteristics of different forms of poetry (including ballads, lyrics, couplets, epics, elegies, odes, and sonnets). • Ballad: a poem that tells a story • Lyric: words set to music • Couplet: two successive lines of verse that rhyme • Epic: a long poem that describes heroic deeds or adventures • Elegy: a mournful poem for the dead • Ode: a poem of praise • Sonnet: a rhymed poem of 14 lines	21	
8.3.2	Evaluate the structural elements of the plot, such as subplots, parallel episodes, and climax; the plot's development; and the way in which conflicts are (or are not) addressed and resolved.	15	
8.3.5	Identify and analyze recurring themes (such as good versus evil) that appear frequently across traditional and contemporary works.	14	
STANDARD 4			
WRITING: Process			
8.4.1	Discuss ideas for writing, keep a list or notebook of ideas, and use graphic organizers to plan writing.		15, 21
8.4.2	Create compositions that have a clear message, a coherent thesis (a statement of position on the topic), and end with a clear and well-supported conclusion.		12, 13
8.4.3	Support theses or conclusions with analogies (comparisons), paraphrases, quotations, opinions from experts, and similar devices.	2, 3	
8.4.4	Plan and conduct multiple-step information searches using computer networks.		14
8.4.6	Use a computer to create documents by using word-processing skills and publishing programs; develop simple databases and spreadsheets to manage information and prepare reports.		20
8.4.9	Revise writing for word choice; appropriate organization; consistent point of view; and transitions among paragraphs, passages, and ideas.		18, 19

Indiana Academic Standards	Part 1	Part 2
STANDARD 5		
WRITING: Applications (Different Types of Writing and Their Characteristics)		
8.5.2 — Write responses to literature that: • demonstrate careful reading and insight into interpretations. • connect response to the writer's techniques and to specific textual references. • make supported inferences about the effects of a literary work on its audience. • support judgments through references to the text, other works, other authors, or to personal knowledge.	17, 18, 19, 20, 23	
8.5.3 — Write research reports that: • define a thesis (a statement of position on the topic). • include important ideas, concepts, and direct quotations from significant information sources, including print reference materials and the Internet, and paraphrase and summarize all perspectives on the topic, as appropriate. • use a variety of primary and secondary sources and distinguish the nature and value of each. • organize and display information on charts, tables, maps, and graphs. • document sources with reference notes and a bibliography.	3, 4	
8.5.4 — Write persuasive compositions that: • include a well-defined thesis that makes a clear and knowledgeable appeal. • present detailed evidence, examples, and reasoning to emotional appeals. • provide details, reasons, and examples, arranging them effectively by anticipating and answering reader concerns and counterarguments.		WP-1, WP-2
8.5.6 — Write using precise word choices to make writing interesting and exact.	Part 2: WP-2	
8.5.7 — Write for different purposes and to a specific audience or person, adjusting tone and style as necessary.		WP-1, WP-2
STANDARD 6		
WRITING: English Language Conventions		
8.6.4 — Edit written manuscripts to ensure that correct grammar is used.		22, 23, 25
8.6.5 — Use correct punctuation.	3	

Name _____ Date _____

Indiana Academic Standards		Part 1	Part 2
STANDARD 7			
LISTENING AND SPEAKING: Skills, Strategies, and Applications			
8.7.1	Paraphrase (restate) a speaker's purpose and point of view and ask questions concerning the speaker's content, delivery, and attitude toward the subject.	10	
8.7.2	Match the message, vocabulary, voice modulation (changes in tone), expression, and tone to the audience and purpose.	6, 7	
8.7.5	Use appropriate grammar, word choice, enunciation (clear speech), and pace (timing) during formal presentations.	7	
8.7.6	Use audience feedback, including both verbal and nonverbal cues, to reconsider and modify the organizational structure and/or to rearrange words and sentences for clarification of meaning.	8	
8.7.12	Deliver research presentations that: • define a thesis • research important ideas, concepts, and direct quotations from significant information sources and paraphrase and summarize important perspectives on the topic • use a variety of research sources and distinguish the nature and value of each • present information in charts, maps, and graphs		16, 17
8.7.13	Deliver persuasive presentations that: • include a well-defined thesis • differentiate fact from opinion and support arguments with detailed evidence, examples, reasoning, and persuasive language • anticipate and effectively answer listener concerns and counterarguments through the inclusion and arrangement of details, reasons, examples, and other elements.	5, 9	4, 5, 6, 7

Name _____ Date _____

Test Score: _____
Teacher Comments: _____

_____
_____
_____
_____
_____
_____
_____

Parent Comments: _____

_____
_____
_____
_____
_____
_____
_____

Student Comments: _____

_____
_____
_____
_____
_____
_____
_____

Name _____ Date _____

ISTEP+ Practice Test

Indiana Academic Standards		Test Item(s)
STANDARD 1		
READING: Word Recognition, Fluency, and Vocabulary Development		
8.1.1	Analyze idioms and comparisons—such as analogies, metaphors, and similes—to infer the literal and figurative meanings of phrases. • Idioms: expressions that cannot be understood just by knowing the meanings of the words in the expression, such as *to be an old hand at something* or *to get one's feet wet* • Analogies: comparisons of the similar aspects of two different things • Metaphors: implied comparisons, such as *The stars were brilliant diamonds in the night sky.* • Similes: comparisons that use *like* or *as*, such as *The stars were like a million diamonds in the sky.*	5, 11, 12
8.1.3	Verify the meaning of a word in its context, even when its meaning is not directly stated, through the use of definition, restatement, example, comparison, or contrast.	12
STANDARD 2		
READING: Comprehension (Focus on Informational Materials)		
8.2.2	Analyze text that uses proposition (statement of argument) and support patterns.	7, 9, 10
8.2.6	Evaluate the logic, internal consistency, and structural patterns of text.	8, 9
STANDARD 3		
READING: Literary Response and Analysis		
8.3.4	Analyze the importance of the setting to the mood, tone, and meaning of the text.	1
8.3.5	Identify and analyze recurring themes (such as good versus evil) that appear frequently across traditional and contemporary works.	6

Indiana Academic Standards		Test Item(s)
8.3.6	Identify significant literary devices, such as metaphor, symbolism, dialect or quotations, and irony, which define a writer's style and use those elements to interpret the work. • Metaphor: an implied comparison in which a word or phrase is used in place of another, such as *He was drowning in money.* • Symbolism: the use of an object to represent something else; for example, a dove might symbolize peace • Dialect: the vocabulary, grammar, and pronunciation used by people in different regions • Irony: the use of words to express the opposite of the literal meaning of the words, often to be humorous	1, 4
8.3.7	Analyze a work of literature, showing how it reflects the heritage, traditions, attitudes, and beliefs of its author.	3, 10

STANDARD 4

WRITING: Process

8.4.1	Discuss ideas for writing, keep a list or notebook of ideas, and use graphic organizers to plan writing.	WP-1
8.4.2	Create compositions that have a clear message, a coherent thesis (a statement of position on the topic), and end with a clear and well-supported conclusion.	WP-1, WP-2
8.4.3	Support theses or conclusions with analogies (comparisons), paraphrases, quotations, opinions from experts, and similar devices.	WP-1, WP-2
8.4.4	Plan and conduct multiple-step information searches using computer networks.	
8.4.5	Achieve an effective balance between researched information and original ideas.	WP-2
8.4.7	Review, evaluate, and revise writing for meaning and clarity.	WP-1, WP-2
8.4.8	Edit and proofread one's own writing, as well as that of others, using an editing checklist or set of rules, with specific examples of corrections of frequent errors.	WP-1, WP-2
8.4.9	Revise writing for word choice; appropriate organization; consistent point of view; and transitions among paragraphs, passages, and ideas.	WP-1, WP-2

Name _____ Date _____

Indiana Academic Standards	Test Item(s)

STANDARD 5

WRITING: Applications (Different Types of Writing and Their Characteristics)

8.5.4	Write persuasive compositions that: • include a well-defined thesis that makes a clear and knowledgeable appeal. • present detailed evidence, examples, and reasoning to emotional appeals. • provide details, reasons, and examples, arranging them effectively by anticipating and answering reader concerns and counterarguments.	WP-1, WP-2
8.5.6	Write using precise word choices to make writing interesting and exact.	WP-1, WP-2
8.5.7	Write for different purposes and to a specific audience or person, adjusting tone and style as necessary.	WP-1, WP-2

STANDARD 6

WRITING: English Language Conventions

8.6.1	Use correct and varied sentence types (simple, compound, complex, and compound-complex) and sentence openings to present a lively and effective personal style.	WP-1, WP-2
8.6.3	Use subordination, coordination, noun phrases that function as adjectives (*These gestures—acts of friendship—were noticed but not appreciated.*), and other devices to indicate clearly the relationship between ideas.	WP-2
8.6.4	Edit written manuscripts to ensure that correct grammar is used.	WP-1, WP-2
8.6.5	Use correct punctuation.	WP-1, WP-2
8.6.6	Use correct capitalization.	WP-1, WP-2
8.6.7	Use correct spelling conventions.	WP-1, WP-2

Teacher Comments: _____

Parent Comments: _____

Student Comments: _____

ANSWERS

Screening Test, p. 1

1. ANS: C	9. ANS: B	17. ANS: D	25. ANS: D
2. ANS: G	10. ANS: H	18. ANS: F	26. ANS: F
3. ANS: D	11. ANS: B	19. ANS: B	27. ANS: B
4. ANS: H	12. ANS: J	20. ANS: G	28. ANS: H
5. ANS: D	13. ANS: D	21. ANS: D	29. ANS: C
6. ANS: H	14. ANS: G	22. ANS: G	30. ANS: F
7. ANS: B	15. ANS: A	23. ANS: B	
8. ANS: F	16. ANS: F	24. ANS: G	

Diagnostic Test 1, p. 7

MULTIPLE CHOICE

1. ANS: B	5. ANS: D	9. ANS: A	13. ANS: D
2. ANS: D	6. ANS: B	10. ANS: B	14. ANS: B
3. ANS: C	7. ANS: A	11. ANS: A	15. ANS: D
4. ANS: B	8. ANS: D	12. ANS: C	

Diagnostic Test 2, p. 10

MULTIPLE CHOICE

1. ANS: C	5. ANS: D	9. ANS: A	13. ANS: B
2. ANS: B	6. ANS: C	10. ANS: B	14. ANS: A
3. ANS: A	7. ANS: B	11. ANS: B	15. ANS: D
4. ANS: D	8. ANS: B	12. ANS: D	

Diagnostic Test 3, p. 13

MULTIPLE CHOICE

1. ANS: D	5. ANS: C	9. ANS: A	13. ANS: B
2. ANS: C	6. ANS: B	10. ANS: B	14. ANS: D
3. ANS: B	7. ANS: A	11. ANS: D	15. ANS: A
4. ANS: C	8. ANS: B	12. ANS: C	

Diagnostic Test 4, p. 16

MULTIPLE CHOICE

1. ANS: B	5. ANS: A	9. ANS: B	13. ANS: A
2. ANS: C	6. ANS: C	10. ANS: A	14. ANS: D
3. ANS: B	7. ANS: D	11. ANS: D	15. ANS: C
4. ANS: B	8. ANS: A	12. ANS: C	

Diagnostic Test 5, p. 19

MULTIPLE CHOICE

1. ANS: D	5. ANS: C	9. ANS: A	13. ANS: B
2. ANS: C	6. ANS: A	10. ANS: D	14. ANS: C
3. ANS: B	7. ANS: D	11. ANS: C	15. ANS: B
4. ANS: B	8. ANS: A	12. ANS: A	

Diagnostic Test 6, p. 22

MULTIPLE CHOICE

1. ANS: D	5. ANS: B	9. ANS: D	13. ANS: B
2. ANS: B	6. ANS: C	10. ANS: D	14. ANS: C
3. ANS: A	7. ANS: D	11. ANS: A	15. ANS: C
4. ANS: A	8. ANS: B	12. ANS: C	

Diagnostic Test 7, p. 25

MULTIPLE CHOICE

1. ANS: C	5. ANS: D	9. ANS: A	13. ANS: C
2. ANS: A	6. ANS: A	10. ANS: C	14. ANS: D
3. ANS: D	7. ANS: D	11. ANS: B	15. ANS: D
4. ANS: B	8. ANS: C	12. ANS: A	

Diagnostic Test 8, p. 28

MULTIPLE CHOICE

1. ANS: B	5. ANS: B	9. ANS: C	13. ANS: D
2. ANS: D	6. ANS: B	10. ANS: A	14. ANS: B
3. ANS: C	7. ANS: C	11. ANS: D	15. ANS: C
4. ANS: D	8. ANS: B	12. ANS: D	

Diagnostic Test 9, p. 31

MULTIPLE CHOICE

1. ANS: C	5. ANS: C	9. ANS: B	13. ANS: C
2. ANS: A	6. ANS: B	10. ANS: A	14. ANS: A
3. ANS: D	7. ANS: C	11. ANS: D	15. ANS: C
4. ANS: D	8. ANS: A	12. ANS: D	

Diagnostic Test 10, p. 34

MULTIPLE CHOICE

1. ANS: B	5. ANS: B	9. ANS: B	13. ANS: C
2. ANS: A	6. ANS: C	10. ANS: A	14. ANS: D
3. ANS: A	7. ANS: D	11. ANS: D	15. ANS: D
4. ANS: C	8. ANS: C	12. ANS: A	

Diagnostic Test 11, p. 37

MULTIPLE CHOICE

1. ANS: D	5. ANS: B	9. ANS: A	13. ANS: A
2. ANS: C	6. ANS: D	10. ANS: C	14. ANS: A
3. ANS: A	7. ANS: D	11. ANS: B	15. ANS: D
4. ANS: A	8. ANS: C	12. ANS: D	

Diagnostic Test 12, p. 40

MULTIPLE CHOICE

1. ANS: C	5. ANS: D	9. ANS: B	13. ANS: C
2. ANS: A	6. ANS: A	10. ANS: D	14. ANS: A
3. ANS: D	7. ANS: B	11. ANS: A	15. ANS: B
4. ANS: B	8. ANS: C	12. ANS: C	

ANSWERS

Benchmark Test 1: Unit 1, Part 1

MULTIPLE CHOICE

1. Story details and your own experience
2. Make a prediction as you read, and then keep reading to see if it comes true.
3. It helps keep the reader actively engaged in the story.
4. Cara will get in the bus when it comes in order to go to school.
5. The sky darkens and the winds begin to blow.
6. Anna will refuse to dance with Jorge when he asks.
7. Jorge motions towards the dance floor.
8. labels and warranties
9. the meaning of the map's symbols
10. a schedule
11. exposition
12. the point of highest tension or suspense
13. A student struggles to come to the right decision.
14. resolution
15. suspense
16. The narrator presents events in the order in which they happened in time.
17. sentence 1
18. sentence 2
19. Jen's struggle to get the Rinaldo brothers to behave at the swimming pool.
20. sentences 6–11
21. *Pre-* and *re-* often have opposite meanings.
22. Before the chapter starts
23. when you had it at least once before
24. A *prefix* is something you fix, or attach, before a word or a root.
25. a line or stanza that is sung over and over in a song
26. A proper noun is more specific than a common noun.
27. three
28. Carmine saw the United Nations and a museum when he visited New York City.
29. To form the plural of a noun that ends in a consonant + *y*, change the *y* to an *i* and add *-es*.
30. The wives used the knives to cut bunches of berries from the leaves.
31. a concrete noun
32. kindness
33. The Miller brothers' invention was a children's game in which each player's marker was a different zoo animal.

ESSAY

1. Students may recount the story or retell it in summarized form. They may include details that point to the new ending or can make it a surprise ending, but the ending should still be in keeping with events and characterizations that come before.

2. Students should use a casual, friendly tone that sounds as if they are speaking to a friend. They should not include background information about themselves that a close friend would know but should instead focus on the situation, giving only sufficient background to explain the new experience.

3. Students should state a main impression of the person and support it with concrete examples and/or personal anecdotes. They should include sensory details about the person's appearance, behavior, and perhaps speech. In giving their thoughts on why the person has made such a strong impression, they may discuss the person's unusual qualities or his or her interactions with others.

SHORT ANSWER

1. Use the details and your own experience to make predictions as you read, keep reading to see if the predictions come true, and change a prediction if new details point to something different.
2. It shows the meaning of the map's symbols.
3. It is the high point of the plot, where the suspense or tension is greatest and the likely outcome is determined.
4. The narrator presents events in the order in which they happened in time.

Benchmark Test 2: Unit 1, Part 2

MULTIPLE CHOICE

1. to entertain readers with an interesting puzzle
2. newspaper editorial
3. facts and technical language
4. persuasion
5. to entertain
6. to share the writer's interesting and amusing experiences as an extra in films
7. the surprising event at the end
8. to inform
9. serious and informative
10. Preview it to see if it will be a useful source of information
11. the feeling or atmosphere that the work creates for the reader
12. the author's attitude toward his or her subject and audience
13. the images and the setting
14. bleak and eerie
15. the cold wind raking
16. barren, crumbling, and inky
17. fairly long sentences
18. plot
19. a biography
20. tense and exciting

21. It emphasizes certain details to add excitement.
22. It turns the word or root into a verb.
23. invention
24. to make special or appropriate to each person
25. replace nouns in sentences
26. four
27. possessive
28. Yvonne and I
29. The boys tried to take care of the problem themselves.
30. Both of the girl had their own bicycle.
31. career
32. They took *possession* of the house last Tuesday.
33. Drop one of the *c's* only.

ESSAY

1. Students' narratives should recount events in chronological order. They should clearly describe the situation and state the change that took place in their outlook.
2. Students should clearly state the situation and give some indication of why they feel it needs improving. They should then suggest the actions to take and/or the change in attitude that they feel would improve the situation or solve the problem entirely.
3. Students should use a consistent first-person point of view and should present a clear sequence of events. They should include their feelings about the incident and make clear why the incident is significant.

SHORT ANSWER

1. to persuade
2. facts and technical writing
3. the feeling or atmosphere that the work creates for the reader
4. plot, characters, and setting

Benchmark Test 3: Unit 2, Part 1

MULTIPLE CHOICE

1. Like Rio de Janeiro, Sao Paolo is a large city on the coast of Brazil.
2. The Nile is in Africa, while the Amazon is in South America.
3. Both authors wrote detective stories.
4. He is very clever.
5. *fewer* and *however*
6. "A Scandal in Bohemia" has events similar to those of "The Purlioned Letter."
7. Franz is more selfish than his sister.
8. Both believe in hard work.
9. a description of a TV show in a TV guide
10. It should include the main ideas of the work it summarizes.
11. mood

12. a historical novel
13. the physical features of the land and weather or the season of the year
14. a calm and cheerful mood
15. a round, dynamic character
16. to create conflict for the main character
17. friendliness
18. vengefulness
19. flat and dynamic
20. She learns a lesson and changes as a result.
21. Latin
22. to identify differences
23. people who watch something
24. In the idea that a simile tells how one thing is like another
25. eyeglasses
26. arrive
27. The roses *smelled* fragrant.
28. present, past, present participle, past participle
29. Their past and past participle have the same form.
30. smiling
31. cost
32. written
33. She *has put* the chair up for bidding.

ESSAY

1. Students should include sensory details that convey how the setting looks, smells, and sounds. The details should work together to capture the mood—either positive or negative—that they associate with the setting.
2. Students should describe the character's physical traits and personality.
3. Students should indicate their opinion of each work and list details to support their opinions.

SHORT ANSWER

1. Students should write a sentence that states a similarity between two or more things.
2. Students should write a sentence that states a difference between two or more things.
3. the mood
4. A round, dynamic character is the most complex.

Benchmark Test 4: Unit 2, Part 2

MULTIPLE CHOICE

1. a logical assumption about something an author leaves unstated
2. connecting several details
3. She is in a supermarket.
4. "her teacher had announced a few hours before" and "study before supper"
5. She is studious and responsible.

6. They eat healthy food.

7. factual details used to convince consumers to buy a product

8. Everyone loves the new Scorpion—the most glamorous car on the road.

9. Scorpion—The car driven by athletes, movie stars, corporate executives . . . and you!

10. *plush, sturdy* and *traditions*

11. the perspective from which the story is told

12. third person, providing the thoughts and impressions of more than one character

13. first person, narrated by Johnny

14. *our, I,* and *me*

15. The theme of a work is often a generalization about life or people.

16. good luck

17. Kindness will be rewarded.

18. Do not judge capability based only on appearances.

19. smallness

20. strength and power

21. It comes from a Latin word meaning "see."

22. A *monologue* is a speech by one person.

23. Latin

24. Words that come before the main part

25. Angela will probably go to the mall next Saturday.

26. Present perfect

27. were

28. Use a form of the helping verb *have* and the past participle of the verb.

29. Gregory and Stuart eat a lot of eggs.

30. A nest of robins sits in the tree.

31. sherbet

32. My sister is applying to *college.*

33. Drop one of the *m*'s only.

SHORT ANSWER

1. a logical assumption about something an author leaves unstated

2. She is in a supermarket shopping.

3. the perspective from which the story is told

4. It is usually a generalization about life or people.

ESSAY

1. Students' dialogues should use words and behavior that seem natural and realistic. They should include details from which a reader can infer the characters' unspoken feelings about the subject of the conversation or about each other. Students should present their dialogues in correct format.

2. Students should identify the work under consideration and clearly state the theme or life lesson that they drew from the work. They should then explain how the theme

or lesson applies to a real-life situation drawn from their own experience.

3. Students should state the theme they wish to convey. They should also indicate the characters in their story, the setting in which the story unfolds, the plot events centering around a conflict that a main character faces, and the outcome of that conflict.

Benchmark Test 5: Unit 3, Part 1

MULTIPLE CHOICE

1. The admittance of Missouri as a state would upset the balance between slave and free states.

2. The Missouri Compromise kept the balance between free and slave states, but it did not stop the argument over slavery.

3. The conflict between the North and the South over slavery grew worse than ever.

4. Stuart learned to believe in himself because he completed the challenging task of writing his report.

5. Stuart worked for six weeks on his report.

6. The main idea is implied in the last two sentences.

7. A game called baseball was played as early as 1744, but it differed in key ways from modern baseball.

8. A game called rounders, similar to modern baseball, was played in 1828.

9. Games similar to modern baseball have been played for over 200 years.

10. Bases were made with posts rather than bags.

11. President Lincoln was shot.

12. President Lincoln and John Wilkes Booth

13. the presidential box in Ford's Theater

14. John Wilkes Booth

15. The writer tells about an important event in the life of another person.

16. Booth's assassination of Lincoln

17. chronological

18. cause and effect

19. educational system in Japan and the United States

20. You could explain the step-by-step process of what happens when the virus enters a human body and makes a person sick.

21. difficulties

22. smart

23. He was overjoyed that the team won its first game of the season.

24. method

25. Andrew was the last to arrive.

26. which one?

27. man

28. in what manner?

29. usually

30. always

31. It is used to compare two items.

32. darkest

33. better

SHORT ANSWER

1. The Missouri Compromise kept the balance between free and slave states, but it did not stop the argument over slavery.

2. President Lincoln was shot.

3. It is an essay in which the writer tells about an important event in the life of another person.

4. With chronological order, you could explain the step-by-step process of what happens when the virus enters a human body and then makes a person sick.

ESSAY

1. Students' essays should contain a clear step-by-step explanation of the process.

2. Students' essays should describe the story or work, tell why it impressed them, and explain how it relates to their lives.

3. Students' essays should clearly describe the person's action and explain why it was admirable.

Benchmark Test 6: Unit 3, Part 2

MULTIPLE CHOICE

1. In 1928, the voting age for women was 21.

2. British Parliament was unfair.

3. Being denied the vote was the worst injustice.

4. Women were not allowed the vote in Great Britain.

5. Hubble is the most sophisticated telescope ever created.

6. People on Earth are lucky to have the Hubble.

7. It is an important invention that will benefit science and humanity.

8. Can the author prove why the Hubble will be a benefit?

9. comparing the Hubble to telescopes on Earth

10. Earth's atmosphere absorbs light, which limits vision.

11. Peace Corps volunteers serve humanity and the cause of peace.

12. by describing how Peace Corps volunteers help others around the world

13. patriotism and a desire to help others

14. Their courage helped awaken the conscience of white Americans.

15. oppressed

16. courageous

17. admiring

18. Their courage helped awaken the conscience of white Americans.

19. words with opposite meanings

20. credible/unbelievable

21. The judge is noted for making fair-minded decisions.

22. props that hold something

23. He presented the facts in a fair manner.

24. Let's review the ground that we have already discussed.

25. words that connect sentence parts

26. It rained in the morning, but the sun came out in the afternoon.

27. They are used to add information to sentences.

28. The judge presented flowers to the winner.

29. coordinating conjunction

30. Because the closest star is so far away, humans will probably never travel there.

31. words that sound alike but have different meanings and spellings

32. bored/board

33. The names of the winners were read aloud.

ESSAY

1. Students' editorials should include a clear statement of the issue, credible support, and persuasive techniques.

2. Students' responses should include a statement of the idea and supporting reasons for agreeing or disagreeing.

3. Students' evaluations should include a description of the commercial and the persuasive techniques used and an evaluation of the commercial's effectiveness.

SHORT ANSWER

1. Possible response: In 1928, the voting age for women in Great Britain was 21.

2. "Lucky" is a judgment word, and the opinion cannot be supported by facts.

3. The author is attempting to persuade readers that Peace Corps volunteers serve humanity and the cause of peace.

4. Possible response: admiring

Benchmark Test 7: Unit 4, Part 1

MULTIPLE CHOICE

1. decaying

2. the word *past*, which suggests something that has died or is dying

3. expressing discontent

4. antonym

5. rest

6. calmly

7. inactive

8. Another, world

9. mixed

10. a tool for lifting food

11. alliteration

12. onomatopoeia

13. Four farmers toiled tirelessly in their field.

14. The grain stalks bowed to one another in the breeze.
15. Pynchon's Pond was as smooth as glass.
16. A rusted stove crouched in the corner.
17. A nonhuman subject is given human characteristics.
18. Using words that appeal to the senses of sight and sound
19. using irony so that readers are surprised to learn what happens at the end
20. full of good qualities
21. the act of putting together
22. having the quality of uneasiness
23. the state of being entertained
24. having an extraordinary quality
25. the state of being satisfied
26. The salesperson who called was he.
27. The best person for the job is she.
28. My dog is master of the household.
29. mule
30. Elyssa handed her dad the purple iris.
31. us
32. Its subject receives the action.
33. The baby is sleeping soundly.

ESSAY

1. Students' ideas should clearly give supporting reasons why the song is important and should cite one or more examples of the use of sound devices in the song.
2. Students' notes should include things that appeal to the senses. For three of the items on the lists, students should write phrases that contain a simile, metaphor, and personification.
3. Students should list three ways that poetry helps us connect with others, such as by expressing feelings that we might share about the power of nature, about the difficulties of growing up, or about the satisfaction of doing a job well.

SHORT ANSWER

1. Possible responses: decaying, crumbling, disappearing
2. calmly
3. onomatopoeia
4. A nonhuman subject is given human characteristics.

Benchmark Test 8: Unit 4, Part 2

MULTIPLE CHOICE

1. A snowstorm has come.
2. The snow blots out everything.
3. People are staying indoors during the storm.
4. after lines 4 and 8
5. Pause briefly after each comma.

6. I cannot resist the call of the wild, free life on the seas/
7. Press the Command, Control, and Power buttons all at the same time.
8. understanding the order of the steps
9. Unplug all devices except the power adapter. Then restart the computer by holding down the Command, Control, and Power keys all at once. Let the battery charge to ten percent before plugging in external devices.
10. lyric poetry
11. The speaker is expressing tender love for someone.
12. a seashore near a town
13. to tell a story
14. the sea-sands damp and brown
15. language that appeals to the senses
16. The icy snow crunched underfoot.
17. a literal description
18. a description of a candle flame that can be compared to a life
19. a dictionary
20. aquarium
21. reception
22. congratulate
23. from
24. The last line of the poem is chilling.
25. in his attic room
26. to read
27. We hope to visit the poet's birthplace.
28. to understand the poem's imagery
29. Huffing and chuffing, the cyclists pedaled slowly up the steep hill.
30. a noun phrase that defines other words in a sentence
31. We found an *affordable* vacation.
32. responsible
33. performance

ESSAY

1. Students' first lines should clearly show whether the poem is to be a lyric or a narrative poem. The first line for a lyric poem should create an impression of the river by describing at least two details about it; the first line for a narrative poem should describe the setting and a main character.
2. Students should identify one example each of specific words and imagery from one of the poems in this test. They should clearly state whether they think the poet uses these effectively in the poem and should give supporting reasons for their opinions.
3. Students should list details that clearly address the writing prompt. They should include at least two similarities and two differences for each mode of travel. The similarities might include that both modes of travel can

be exciting and that both afford interesting perspectives; differences might include that travel by car is slower and less convenient than travel by plane and that travel by car affords a better sense of the changing country than does travel by plane.

SHORT ANSWER

1. Possible response: Neighbors are isolated from one another by the storm.
2. Possible response: I cannot resist the call of the wild, free life on the seas.
3. to tell a story
4. language that appeals to the senses

Benchmark Test 9: Unit 5, Part 1

MULTIPLE CHOICE

1. connecting important details
2. a decision
3. observing characters' interactions with each other
4. Patrick is wary of new situations.
5. It is a volunteer project to help others.
6. Thomas feels that Patrick will benefit from helping on the project.
7. Thomas likes to help others.
8. It applies to many examples.
9. noting common elements as you read
10. Most supermarkets sell fresh fruit.
11. notes that tell how a play should be performed
12. a description of sounds
13. The setting is night, on a cabin porch.
14. how they feel about each other
15. to someone reading the play
16. a work changed to fit a different form
17. a novel made into a movie
18. differences between the literary forms
19. to take
20. to take upon oneself
21. strong
22. strong and brave
23. take place again
24. lower in worth
25. a participle that, with its modifiers, acts as an adjective
26. spotting
27. The team, encouraged by the crowd, scored ten points.
28. Thinking he was on the right trail, the hoker whistled as he walked.
29. a verb form ending in -ing that is used as a noun
30. drinking
31. Steve reached a surprising conclusion.
32. Celina likes reading mysteries.

ESSAY

1. Students' sentences should clearly state the situation on which the scene with dialogue will be based. Their lines of dialogue should show each character's name, followed by the character's words.
2. Students' responses should clearly show the characters' names, followed by lines of dialogue in which two or more characters are interacting.
3. Students' sentences should clearly state their reason or reasons for writing the letter of complaint.
4. Students' paragraphs should contain appropriate language for a business letter and should clearly state three reasons why they should be hired for the job.

SHORT ANSWER

1. Possible responses: Listen for statements that show characters' ideas and attitudes; watch characters' interactions; notice actions that show a pattern of behavior
2. Possible responses: It is a broad statement. It applies to many examples.
3. They are notes that tell how a play should be performed
4. It is a work that is changed to fit a different form.

Benchmark Test 10: Unit 5, Part 2

MULTIPLE CHOICE

1. using background information
2. The priest is determined to work for justice for the peasants.
3. People are being punished for working for reforms.
4. Are two or more events really related?
5. One cause can have multitude effects.
6. One cause produces two effects.
7. section headings
8. a timeline of major events
9. a home page
10. dialogue
11. He cares deeply about the safety of his country.
12. a conflict between England and the Nazis
13. the reason a character takes an action
14. compassion
15. discomfort
16. a play adapted from another work
17. comparing a journal and a play based on the journal
18. to make
19. to follow
20. makes easier
21. one event following another
22. one who makes a contribution
23. the part that follows
24. a group of words with its own subject and verb

25. When Ian finished the book, he gave it to Sean.

26. When I write, I prefer pen and paper.

27. Lijia kept yelling until someone finally rescued her.

28. a clause that cannot stand by itself as a sentence

29. to show connections between ideas

30. Although *cogent* was unfamiliar to Ty, he spelled it correctly.

31. beliefs

32. Two white *geese* honked as they flew.

33. The store carries five *varieties* of pears.

ESSAY

1. Students' sentences should clearly refer to a specific historical event and should be written from a first-person point of view.

2. Students' sentences should clearly describe their original play and give a statement of purpose for the letter.

3. Students' topics should be clearly stated. Their questions should relate directly to their topic.

SHORT ANSWER

1. You might look at the home page

2. Possible responses: Are the events really related? What causes might have triggered the effect? What are all the possible effects, or chains of effects, that might result from the cause?

3. It is the reason a character takes a particular action.

4. It is a play that has been adapted from another work.

Benchmark Test 11: Unit 6, Part 1

MULTIPLE CHOICE

1. A good summary restates a work's main ideas in as few words as possible.

2. It can provide a quick way to previewing or reviewing the original work.

3. The Art Institute of Chicago has a huge collection of works from many cultures and eras.

4. During the storm, we found shelter in a cave.

5. Janine and I had not found many specimens for our project.

6. a time line

7. a description of a TV show in a TV guide

8. sentences 1 and 7

9. sentences 2, 3, and 4

10. sentences 5 and 6

11. to explain natural occurrences or events in the peoples' history

12. They often display human qualities.

13. the origins of the seasons

14. power guided by compassion

15. Agriculture was an important activity.

16. It includes legends, folk songs, folk tales, and tall tales.

17. the language and grammar of a particular region or people

18. It uses dialect and repetition.

19. He is a heroic character whose admirable qualities are exaggerated.

20. It was a society where compassion for the poor was deeply admired.

21. aristocrats

22. They can change a word into its antonym.

23. a baseball and a noodle

24. unnecessary

25. to *discredit* is to take away the credit, reputation, or believability of someone or something

26. a nonconformist

27. The government collapsed and complete *anarchy* followed.

28. simple

29. She could do to work herself or hire a secretary.

30. Add a comma after *Spain, Madrid,* and *Seville* and keep the comma after *Grenada.*

31. Add a comma after *rain* and change the comma after *cancelled* to a semicolon.

32. If you visit on a busy weekend, you will probably wait in line at opening time.

33. They traveled far.

ESSAY

1. Students should choose a modern subject and explain it in mythic terms. To make the myth entertaining, they might include dialect, modern slang, idioms, and humor.

2. Students should discuss the character's personality, talents, and deeds as well as the effectiveness with which he or she is portrayed. They should cite specific examples from the work to support their general statements about it.

3. Students might list written material, illustrations, audio material, and video material that they would include in their reports. They should indicate several sources for their materials, perhaps including both library and on-line sources.

SHORT ANSWER

1. It restates a work's main ideas in as few words as possible.

2. Possible responses: A description of a TV show in a TV guide or a movie in a movie guide usually consists of a summary. A book report generally contains a summary.

3. They did so to explain natural occurrences or events in the peoples' history.

4. Possibilities include myths, legends, folk songs, folk tales, and tall tales.

Benchmark Test 12: Unit 6, Part 2

MULTIPLE CHOICE

1. before you read
2. what you already *know* about the topic
3. Read more slowly when you are reading to learn new information.
4. to learn about the early history of flying
5. to be entertained with amusing historical anecdotes
6. Take notes on sentences 3–6 only.
7. What was unusual about the Wright Brothers' achievement?
8. a complete written record of a spoken event
9. a public affairs program on TV
10. Jewish Americans
11. The family must leave their immigrant community for an unfamiliar American city.
12. She is upset with the changes and relies more on her daughter.
13. She likes some of the changes but misses her friends from New York City.
14. her portrayal of changing times in English society
15. She obtained knowledge of poisons to use as murder weapons.
16. the fact that she married an archeologist and went on digs with him in the Middle East
17. an insight, major idea, or underlying message that appears in many cultures
18. Change is not always an improvement.
19. The first story puts more emphasis on social customs.
20. canyon
21. chef
22. typhoon
23. yellow brown
24. the enclosure for holding the animals
25. I went to the Lost and Found; the hat was there.
26. Change the first comma to a semicolon and the second comma to a colon.
27. Last Thanksgiving my parents and I visited the city of Atlanta.
28. Yesterday Miss Duncan asked the class, "How many of you like to read poetry?"
29. for shorter quotes only
30. a longer quotation that is set off by indenting
31. pleasant
32. The 30 percent discount makes the bathing suit a real *bargain.*
33. Change the first *u* to *a.*

ESSAY

1. Students should write questions that seem useful for researching the period they choose. They should identify appropriate research sources.
2. Students should include factual historical information about the person. They should indicate the qualities or achievements that they admire in the person and give details that support or illustrate their statements.
3. Students should explain how one or more events or situations resulted in one or more other events or situations. They should supply accurate facts and provide sufficient details to make the events clear. They should use transition words such as *because, since,* and *therefore* to make the cause-and-effect organization clear.

SHORT ANSWER

1. Possible response: When you are reading to learn information, you need to read more slowly.
2. a complete written record of a spoken event
3. the social and historical environment in which the characters live
4. an insight, major idea, or underlying message that appears in many cultures

ANSWERS

Grade 8 OUTCOME TEST: PART 1

1. Write a list of questions to ask.
2. Take notes as the mayor talks.
3. both A and B
4. They yield information that helps you answer the questions "who," "what," "where," "when," "why," and "how."
5. to persuade listeners to wear seat belts whenever they ride in an automobile
6. serious and professional
7. Make eye contact with the audience.
8. to provide more information and clarify your points
9. Stay focused on your main idea.
10. Observe their performances, taking notes on strengths and weaknesses.
11. All of the above
12. to persuade
13. The spotlight was a great eye looking down upon us.
14. Do not give up freedom for something less important.
15. The peacock tries to adjust to his new limitations.
16. Habitats
17. "Lesson Plan"
18. "Lesson Plan"
19. He enjoys music and likes the group's work.
20. "Lesson Plan" is in first person; "The Return" is in third person.
21. to show that the knocking is continuous
22. wagon
23. All of the above
24. disturbing
25. three

Grade 8 OUTCOME TEST: PART 2

1. The book functions as a kind of textbook on magic.
2. It would take away the right of parents to decide what their children should read.
3. Informative people will agree that "The Wizard Walks" poses no threat to children and should not be banned from the public library.
4. To persuade the audience by comparing and contrasting different viewpoints
5. Show a copy of "The Wizard Walks" along with several classic works of literature that have been banned in the past.
6. Only a few books should ever be banned from the library.
7. The speaker states the issues, gives examples, and presents a solution.
8. Check that the mixer is turned off and unplugged.
9. Wash and dry the beaters and mixing bowl.
10. The passage informs how to use the Chef's Gourmet Hand Mixer.
11. The mixer should be operated near an electrical outlet.
12. More people visit Lake Louise than anywhere else in the Canadian Rockies.
13. People enjoy the spectacular scenery at Lake Louise.
14. Use the Internet to find out more about Banff National Park.
15. Why Dickson made his own bandage
16. Band-Aids® were popular right away.
17. One man's homemade bandages became Band-Aids®.
18. Young stars such as Andy Roddick and Serena Williams have made the sport of tennis more popular with children and teenagers.
19. As a result,
20. Both B and C
21. the first sentence
22. make
23. he or she
24. "tragedy" is to "misfortune"
25. cover

ISTEP Practice Test

1. humorous

2. Sample answers: Reason: He took it thinking it would be more of an adventure than the more-traveled road. Example: Because it was grassy and wanted wear.

3. 1) Then took the others, just as fair,/And having perhaps the better claim; 2) I took the one less traveled by,/And that has made all the difference.

4. process of making decisions

5. Where no evidence of travel was visible

6. taking the less traveled road made a difference in his life.

7. It tells a story about the narrator's experiences.

8. study a cyclical process of nature

9. Sample answers: 1) they are thrilled and pleased by the brilliant colors. 2) They can find comfort and understanding of death's role in their own lives.

10. They are concealed.

11. It is a metaphor. Sample answer: The barbed wire has pointy knots of wire throughout its length. When the frost turns these knots white, they look like small stars.

12. inclined to like something in advance

ITBS Mastery Test: Answer Key

Vocabulary
1.	D	6.	K	11.	D
2.	J	7.	C	12.	M
3.	C	8.	J	13.	C
4.	J	9.	B	14.	L
5.	B	10.	K		

Reading Comprehension
1.	D	11.	A	21.	A
2.	J	12.	M	22.	J
3.	C	13.	D	23.	B
4.	M	14.	L	24.	M
5.	B	15.	B	25.	B
6.	K	16.	K	26.	J
7.	C	17.	D	27.	C
8.	L	18.	K	28.	J
9.	B	19.	D	29.	B
10.	K	20.	L	30.	K

Spelling
1.	A	6.	L	11.	C
2.	L	7.	B	12.	M
3.	D	8.	N	13.	D
4.	N	9.	A	14.	K
5.	D	10.	L		

Capitalization
1.	C	5.	A	9.	B
2.	J	6.	K	10.	L
3.	D	7.	B	11.	B
4.	L	8.	L	12.	L

Punctuation
1.	B	5.	C	9.	B
2.	K	6.	L	10.	J
3.	A	7.	A	11.	D
4.	K	8.	K	12.	K

Usage and Expression
1.	B	8.	J	15.	C
2.	K	9.	C	16.	K
3.	A	10.	M	17.	D
4.	M	11.	A	18.	M
5.	B	12.	K	19.	B
6.	J	13.	A	20.	J
7.	D	14.	J		

TerraNova Mastery Test: Answer Key

Sample A: B   Sample B: F   Sample C: B

1.	C	7.	C	13.	B
2.	G	8.	F	14.	J
3.	A	9.	B	15.	C
4.	J	10.	H	16.	H
5.	B	11.	A	17.	D
6.	F	12.	F		

18. "The fact that most network interactions are limited to written words can be the source of misunderstandings."

Sample sentence in student's own words:

Since all people see are the words you type, you can easily be misunderstood in network interactions.

Messages to friends should correctly use at least two emoticons and two abbreviations.

TerraNova Mastery Test: Answer Key *(continued)*

Rubric:

2 Points	1 Point	0 Points
The student's response fulfills the task specifications.	The student's response fulfills some of the task specifications.	The student's response does not fulfill the task specifications.

19. A volcano is a vent in the surface of the earth through which hot gases and ashes sometimes <u>flow</u>. When the gases and ashes flow out of the top of a <u>volcano, it's</u> said to be active. When this activity stops, the <u>volcano</u> is considered dormant. One of the most <u>famous</u> volcanoes is Mt. St. Helen's in Washington. After being dormant for over 120 years, the volcano erupted on May 18, 1980. While the major activity <u>has stopped</u>, Mt. St. Helen's is still considered active.

20. Rubric:

2 Points	1 Point	0 Points
The student's response fulfills the task specifications. The response is cohesive and well-organized. Ideas are supported by relevant facts and details. The response is text-based.	The student's response fulfills some of the task specifications. The response is not completely cohesive and organized. Ideas are not sufficiently supported. The response does not make adequate use of the text.	The student's response does not fulfill the task specifications. The response has no cohesiveness or organization. Ideas are not developed or supported. The response does not make use of the text.

SAT 10 Practice Test: Answer Key

Vocabulary

1 B	4 F		
2 F	5 B		
3 C	6 H		

Reading Comprehension

1 D	6 H	11 C
2 J	7 D	12 G
3 B	8 G	13 D
4 H	9 A	14 F
5 B	10 J	

Spelling

1 D	9 A	17 C
2 F	10 J	18 G
3 B	11 C	19 A
4 F	12 J	20 J
5 B	13 B	21 B
6 H	14 F	22 J

7 D	15 B
8 G	16 F

Language

1 D	11 A	21 D
2 F	12 F	22 H
3 A	13 D	23 D
4 H	14 F	24 G
5 C	15 B	25 B
6 G	16 H	26 F
7 C	17 A	27 A
8 H	18 H	28 F
9 D	19 A	29 C
10 G	20 F	30 J

Listening

1 C	4 G
2 G	5 D
3 D	

Name _____ Date _____

Answer Sheet

•••

1.	Ⓐ	Ⓑ	Ⓒ	Ⓓ	31.	Ⓐ	Ⓑ	Ⓒ	Ⓓ
2.	Ⓐ	Ⓑ	Ⓒ	Ⓓ	32.	Ⓐ	Ⓑ	Ⓒ	Ⓓ
3.	Ⓐ	Ⓑ	Ⓒ	Ⓓ	33.	Ⓐ	Ⓑ	Ⓒ	Ⓓ
4.	Ⓐ	Ⓑ	Ⓒ	Ⓓ	34.	Ⓐ	Ⓑ	Ⓒ	Ⓓ
5.	Ⓐ	Ⓑ	Ⓒ	Ⓓ	35.	Ⓐ	Ⓑ	Ⓒ	Ⓓ
6.	Ⓐ	Ⓑ	Ⓒ	Ⓓ	36.	Ⓐ	Ⓑ	Ⓒ	Ⓓ
7.	Ⓐ	Ⓑ	Ⓒ	Ⓓ	37.	Ⓐ	Ⓑ	Ⓒ	Ⓓ
8.	Ⓐ	Ⓑ	Ⓒ	Ⓓ	38.	Ⓐ	Ⓑ	Ⓒ	Ⓓ
9.	Ⓐ	Ⓑ	Ⓒ	Ⓓ	39.	Ⓐ	Ⓑ	Ⓒ	Ⓓ
10.	Ⓐ	Ⓑ	Ⓒ	Ⓓ	40.	Ⓐ	Ⓑ	Ⓒ	Ⓓ
11.	Ⓐ	Ⓑ	Ⓒ	Ⓓ	41.	Ⓐ	Ⓑ	Ⓒ	Ⓓ
12.	Ⓐ	Ⓑ	Ⓒ	Ⓓ	42.	Ⓐ	Ⓑ	Ⓒ	Ⓓ
13.	Ⓐ	Ⓑ	Ⓒ	Ⓓ	43.	Ⓐ	Ⓑ	Ⓒ	Ⓓ
14.	Ⓐ	Ⓑ	Ⓒ	Ⓓ	44.	Ⓐ	Ⓑ	Ⓒ	Ⓓ
15.	Ⓐ	Ⓑ	Ⓒ	Ⓓ	45.	Ⓐ	Ⓑ	Ⓒ	Ⓓ
16.	Ⓐ	Ⓑ	Ⓒ	Ⓓ	46.	Ⓐ	Ⓑ	Ⓒ	Ⓓ
17.	Ⓐ	Ⓑ	Ⓒ	Ⓓ	47.	Ⓐ	Ⓑ	Ⓒ	Ⓓ
18.	Ⓐ	Ⓑ	Ⓒ	Ⓓ	48.	Ⓐ	Ⓑ	Ⓒ	Ⓓ
19.	Ⓐ	Ⓑ	Ⓒ	Ⓓ	49.	Ⓐ	Ⓑ	Ⓒ	Ⓓ
20.	Ⓐ	Ⓑ	Ⓒ	Ⓓ	50.	Ⓐ	Ⓑ	Ⓒ	Ⓓ
21.	Ⓐ	Ⓑ	Ⓒ	Ⓓ	51.	Ⓐ	Ⓑ	Ⓒ	Ⓓ
22.	Ⓐ	Ⓑ	Ⓒ	Ⓓ	52.	Ⓐ	Ⓑ	Ⓒ	Ⓓ
23.	Ⓐ	Ⓑ	Ⓒ	Ⓓ	53.	Ⓐ	Ⓑ	Ⓒ	Ⓓ
24.	Ⓐ	Ⓑ	Ⓒ	Ⓓ	54.	Ⓐ	Ⓑ	Ⓒ	Ⓓ
25.	Ⓐ	Ⓑ	Ⓒ	Ⓓ	55.	Ⓐ	Ⓑ	Ⓒ	Ⓓ
26.	Ⓐ	Ⓑ	Ⓒ	Ⓓ	56.	Ⓐ	Ⓑ	Ⓒ	Ⓓ
27.	Ⓐ	Ⓑ	Ⓒ	Ⓓ	57.	Ⓐ	Ⓑ	Ⓒ	Ⓓ
28.	Ⓐ	Ⓑ	Ⓒ	Ⓓ	58.	Ⓐ	Ⓑ	Ⓒ	Ⓓ
29.	Ⓐ	Ⓑ	Ⓒ	Ⓓ	59.	Ⓐ	Ⓑ	Ⓒ	Ⓓ
30.	Ⓐ	Ⓑ	Ⓒ	Ⓓ	60.	Ⓐ	Ⓑ	Ⓒ	Ⓓ

Answer Sheet for ITBS

Vocabulary

1. Ⓐ Ⓑ Ⓒ Ⓓ	5. Ⓐ Ⓑ Ⓒ Ⓓ	9. Ⓐ Ⓑ Ⓒ Ⓓ	13. Ⓐ Ⓑ Ⓒ Ⓓ
2. Ⓙ Ⓚ Ⓛ Ⓜ	6. Ⓙ Ⓚ Ⓛ Ⓜ	10. Ⓙ Ⓚ Ⓛ Ⓜ	14. Ⓙ Ⓚ Ⓛ Ⓜ
3. Ⓐ Ⓑ Ⓒ Ⓓ	7. Ⓐ Ⓑ Ⓒ Ⓓ	11. Ⓐ Ⓑ Ⓒ Ⓓ	
4. Ⓙ Ⓚ Ⓛ Ⓜ	8. Ⓙ Ⓚ Ⓛ Ⓜ	12. Ⓙ Ⓚ Ⓛ Ⓜ	

Reading Comprehension

1. Ⓐ Ⓑ Ⓒ Ⓓ	7. Ⓐ Ⓑ Ⓒ Ⓓ	13. Ⓐ Ⓑ Ⓒ Ⓓ	19. Ⓐ Ⓑ Ⓒ Ⓓ	25. Ⓐ Ⓑ Ⓒ Ⓓ
2. Ⓕ Ⓖ Ⓗ Ⓙ	8. Ⓕ Ⓖ Ⓗ Ⓙ	14. Ⓕ Ⓖ Ⓗ Ⓙ	20. Ⓕ Ⓖ Ⓗ Ⓙ	26. Ⓕ Ⓖ Ⓗ Ⓙ
3. Ⓐ Ⓑ Ⓒ Ⓓ	9. Ⓐ Ⓑ Ⓒ Ⓓ	15. Ⓐ Ⓑ Ⓒ Ⓓ	21. Ⓐ Ⓑ Ⓒ Ⓓ	27. Ⓐ Ⓑ Ⓒ Ⓓ
4. Ⓕ Ⓖ Ⓗ Ⓙ	10. Ⓕ Ⓖ Ⓗ Ⓙ	16. Ⓕ Ⓖ Ⓗ Ⓙ	22. Ⓕ Ⓖ Ⓗ Ⓙ	28. Ⓕ Ⓖ Ⓗ Ⓙ
5. Ⓐ Ⓑ Ⓒ Ⓓ	11. Ⓐ Ⓑ Ⓒ Ⓓ	17. Ⓐ Ⓑ Ⓒ Ⓓ	23. Ⓐ Ⓑ Ⓒ Ⓓ	29. Ⓐ Ⓑ Ⓒ Ⓓ
6. Ⓕ Ⓖ Ⓗ Ⓙ	12. Ⓕ Ⓖ Ⓗ Ⓙ	18. Ⓕ Ⓖ Ⓗ Ⓙ	24. Ⓕ Ⓖ Ⓗ Ⓙ	30. Ⓕ Ⓖ Ⓗ Ⓙ

Spelling

1. Ⓐ Ⓑ Ⓒ Ⓓ Ⓔ	4. Ⓙ Ⓚ Ⓛ Ⓜ Ⓝ	7. Ⓐ Ⓑ Ⓒ Ⓓ Ⓔ	10. Ⓙ Ⓚ Ⓛ Ⓜ Ⓝ	13. Ⓐ Ⓑ Ⓒ Ⓓ Ⓔ
2. Ⓙ Ⓚ Ⓛ Ⓜ Ⓝ	5. Ⓐ Ⓑ Ⓒ Ⓓ Ⓔ	8. Ⓙ Ⓚ Ⓛ Ⓜ Ⓝ	11. Ⓐ Ⓑ Ⓒ Ⓓ Ⓔ	14. Ⓙ Ⓚ Ⓛ Ⓜ Ⓝ
3. Ⓐ Ⓑ Ⓒ Ⓓ Ⓔ	6. Ⓙ Ⓚ Ⓛ Ⓜ Ⓝ	9. Ⓐ Ⓑ Ⓒ Ⓓ Ⓔ	12. Ⓙ Ⓚ Ⓛ Ⓜ Ⓝ	

Capitalization

1. Ⓐ Ⓑ Ⓒ Ⓓ	4. Ⓙ Ⓚ Ⓛ Ⓜ	7. Ⓐ Ⓑ Ⓒ Ⓓ	10. Ⓙ Ⓚ Ⓛ Ⓜ
2. Ⓙ Ⓚ Ⓛ Ⓜ	5. Ⓐ Ⓑ Ⓒ Ⓓ	8. Ⓙ Ⓚ Ⓛ Ⓜ	11. Ⓐ Ⓑ Ⓒ Ⓓ
3. Ⓐ Ⓑ Ⓒ Ⓓ	6. Ⓙ Ⓚ Ⓛ Ⓜ	9. Ⓐ Ⓑ Ⓒ Ⓓ	12. Ⓙ Ⓚ Ⓛ Ⓜ

Punctuation

1. Ⓐ Ⓑ Ⓒ Ⓓ	4. Ⓙ Ⓚ Ⓛ Ⓜ	7. Ⓐ Ⓑ Ⓒ Ⓓ	10. Ⓙ Ⓚ Ⓛ Ⓜ
2. Ⓙ Ⓚ Ⓛ Ⓜ	5. Ⓐ Ⓑ Ⓒ Ⓓ	8. Ⓙ Ⓚ Ⓛ Ⓜ	11. Ⓐ Ⓑ Ⓒ Ⓓ
3. Ⓐ Ⓑ Ⓒ Ⓓ	6. Ⓙ Ⓚ Ⓛ Ⓜ	9. Ⓐ Ⓑ Ⓒ Ⓓ	12. Ⓙ Ⓚ Ⓛ Ⓜ

Usage and Expression

1. Ⓐ Ⓑ Ⓒ Ⓓ	5. Ⓐ Ⓑ Ⓒ Ⓓ	9. Ⓐ Ⓑ Ⓒ Ⓓ	13. Ⓐ Ⓑ Ⓒ Ⓓ	17. Ⓐ Ⓑ Ⓒ Ⓓ
2. Ⓙ Ⓚ Ⓛ Ⓜ	6. Ⓙ Ⓚ Ⓛ Ⓜ	10. Ⓙ Ⓚ Ⓛ Ⓜ	14. Ⓙ Ⓚ Ⓛ Ⓜ	18. Ⓙ Ⓚ Ⓛ Ⓜ
3. Ⓐ Ⓑ Ⓒ Ⓓ	7. Ⓐ Ⓑ Ⓒ Ⓓ	11. Ⓐ Ⓑ Ⓒ Ⓓ	15. Ⓐ Ⓑ Ⓒ Ⓓ	19. Ⓐ Ⓑ Ⓒ Ⓓ
4. Ⓙ Ⓚ Ⓛ Ⓜ	8. Ⓙ Ⓚ Ⓛ Ⓜ	12. Ⓙ Ⓚ Ⓛ Ⓜ	16. Ⓙ Ⓚ Ⓛ Ⓜ	20. Ⓙ Ⓚ Ⓛ Ⓜ

Answer Sheet for TerraNova

1.	Ⓐ	Ⓑ	Ⓒ	Ⓓ		31.	Ⓐ	Ⓑ	Ⓒ	Ⓓ
2.	Ⓕ	Ⓖ	Ⓗ	Ⓙ		32.	Ⓕ	Ⓖ	Ⓗ	Ⓙ
3.	Ⓐ	Ⓑ	Ⓒ	Ⓓ		33.	Ⓐ	Ⓑ	Ⓒ	Ⓓ
4.	Ⓕ	Ⓖ	Ⓗ	Ⓙ		34.	Ⓕ	Ⓖ	Ⓗ	Ⓙ
5.	Ⓐ	Ⓑ	Ⓒ	Ⓓ		35.	Ⓐ	Ⓑ	Ⓒ	Ⓓ
6.	Ⓕ	Ⓖ	Ⓗ	Ⓙ		36.	Ⓕ	Ⓖ	Ⓗ	Ⓙ
7.	Ⓐ	Ⓑ	Ⓒ	Ⓓ		37.	Ⓐ	Ⓑ	Ⓒ	Ⓓ
8.	Ⓕ	Ⓖ	Ⓗ	Ⓙ		38.	Ⓕ	Ⓖ	Ⓗ	Ⓙ
9.	Ⓐ	Ⓑ	Ⓒ	Ⓓ		39.	Ⓐ	Ⓑ	Ⓒ	Ⓓ
10.	Ⓕ	Ⓖ	Ⓗ	Ⓙ		40.	Ⓕ	Ⓖ	Ⓗ	Ⓙ
11.	Ⓐ	Ⓑ	Ⓒ	Ⓓ		41.	Ⓐ	Ⓑ	Ⓒ	Ⓓ
12.	Ⓕ	Ⓖ	Ⓗ	Ⓙ		42.	Ⓕ	Ⓖ	Ⓗ	Ⓙ
13.	Ⓐ	Ⓑ	Ⓒ	Ⓓ		43.	Ⓐ	Ⓑ	Ⓒ	Ⓓ
14.	Ⓕ	Ⓖ	Ⓗ	Ⓙ		44.	Ⓕ	Ⓖ	Ⓗ	Ⓙ
15.	Ⓐ	Ⓑ	Ⓒ	Ⓓ		45.	Ⓐ	Ⓑ	Ⓒ	Ⓓ
16.	Ⓕ	Ⓖ	Ⓗ	Ⓙ		46.	Ⓕ	Ⓖ	Ⓗ	Ⓙ
17.	Ⓐ	Ⓑ	Ⓒ	Ⓓ		47.	Ⓐ	Ⓑ	Ⓒ	Ⓓ
18.	Ⓕ	Ⓖ	Ⓗ	Ⓙ		48.	Ⓕ	Ⓖ	Ⓗ	Ⓙ
19.	Ⓐ	Ⓑ	Ⓒ	Ⓓ		49.	Ⓐ	Ⓑ	Ⓒ	Ⓓ
20.	Ⓕ	Ⓖ	Ⓗ	Ⓙ		50.	Ⓕ	Ⓖ	Ⓗ	Ⓙ
21.	Ⓐ	Ⓑ	Ⓒ	Ⓓ		51.	Ⓐ	Ⓑ	Ⓒ	Ⓓ
22.	Ⓕ	Ⓖ	Ⓗ	Ⓙ		52.	Ⓕ	Ⓖ	Ⓗ	Ⓙ
23.	Ⓐ	Ⓑ	Ⓒ	Ⓓ		53.	Ⓐ	Ⓑ	Ⓒ	Ⓓ
24.	Ⓕ	Ⓖ	Ⓗ	Ⓙ		54.	Ⓕ	Ⓖ	Ⓗ	Ⓙ
25.	Ⓐ	Ⓑ	Ⓒ	Ⓓ		55.	Ⓐ	Ⓑ	Ⓒ	Ⓓ
26.	Ⓕ	Ⓖ	Ⓗ	Ⓙ		56.	Ⓕ	Ⓖ	Ⓗ	Ⓙ
27.	Ⓐ	Ⓑ	Ⓒ	Ⓓ		57.	Ⓐ	Ⓑ	Ⓒ	Ⓓ
28.	Ⓕ	Ⓖ	Ⓗ	Ⓙ		58.	Ⓕ	Ⓖ	Ⓗ	Ⓙ
29.	Ⓐ	Ⓑ	Ⓒ	Ⓓ		59.	Ⓐ	Ⓑ	Ⓒ	Ⓓ
30.	Ⓕ	Ⓖ	Ⓗ	Ⓙ		60.	Ⓕ	Ⓖ	Ⓗ	Ⓙ

Answer Sheet for SAT 10

Vocabulary

1. Ⓐ Ⓑ Ⓒ Ⓓ	4. Ⓕ Ⓖ Ⓗ Ⓙ
2. Ⓕ Ⓖ Ⓗ Ⓙ	5. Ⓐ Ⓑ Ⓒ Ⓓ
3. Ⓐ Ⓑ Ⓒ Ⓓ	6. Ⓕ Ⓖ Ⓗ Ⓙ

Reading Comprehension

1. Ⓐ Ⓑ Ⓒ Ⓓ	6. Ⓕ Ⓖ Ⓗ Ⓙ	11. Ⓐ Ⓑ Ⓒ Ⓓ
2. Ⓕ Ⓖ Ⓗ Ⓙ	7. Ⓐ Ⓑ Ⓒ Ⓓ	12. Ⓕ Ⓖ Ⓗ Ⓙ
3. Ⓐ Ⓑ Ⓒ Ⓓ	8. Ⓕ Ⓖ Ⓗ Ⓙ	13. Ⓐ Ⓑ Ⓒ Ⓓ
4. Ⓕ Ⓖ Ⓗ Ⓙ	9. Ⓐ Ⓑ Ⓒ Ⓓ	14. Ⓕ Ⓖ Ⓗ Ⓙ
5. Ⓐ Ⓑ Ⓒ Ⓓ	10. Ⓕ Ⓖ Ⓗ Ⓙ	

Spelling

1. Ⓐ Ⓑ Ⓒ Ⓓ	6. Ⓕ Ⓖ Ⓗ Ⓙ	11. Ⓐ Ⓑ Ⓒ Ⓓ	16. Ⓕ Ⓖ Ⓗ Ⓙ	21. Ⓐ Ⓑ Ⓒ Ⓓ
2. Ⓕ Ⓖ Ⓗ Ⓙ	7. Ⓐ Ⓑ Ⓒ Ⓓ	12. Ⓕ Ⓖ Ⓗ Ⓙ	17. Ⓐ Ⓑ Ⓒ Ⓓ	22. Ⓕ Ⓖ Ⓗ Ⓙ
3. Ⓐ Ⓑ Ⓒ Ⓓ	8. Ⓕ Ⓖ Ⓗ Ⓙ	13. Ⓐ Ⓑ Ⓒ Ⓓ	18. Ⓕ Ⓖ Ⓗ Ⓙ	
4. Ⓕ Ⓖ Ⓗ Ⓙ	9. Ⓐ Ⓑ Ⓒ Ⓓ	14. Ⓕ Ⓖ Ⓗ Ⓙ	19. Ⓐ Ⓑ Ⓒ Ⓓ	
5. Ⓐ Ⓑ Ⓒ Ⓓ	10. Ⓕ Ⓖ Ⓗ Ⓙ	15. Ⓐ Ⓑ Ⓒ Ⓓ	20. Ⓕ Ⓖ Ⓗ Ⓙ	

Language

1. Ⓐ Ⓑ Ⓒ Ⓓ	7. Ⓐ Ⓑ Ⓒ Ⓓ	13. Ⓐ Ⓑ Ⓒ Ⓓ	19. Ⓐ Ⓑ Ⓒ Ⓓ	25. Ⓐ Ⓑ Ⓒ Ⓓ
2. Ⓕ Ⓖ Ⓗ Ⓙ	8. Ⓕ Ⓖ Ⓗ Ⓙ	14. Ⓕ Ⓖ Ⓗ Ⓙ	20. Ⓕ Ⓖ Ⓗ Ⓙ	26. Ⓕ Ⓖ Ⓗ Ⓙ
3. Ⓐ Ⓑ Ⓒ Ⓓ	9. Ⓐ Ⓑ Ⓒ Ⓓ	15. Ⓐ Ⓑ Ⓒ Ⓓ	21. Ⓐ Ⓑ Ⓒ Ⓓ	27. Ⓐ Ⓑ Ⓒ Ⓓ
4. Ⓕ Ⓖ Ⓗ Ⓙ	10. Ⓕ Ⓖ Ⓗ Ⓙ	16. Ⓕ Ⓖ Ⓗ Ⓙ	22. Ⓕ Ⓖ Ⓗ Ⓙ	28. Ⓕ Ⓖ Ⓗ Ⓙ
5. Ⓐ Ⓑ Ⓒ Ⓓ	11. Ⓐ Ⓑ Ⓒ Ⓓ	17. Ⓐ Ⓑ Ⓒ Ⓓ	23. Ⓐ Ⓑ Ⓒ Ⓓ	29. Ⓐ Ⓑ Ⓒ Ⓓ
6. Ⓕ Ⓖ Ⓗ Ⓙ	12. Ⓕ Ⓖ Ⓗ Ⓙ	18. Ⓕ Ⓖ Ⓗ Ⓙ	24. Ⓕ Ⓖ Ⓗ Ⓙ	30. Ⓕ Ⓖ Ⓗ Ⓙ

Listening

1. Ⓐ Ⓑ Ⓒ Ⓓ	4. Ⓕ Ⓖ Ⓗ Ⓙ
2. Ⓕ Ⓖ Ⓗ Ⓙ	5. Ⓐ Ⓑ Ⓒ Ⓓ
3. Ⓐ Ⓑ Ⓒ Ⓓ	

Answer Sheet

Short Answer/Essay

_____

_____

_____

_____

_____

_____

_____

_____

_____

_____

_____

_____

_____

_____

_____

_____

_____

_____

_____

_____

_____

_____

_____

_____

_____

PARENT WELCOME

Date:_____

Dear Parent or Guardian:

Recent studies indicate how important parental involvement is in helping students to achieve success in school. Because I know that you want your child to have an excellent year in English Language Arts class, I'm pleased to tell you about our curriculum and suggest some ways that you can participate in improving your child's performance.

Our English Language Arts textbook this year will be *Prentice Hall Literature: The Penguin Edition.* This program combines a wide variety of quality reading selections with literary analysis, critical thinking and reading skills, and composition. Importantly, it focuses on a different genre in each unit and offers students with two options for covering the same skills, depending on their reading level.

You can help your child get the most from this program and from all of his or her homework by following this expert-tested advice:

- **Find the best time for studying.** Work hard with your child to decide on the best time for studying. Then, set that time aside at least five days out of every week. If there is no homework, your child can use the time to review and plan ahead.
- **Eliminate common distractions.** Set aside a study area that is free from noise and other distractions. Turn off the TV. Research indicates that watching television allows students to "turn off their minds" because it requires no further action or interaction.
- **Avoid common interruptions.** Take messages if the telephone rings, and have your child alert his or her friends not to drop by during the established study time.
- **Provide physical conditions that help concentration.** Ensure that the study area has adequate lighting and is kept at a comfortable temperature. Provide a table or desk that has enough space for writing.
- **Keep supplies handy.** Keeping study materials nearby saves time. Placing them in a small bucket or box makes it easy to move them to the study area.
- **Encourage computer literacy.** Help your child to understand the value of using the computer to write compositions and other assignments. Encourage your child to use the computers at home, school, or the public library.
- **Ask to see your child's books.** Looking through the books gives you a better idea of what your teenager is learning and shows him or her that you consider the material important.
- **Ask to see your child's work on a regular basis.** You do not need to criticize or regrade the papers—that will only make your teenager less willing to show you his or her work. Just show that you are interested.
- **Read.** By watching you read, your child will see reading as a valuable activity. You can be especially effective if you occasionally read and discuss one of the selections your child is studying in class.

I look forward to working with you and your child and hope that you will contact me if you have any questions during the school year.

Cordially,

_____

PARENT LETTER:
REVIEW OF INDIANA ACADEMIC STANDARDS

Date:_____

Dear Parent or Guardian:

The state of Indiana has established a set of English Language Arts Indiana Academic Standards to ensure that all students in the state develop grade-level appropriate proficiencies in the Language Arts each year. I have attached the Indiana Academic Standards to this sheet for your review. Throughout the school year, your students will be taking Benchmark Tests, which assess their mastery of these standards. Each test will be sent home with a report, indicating strengths or weaknesses.

Please read, sign, and return this form. Feel free to indicate any questions or concerns that you have. I will work to address any concerns you have about the instructional goals for this academic year.

Cordially,

_____

_____

I, the parent or guardian of_____, have reviewed Indiana's Academic Standards for English Language Arts for this academic year. I understand that these standards form the foundation for the instruction and educational expectations in the classroom.

_____
Parent

Please use these lines to indicate any questions, concerns, or comments you would like the teacher to address:

_____

_____

_____